# THE COMPLETE WORKS

OF

# JAMES WHITCOMB RILEY

IN SIX VOLUMES

From a photograph taken in 1895

*4698.*

# THE COMPLETE WORKS

OF

# JAMES WHITCOMB RILEY

IN WHICH THE POEMS, INCLUDING A NUMBER HERETOFORE UNPUBLISHED,
ARE ARRANGED IN THE ORDER IN WHICH THEY WERE WRITTEN,
TOGETHER WITH PHOTOGRAPHS, BIBLIOGRAPHIC NOTES,
AND A LIFE SKETCH OF THE AUTHOR

COLLECTED AND EDITED BY

## EDMUND HENRY EITEL

BIOGRAPHICAL EDITION
VOLUME SIX

INDIANAPOLIS
THE BOBBS-MERRILL COMPANY
PUBLISHERS

PRESS OF
BRAUNWORTH & CO.
BOOKBINDERS AND PRINTERS
BROOKLYN, N. Y.

# CONTENTS

# THE COMPLETE WORKS

OF

# JAMES WHITCOMB RILEY

IN SIX VOLUMES

# TOD

STODDARD ANDERSON was the boy's name,
though had you made inquiry for Stoddard Anderson of any boy of the town in which he lived—
and I myself lived there, a handy boy in the dim
old days—you doubtless would have been informed
that nobody of that name was there. Your juvenile informant, however, by way of gratuitous intelligence, might have gone on to state that two
families of the name of Anderson resided there,—
"Old Do-good" Anderson, the preacher, and his
brother John. But had you asked for "Tod" Anderson, or simply "Tod," your boy would have known
Tod; your boy, in all likelihood, would have had
especial reasons for remembering Tod, although his
modesty, perhaps, might not allow him to inform
you how Tod had "waxed it to him more'n onc't"!
But he would have told you, as I tell you now, that
Tod Anderson was the preacher's boy, and lived at
the parsonage. Tod was a queer boy.

Stoddard Anderson was named in honor of some
obscure divine his father had joined church under
when a boy. It was a peculiar weakness of the
father to relate the experience of his early conviction; and as he never tired of repeating it, by way

of precept and admonition to the wayward lambkins of his flock, Tod mastered its most intricate and sacred phraseology, together even with the father's more religious formulas, to a degree of perfection that enabled him to preside at mock meetings in the hay-loft, and offer the baptismal service at the "swimmin'-hole."

In point of personal or moral resemblance, Tod was in nowise like his father. Some said he was the picture of his mother, they who could remember her, for she fell asleep when Tod was three days old, with her mother-arms locked around him so closely that he cried, and they had to take him away from her. No.—Death had taken her away from him.

It needs now no chronicle to tell how Tod thrived in spite of his great loss, and how he grew to be a big, fat, two-fisted baby with a double chin, the pride and constant worry of the dear old grandmother into whose care he had fallen. It requires no space in history's crowded page to tell how he could stand up by a chair when eight months old, and crow and laugh and doddle his little chubby arms till he quite upset his balance, and, pulling the chair down with him, would laugh and crow louder than ever, and kick, and crawl, and sprawl, and jabber; and never lift a whimper of distress but when being rocked to sleep. Let a babyhood of usual interest be inferred—then add a few more years, and you will have the Tod of ten I knew.

O moral, saintlike, and consistent Christian, what is it in the souls of little children so antagonistic to

your own sometimes? What is it in their wayward
and impulsive natures that you can not brook? And
what strange tincture of rebellious feeling is it that
embitters all the tenderness and love you pour out
so lavishly upon their stubborn and resentful hearts?
Why is it you so covetously cherish the command
divine, "Children, obey your parents," and yet find
no warm nook within the breast for that old house-
less truth that goes wailing through the world:

"A boy's will is the wind's will,
And the thoughts of youth are long, long thoughts"?

Tod went to school—the thriftless Tod!—not
wholly thriftless, either; for, although he had not
that apt way of skimming like a swallow down the
placid rills of learning, he did possess, in some mysterious strength, a most extraordinary knack of ac-
quiring just such information as was not taught at
school, and had no place within the busy hive of
knowledge.

Tod was a failure in arithmetic. Tod couldn't tell
twice ten from twice eternity. Tod knew absolutely
nothing of either Christopher Columbus or the glorious country he discovered expressly for the use of
industry and learning, as the teacher would have had
him implicitly believe. Tod couldn't tell you anything of John Smith, even, that very noted captain
who walks cheek by jowl with the dusky Pocahontas
across the illimitable fancy of the ten-year-old
schoolboy of our glorious republic. Tod knew all
about the famous Captain Kidd, however. In fact,

Tod could sing his history with more lively interest and real appreciation than his fellow schoolmates sang geography. The simple Tod once joined the geographical chorus with:

> "I'd a Bible in my hand,
>   As I sailed, as I sailed,
> And I sunk her in the sand,
>   As I sailed."

And Tod—not Captain Kidd—had a ringing in his ears as he sang, as he sang, and an overflow of tears as he sang. And then he ran away from school that afternoon, and sang Captain Kidd, from A to izzard, in the full hearing of the "Industrial Hive," to the very evident amusement of "the workers," and the discomfiture of the ruler of "the swarm."

The teacher called on the good minister that evening, and after a long talk on the back porch, left late in the dusk, wiping his eyes with one hand, and shaking the other very warmly with the preacher. And Tod slipped noiselessly along the roof above them, and slid down the other side, and watched the teacher's departure with a puzzled face.

Tod was at school next morning long before the call of "Books"; in fact, so early, that he availed himself of his isolated situation to chalk the handle of the teacher's pointer, to bore a gimlet-hole in the water-bucket, to slip a chip under one corner of the clock in order to tilt it out of balance and time, and in many more ingenious ways to contribute to the coming troubles of the day. The most audacious act, however, was to climb above the teacher's desk and paste a paper scrap over a letter "o" in the motto, "Be good," that had offered him its vain advice for years. As one by one these depredations met the teacher's notice through the day, the culprit braced himself for some disastrous issue, but his only punishment was the assured glance the teacher always gave him, and the settled yet forbearing look of pain upon his face. In sheer daring Tod laughed aloud—a hollow, hungry laugh that had no mirth in it—but as suddenly subsided in a close investigation of a problem in mental arithmetic, when the teacher backed slowly toward his desk and stood covertly awaiting further developments. But Tod was left again to his own inclinations, after having, with a brazen air of innocence, solicited and gained the master's assistance in the solution of a very knotty problem, which it is needless to say he knew no more of than before. Throughout the remainder of the day Tod was thoughtful, and was evidently evolving in his mind a problem far more serious than could be found in books. Of his own accord, that evening at the close of school, he stayed in for some mysterious reason that even his own deskmate could not comprehend. When, an hour later, this latter worthy, from the old barn opposite, watched Tod and the teacher hand in hand come slowly down the walk, he whispered to himself with bated breath: "What's the durn fool up to, anyhow?"

From that time Tod grew to be a deeper mystery than he could fathom, inasmuch as some strange spirit of industry fell upon him, and he became a student.

Though a perverse fate had seemingly decreed that Tod should remain a failure in all branches wherein most schoolboys readily succeed, he rapidly advanced in reading; and in the declamatory art he soon acquired a fame that placed him high above the reach of competitors.

Tod never cried when he got up to "speak." Tod never blanched, looked silly, and hung down his head. Tod never mumbled in an undertone, was never at a loss to use his hands, nor ever had "his piece" so poorly memorized that he must hesitate with awkward repetitions, to sit down at last in wordless misery among the unfeeling and derisive plaudits of the school. Tod, in a word, knew no such word as fail when his turn was called to entertain his hearers either with the gallant story of the youthful "Casabianca," "The Speech of Logan," or "Catiline's Defiance." Let a pupil be in training for the old-time exercises of Friday afternoon, and he was told to speak out clear and full—not hang his head—not let his arms hang down like empty sleeves,—but to stand up like a king, look everybody in the face, as though he were doing something to be proud of—in short, to take Tod for his model, and "speak out like a man"!

When Tod failed to make his appearance with his usual promptness one Friday afternoon, and the last day of the term, there was evidence of general disappointment. Tod was to deliver an oration written especially for that occasion by the teacher. The visitors were all there—the school committee, and the minister, Tod's father, who occupied Tod's desk alone when "Books" was called. The teacher, with his pallid, care-worn face, tiptoed up and down the aisles, bending occasionally to ask a whispered question, and to let the look of anxious wonder deepen on his face as the respectful pupils shook their heads in silent response. But upon a whispered colloquy with the minister, his face brightened, as he learned that "Tod was practising his oration in the wood-house half an hour before the ringing of the bell."

A boy was sent to bring him, but returned alone, to say that he had not been able to find any trace of him.

"Oh, he'll be here in time enough," said the teacher apologetically to the sad-faced minister. "He's deeply interested in his effort for this after-noon, and I'm certain he wouldn't purposely dis-appoint me." The good man in reply shook his head resignedly, with a prayerful flight of the eyes in-dicative of long-suffering and forbearance.

The opening services of singing and prayer. No Tod.

First class in arithmetic called—examined. No Tod.

Second class, ditto; still no Tod. Primary class in ditto, composed of little twin sisters, aged six, with very red hair and very fair skin, and very short dresses and very slim legs. Tod failed to join his class.

The long-suffering minister was ill at ease. The exercise failed in some way to appease the hunger of the soul within. He looked out of the open window nervously, and watched a saucy little sapsucker hopping up and down a tree; first up one side and then down the other, suddenly disappearing near the roots, and as suddenly surprising him with a mischievous pecking near the top fork. He thought of his poor, wayward boy, with a vague, vague hope that he might yet, in some wise ruling of a gracious Providence, escape the gallows; and with a deep sigh turned to the noisy quiet of the schoolroom; he did not even smile as he took up Tod's geography, opened at the boy's latest work,—a picture of the State seal, where a stalwart pioneer in his shirtsleeves hacked away at a gnarled and stubborn-looking tree, without deigning to notice a stampeding herd of buffalo that dashed by in most alarming proximity. The nonchalance of the sturdy yeoman was intensified by Tod's graphic pen, which had mounted each plunging monster with a daring rider, holding a slack bridle-rein in one hand, and with the other swinging a plug-hat in the most exultant and defiant manner. This piece of grotesque art and others equally suggestive of the outcropping genius of their author, were put wearily aside, only serving, as it seemed, to deepen rather than dissolve the gloom enshrouding the good father's face. And so the exercises wore along till recess came, and with it came the missing Tod.

"I'm in time, am I? Goody!" shouted Tod, jumping over a small boy who had stooped to pick up a slate-pencil, and stopping abruptly in front of the teacher's desk.

"Why, Tod; what in the world!"

Tod's features wore a proud, exultant smile, though somewhat glamoured with a network of spiteful-looking scratches; and his eyes were more than usually bright, although their lids were blue, and swollen to a size that half concealed them. His head, held jauntily erect, suggested nothing but boyish spirit; but his hair, tousled beyond all reason, with little wisps of it glued together with clots of blood; his best clothes soiled and torn; a bruised and naked knee showing through a straight rent across one leg of his trousers, conveyed the idea of a recent passage through some gantlet of disastrous fortune.

It was nothing, Tod said, only on his way to school he had come upon a blind man who played the fiddle and sold lead-pencils, and the boy who had been leading him had stolen something from him; and Tod had voluntarily started in pursuit of the fugitive, to overtake him only after a prolonged chase of more than a mile. "And now I've got you out o' town," said the offender, wheeling suddenly upon him, "I'll jes' meller your head fer you!" After a long pause, in which Tod's face was hidden from the curious group about him, as the teacher bent above him at the back steps pouring water on his head, he continued: "Didn't think the little cuss was so stout! Oh! I'm scratched up, but you ought to see him! And you ought to hear him holler 'Nuff!' and you ought to see him hand over three boxes of pens and them penholders and pencils he stol'd, and a whole bunch o' envelopes; there's blood on some of 'em, and the blind man said I could keep 'em, and he give me a lead-pencil, too, with red in one end and blue in the other. Father, you sharpen it."

Tod never spoke better in his life than on that memorable afternoon—so well indeed did he acquit himself that the good old father failed to censure him that evening for the sin of fighting, and perhaps never would have done so had not the poor blind man so far forgotten the dignity of his great affliction as to get as drunk as he was blind two evenings following, and play the fiddle in front of the meeting-house during divine service.

It was in the vacation following these latter-mentioned incidents that a far more serious occurrence took place.

Tod had never seen a circus, for until this eventful epoch in our simple history the humble little village had never been honored with the presence of this "most highly moral and instructive exhibition of the age." When the grand cavalcade, with its blaring music and its richly caparisoned horses, with their nodding plumes and spangles, four abreast,

drawing the identical "fiery chariot" Tod had heard
his father talk about; when all the highly painted
wagons with their mysterious contents, and the cunning fairy ponies with their little, fluffy manes and
flossy tails—when all this burst upon Tod's en-
raptured eyes, he fell mutely into place behind the
band-wagon, with its myriad followers; and so,
dazed, awestricken and entranced, accompanied the
pageant on its grand triumphal march around the
town.

Tod carried water for the animals; Tod ran errands of all kinds for the showmen; Tod looked
upon the gruff, ill-tempered canvas-hand with an
awe approaching reverence. Tod was going to the
show, too, for he had been most fortunate in ex-
changing his poor services of the morning for the
"open sesame" of all the dreamed-of wonders of the
arena. Tod would laugh and whisper to himself,
hugging the ticket closely to his palpitating side, as
he ran about on errands of a hundred kinds, oc-
cupying every golden interlude of time in drawing
the magic passport from his pocket and gloating
over the cabalistic legend "Complimentary," with
the accompanying autograph of the fat old manager
with the broad, bejeweled expanse of shirt-front,
and a watch-seal as big as a walnut; while on the
reverse side he would glut his vision with an "exterior view of the monster pavilion," where a "girl
poised high in air on a cord, in spangled dress,"
was kissing her hand to a mighty concourse of people, who waved their hats and handkerchiefs in wild-

est token of approval and acclaim. Nor was this the
sole cause of Tod's delight, for the fat man with
the big watch-seal had seemed to take a special
fancy to him, and had told him he might bring a
friend along, that his ticket would pass two. As the
gleeful Tod was scampering off to ask the teacher
if he wouldn't go, he met his anxious father in a
deep state of distress, and was led home to listen
in agony and tears to a dismal dissertation on the
wickedness of shows, and the unending punishment
awaiting the poor, giddy moths that fluttered round
them. Tod was missed next morning. He had retired very early the evening previous. "He acted
strange-like," said the good grandmother, recalling
vaguely that he hadn't eaten any supper, "and I
thought I heard him crying in the night. What was
the matter with him, Isaac?"

Two weeks later Tod was discovered by his distracted father and an officer, cowering behind a roll
of canvas, whereon a fat man sat declaring with a
breezy nonchalance that no boy of Tod's description was "along o' this-'ere party." And the defiant
Tod, when brought to light, emphatically asserted
that the fat man was in nowise blamable; that he
had run away on his own hook, and would do it
again if he wanted to. But he broke there with a
heavy sob; and the fat man said: "There! there!
Cootsey, go along with the old 'un, and here's a
dollar for you." And Tod cried aloud.

The good minister had brought a letter for him,

too, and as the boy read it through his tears he turned homeward almost eagerly.

DEAR TOD [it ran], I have been quite sick since you left me. You must come back, for I miss you, and I can never get well again without you. I've got a new kink on a pair of stilts I've made you, but I can't tell how long to make them till you come back. Fanny comes over every day, and talks about you so much I half believe sometimes she likes you better than she does her old sick uncle; but I can stand that, because you deserve it, and I'm too old for little girls to like very much. It'll soon be the Fourth, you know, and we must be getting ready for a big time. Come home at once, for I am waiting.

To Stoddard Anderson, from his old friend and teacher.

Tod went home. He hastened to the teacher's darkened room. The dear old face had grown pale —so very pale! The kindly hand reached out to grasp the boy's was thin and wasted, and the gentle voice that he had learned to love was faint and low —so very low, it sounded like a prayer. The good minister turned silently and left the two old friends together; and there were tear-drops in his eyes.

And so the little, staggering life went on alone. Some old woman gossip, peering through the eye of a needle on the institution known as the "Ladies' Benevolent Sewing Society," said that it 'peared to her like that boy of the preacher's jes' kep' a-pinin' and a-pinin' away like, ever sence they fetched him back from his runaway scrape. She'd seen him time and time again sence then, and although the little snipe was innocent-like to all ap-

pearances, she'd be bound that he was in devilment
enough! Reckoned he was too proud to march in
the school p'cession at the teacher's funer'l; and he
didn't go to the meetin'-house at all, but putt off to
the graveyard by hisse'f; and when they got there
with the corpse, Tod was a-settin' with his legs
a-hangin' in the grave, and a-pitchin' clods in, and
a-smilin'. "And only jes' the other evening," she
continued, "as I was comin' past there kind o' in
the dusk-like, that boy was a-settin' a-straddle o' the
grave, and jes' a-cryin'! And I thought it kind o'
strange-like, and stopped and hollered: 'What's the
matter of ye, Tod?' and he ups and hollers back:
'Stumpt my toe, durn ye!' and thinks I, 'My youngster, they'll be a day o' reckonin' fer you!'"

The old world worried on, till July came at last,
and with it that most glorious day that wrapped the
baby nation in its swaddling-clothes of stripes and
stars and laid it in the lap of Liberty. And what a
day that was! And how the birds did sing that morning from the green tops of the trees when the glad
sunlight came glancing through the jeweled leaves
and woke them! And not more joyous were the
birds, or more riotous their little throbbing hearts
to "pipe the trail and cheep and twitter twenty million loves," than the merry children that came fluttering to the grove to join their revelry.

O brighter than a dream swept the procession
of children from the town toward the boy that
swung his hat from the tree-top near the brook.
And he flushed with some strange ecstasy as he saw

a little girl in white, with a wreath of evergreen,
wave her crimson sash in answer to him, while the
column slowly filed across the open bridge, where
yet again he saw her reappear in the reflection in the
stream below.   Then, after the dull opening of
prayer, and the more tedious exercises following,
how the woods did ring with laughter; how the boys
vied with one another in their labors of arranging
swings and clearing underbrush away preparatory
to a day of unconfined enjoyment; and how the girls
shrieked to "see the black man coming," and how
coquettishly they struggled when captured and carried off by that dread being, and yet what eagerness
they displayed in his behalf! And "Ring"—men
and women even joining in the game, and kissing
one another's wives and husbands like mad. Why,
even the ugly old gentleman with a carbuncle on
the back of his neck, grew riotous with mirth, and
when tripped full length upon the sward by the
little widow in half-mourning, bustled nimbly to his
feet and kissed her, with some wicked pun about
"grass" widows, that made him laugh till his face
grew as red as his carbuncle.   That bashful young
man who had straggled off alone, sitting so uncom-
fortably upon a log, killing bugs and spiders, like an
ugly giant with a monster club—how he must have
envied the airy freedom of those "old boys and
girls."

Then there was a group of older men talking so
long and earnestly about the weather and the crops
that they had not discovered that the shade of the

old beech they sat beneath had stolen silently away
and left them sitting in the sun, and was even then
performing its refreshing office for a big, sore-eyed
dog, who, with panting jaws and lolling tongue, was
winking away the lives of a swarm of gnats with
the most stoical indifference.

And so time wore along till dinner came, and
women, with big open baskets, bent above the snowy
cloths spread out upon the grass, arranging "the
substantials" and the dainties of a feast too varied
and too toothsome for anything but epicurean memories to describe. And then the abandon of the vo-
racious guests! No dainty affectations—no formal-
ity—no etiquette—no anything but the full sway of
healthful appetites incited by the exhilarant exercises of the day into keenest rapacity and relish.

"Don't you think it's goin' to rain?" asked some
one, suddenly. A little rosy-gilled gentleman, with
the aid of a chicken-leg for a lever, raised his fat
face skyward, and after a serious contemplation of
the clouds, wouldn't say for certain whether it would
rain or not, but informed the unfortunate querist,
after pulling his head into its usual position and laying down the lever to make room for a bite of bread,
that "if it didn't rain there'd be a long dry spell";
and then he snorted a mimic snow-storm of bread-
crumbs on his vis-à-vis, who looked wronged, and
said he "guessed he'd take another piece of that-air
pie down there."

It was looking very much like rain by the time
the dinner things were cleared away. Anxious

mothers, with preserve-stains on their dresses, were running here and there with such exclamations to the men-folks as "Do hurry up!" and "For goodness' sake, John, take the baby till I find my parasol," and "There, Thomas, don't lug that basket off till I find my pickle-dish!"

Already the girls had left the swings, which were being taken down, and were tying handkerchiefs over their hats and standing in despairing contemplation of the ruin of their dresses. Some one called from the stand for the ladies not to be at all alarmed, it wasn't going to rain, and there wasn't a particle of danger of —— ; but there a clap of thunder interrupted, and went on growling menacingly, while a little girl, with her hair blown wildly over her bare shoulders, and with a face, which a moment before glowed like her crimson scarf, now grown whiter than her snowy dress, ran past the stand and fell fainting to the ground. "Is there a doctor on the grounds?" called a loud voice in the distance, and, without waiting for a response—"For God's sake, come here quick ; a boy has fallen from the swing, and maybe killed himself!"

And then the crowd gathered round him there, men with white faces, and frightened women and little, shivering children.

"Whose boy is it?"

"Hush ; here comes his father." And the good minister, with stark features and clenched hands, passed through the surging throng that closed behind him even as the waves on Pharaoh.

Did I say all were excited? Not all; for there was one calm face, though very pale—paler yet for being pillowed on the green grass and the ferns.

"You mustn't move me," the boy said when he could speak; "tell 'em to come here." He smiled and tried to lift and fold his arms about his father's neck. "Poor father! poor father!" as though speaking to himself, "I always loved you, father, only you'd never believe it—never believe it. Now you will. I'll see mother, now—mother. Don't cry— I'm hurt, and I don't cry. And I'll see the teacher, too. He said I would. He said we would always be together there. Where's Fanny? Tell her—tell her—" But that strange unending silence fell upon his lips, and as the dying eyes looked up and out beyond the sighing tree-tops, he smiled to catch a gleam of sunshine through the foolish cloud that tried so hard to weep.

## A REMARKABLE MAN

IN the early winter 1875, returning from a rather
lengthy sojourn in the Buckeye State, where
a Hoosier is scrutinized as critically as a splinter
in the thumb of a near-sighted man, I mentally
resolved that just as soon as the lazy engine
dragging me toward home had poked its smutty
nose into the selvage of my native state, I would
disembark, lift my voice, and shout for joy for being
safely delivered out of a land of perpetual strangers.

This opportunity was afforded me at Union City
—a fussy old-hen-of-a-town, forever clucking over
its little brood of railroads, as though worried to see
them running over the line, and bristling with the
importance of its charge.

The place is not an attractive one, as one steps
from the train in the early dusk of a December evening; in fact, the immediate view of the town is almost entirely concealed by a big square-faced hotel,
standing, as it were, on the very platform, as though
its "runners" were behind time, and it had come
down to solicit its own custom. A walk of sixty
steps, however, gave me a sweeping view of the
main business street of the city; and here it was,

19

by one of those rare freaks of circumstance, that I
suddenly found myself standing face to face with an
old friend. "Smith!" said I. "Correct!" said he,
and all lacking to complete the tableau was the red
light. And now, as my story has more to do with
a more remarkable man than either Smith or myself, I shall hasten to that notable—only introducing
humbler personages as necessity demands.

That night was a bragging, blustering, bullying
sort of a night. The wind was mad—stark, staring
mad; running over and around the town, howling
and whooping like a maniac. It whirled and
whizzed, and wheeled about and whizzed again.
It pelted the pedestrian's face with dust that stung
like sleet. It wrenched at the signs, and rattled the
doors and windows till the lights inside shivered as
with affright. The unfurled awnings fluttered and
flapped over the deserted streets like monstrous bats
or birds of prey; and, gritting their iron teeth, the
shutters lunged and snapped at their fastenings con-
vulsively. Such a night as we like to hide away
from, and with a good cigar, a good friend, and a
good fire, talk of soothing things and dream. My
friend and I were not so isolated, however, upon this
occasion; for the suddenness of the storm had driven
us, for shelter, into "Bower's Emporium"; and,
seated in the rear of the spacious and brightly illuminated store, we might almost dream we "dwelt
in marble halls," were it not for the rather profuse
display of merchandise and a voluminous comple-
ment of show-cards, reading "Bargains in Over-

coats," "Best and Cheapest Underwear," "Buy
Bowers's Boots!" etc.

The clerks were all idle, and employing their leisure in listening to a "fine-art" conversation, casually introduced by my friend's remarking the extraordinary development of the bust and limbs of a
*danseuse* on a paper collar-box; and after deploring
the prostitution to which real talent was subjected,
and satirizing the general degeneracy of modern art,
he had drifted back to the rare old days of Hans
Holbein, Albert Dürer, and that guild. And while
dwelling enthusiastically upon the genius of Angelo,
I became aware that among the listeners was a remarkable man. It was not his figure that impressed
me, for that was of the ordinary mold, and rather
shabbily attired in a tattered and ill-fitting coat of
blue, sadly faded and buttonless; a short-waisted
vest of no particular pattern, fastened together by
means of a loosened loop of binding pulled through
a buttonhole, and held to its place by a stumpy lead-
pencil with a preponderance of rubber at the end;
the pantaloons very baggy and fraying at the bot-
toms, as though in excessive sympathy with a pair
of coarse, ungainly army shoes that wore the appearance of having been through Sherman's march
to the sea.

Not remarkable, I say, in these particulars, for
since "tramping" has arrived at the dignity of a
profession, such characteristics are by no means uncommon; but when taken in conjunction with a head
and face that would have served as model for either

Abraham, Isaac, or Jacob, in patriarchal cast of feature and flow of beard, it is no wonder that my fancy saw in the figure before me a remarkable man. He stood uncovered, and in an eager listening attitude, as though drinking every syllable to the very dregs. His eyes were large and lustrous, and with that dreamy, far-off look peculiar to that quality of mind that sees what is described, even though buried in Pompeian ruins, or under the pyramids of Egypt.

He met my rather scrutinizing gaze with a friendly and forgiving expression—adding an intuitive affinity by a nestling of the palms one within the other and a genial friction indicative of warm impulse and openness, yet withal suggesting a due subservience to my own free will to accept the same as token of genuine esteem and admiration.

I thought I read his character aright in fancying, "Here is a man of more than ordinary culture and refinement," and I determined, if it were possible, to know him better. When I took an early opportunity to refer to him for information he responded eagerly, and in so profuse and elegant a style of diction that I was surprised.

He referred to Angelo as "that master whose iron pencil painted language on lips of stone, and whose crudest works in clay might well outlive the marble monuments of modern art." He glanced from one topic to another with a grace and ease that not only betokened a true mastery of the language, but an inexhaustible fund of information; nor was it long

ere my "stock in hand" had dwindled down to the
insignificant "yes-and-of-course" verbosity that is
not worth the giving away. He dwelt with particular fondness upon literature; frequently asking me
what works I most admired, and pointing out the
beauties and excellence of old authors—Shakespeare, Milton, Pope, Dryden, and a host of others
long dead and gone, whose works live on eternally.
All these, as they were successively reviewed, he
quoted in a manner that evinced a thorough knowledge of their worth.

At last, after no little artifice and strategy, I drew
him to his own history, which grew fantastically interesting as he proceeded. His father, passing rich,
had educated him for the ministry; but the profession did not suit him—or, rather, he did not suit
the profession; for to be frank he was rather inclined
in his younger days to be a "graceless dog"; and so,
when it became evident that he must shift for himself, more at the instigation of literary friends than
from any ambition or choice, he entered the field
of journalism, beginning at the bottom of the lad-
der—the bottom—and gradually rising from the
compositor's case to the very rung of editorial success—when there came a crash,—a flaw in the grain,
my boy, a flaw in the grain—and that flaw— Well,
no matter!—The noblest minds had toppled from
the height, and crumbled to the merest débris of
pauper intellect. The grandest tomb the finger of
the nation could point out was glutted with such
food. Did he not remember poor Prentice, and, in

memory, recall him now as vividly as though but yesterday, entering the sanctum of the Louisville *Journal,* with the old-time greeting: "Ah, Charles; ready for work, I see. Well, here am I—punctual as Death." And then, after a good stiff brandy, which he could hardly raise to his lips with both trembling hands, poor George! how he would dictate, so rapidly that he (Charles) could scarcely put it down, although a clever hand at writing in those days. Served as amanuensis for five years, and transcribed with his own hand, " 'Tis Midnight's Holy Hour," at ten o'clock in the morning, and had the poem entire ready for the compositor at half past. At such times it was nothing uncommon for George to say, "Well done, thou Good and Faithful! the big end of the day is left you to transcribe as your pleasure may dictate. Only bear in mind, I shall expect a little gem from your individual pen for to-morrow's issue!"

"And do you write?" I broke in abruptly.

"I used to write," he answered, as though loath to make the acknowledgment—"that is, I sometimes rode Pegasus as a groom might ride his master's horse—but my flights were never high—never high!"

"For what reason, may I inquire? Surely you had no lack of inspiration with such men as Prentice about you?"

"Ay, there's the rub!" he sighed, with a negative shake. "The association of great men does not always tend to develop genius; the more especially when one's subservient position causes one to degenerate into a mere machine. Yet I found some time, of course, for verse-making; and, chiefly owing to the kindly encouragement of Mr. Prentice, I 'gave to the world,' as he was pleased to say, many little poems; but of them those that survive to-day are vagrants, like myself, and are drifting about at the mercy of the press." Here the old man sighed heavily and mechanically fumbled his pencil.

I was growing deeply interested in the strange character before me, and although the faces of the group smiled at me significantly, I was not to be beguiled from my new acquaintance.

"There is a question," said I, "I would like to ask you, since from actual experience you are doubtless well informed upon it:—I have often heard it argued that the best productions of authors—poets in particular—are written under the influence of what they are pleased to term 'inspiration.' Can you enlighten me as to the truth of that assertion?"

"I can say in reply," said the old man, with his unwavering eyes fixed upon mine—"I can say in reply that the best productions of authors—poets in particular—*are* written under the influence of what they are pleased to term 'inspiration.' I have seen it proved."

"How proved?" I asked.

"Listen. Take, for example, an instance I will cite: A man worn and enfeebled by age, whose eyes are dimmed almost to sightlessness; whose mind, once clear and vivid as the light of day, is now wav-

ering and fickle as the wind: and yet at times this
influence comes upon him like an avalanche, and as
irresistible; a voice cries, 'Write! write! write!' nor
does he know, when he has obeyed that summons,
what his trembling hand has written. Further proof
that this is divine inspiration is that his fragmentary
productions will oftentimes be in the exact manner
and diction of writers long since passed away; and
I am satisfied they are produced at the direct dicta-
tion of the departed. I know this!"

"You astonish me," said I, in unfeigned wonder;
"you say you know this—how do you know it?"

"Because I am the man."

Although the assertion, in my mind, was simply
preposterous, there was a certain majesty in the
utterance that held me half in awe. I looked upon
him as one might look upon some curious being
from an unknown world. He was moving now—
pacing grotesquely up and down a little space of half
a dozen steps, and wheeling, at the limits of his
walk, as nimbly as the harlequin in the pantomime,
and repeating, as though to himself, "I am the man;
I am the man."

"Well, sir," said I, forcing myself into an air of
indifference I did not feel—"well, sir, not for a
moment questioning your own belief as to this
strange influence which may possess you at times,
you will pardon me for expressing the vaguest
skepticism, since I have never been so fortunate as
to witness an actual demonstration." He was about
to interrupt me, but I continued coolly, "By what

circumstance is this influence introduced—or how produced—is it—"

He broke in on me with a keen little pang of a laugh that almost made me shudder. "You are my convert," he exclaimed excitedly. "Quick! Give me paper—give me paper!" But before I could take my note-book from my pocket he had hurriedly snatched a scrap of wrapping-paper from the counter, and bending over it, was writing with great rapidity.

His manner was decidedly singular. In the occasional pauses he made, he would lean his forehead in the palm of his left hand, with the fingers dancing nervously upon the bald spot on the summit of his head, while with the hand that held the pencil he kept up a continued rotary movement in the air. Then he would suddenly pounce down upon the paper before him as though in a perfect frenzy of delight, and line after line would appear as if by magic, each succeeding one preluded by that sharp little yelp of a laugh: and ere three minutes had elapsed, he had covered both sides of the paper. He then threw down his pencil, as though reluctantly, pushed me the scrap and motioned me to read.

I was at first completely mystified, for what I had confidently expected to be rhyme was prose; but ere I had examined it far I was as highly gratified as at first disappointed. The writing, although so recklessly scrawled, was quite legible, and here and there gave evidence of more than ordinary grace

and elegance; the punctuation, so far as I was able
to judge, seemed perfect in every part; and, in fact,
the entire production bore the appearance of having
been executed by a skilful hand.

I copy it verbatim from the original scrap, which
now lies before me:

> By this time they had come upon the figure of the old
> hag, seated by the roadside, and, in a harsh, cracked
> voice, crooning a dismal ballad. "By God's rood," quoth
> the knight, in a burst of admiration, "did I not tell thee
> 'twas some fair princess, decoyed from her father's castle
> and thus transformed, through the despicable arts of
> some wicked enchanter; for thou hast but to perk an ear
> to have the sense of hearing bathed and overflowed with
> melody. Dost thou not also note rare grace and sweetest
> dignity voiced, as it were, from the very tatters that en-
> clothe her form?" "Indeed thou mayest," said the squire;
> "for I have heard it said 'rags may enfold the purest
> gold.'—Yet in this instance I am restrained to think it
> more like the hidalgo's dinner—'very little meat and a
> good deal of tablecloth.'" "Hold thy peace, bladderhead,"
> exclaimed the knight, "lest I make thee gnaw thy words
> with loosened teeth. Listen what liquid syllables are
> spilled upon the atmosphere:"

> > "My father's halls, so rich and rare,
> > Are desolate and bleak and bare;
> > My father's heart and halls are one,
> > Since I, their life and light, am gone.

> > "O, valiant knight, with hand of steel
> > And heart of gold, hear my appeal:
> > Release me from the spoiler's charms,
> > And bear me to my father's arms."

> The knight had by this time thrown himself from his

steed, and with lance reversed and visor doffed he sank
upon his knees in the slime and ooze of the dike, ex-
claiming: "Be of good heart, fair princess! Thy suc-
cor is at hand, since the Fates have woven thee—the
pearl of pearls—into the warp and woof of my great
destiny. Nay, nay! No thanks! Thy father's beaming
eye alone shall be my guerdon, for home thou shalt go,
even though I must needs truckle thee thither on a bar-
row."

"Good," said I, grasping the old man by the
hand. "Hail, Cervantes!"

"Cervantes? Cervantes?" he mused, as though
bewildered; "why, what have I been writing? Is
it not poetry?"

"Yes," I replied enthusiastically, "both prose and
poetry, and that of the rarest school. Read for
yourself."

I handed him the scrap, but he pushed it from him
with a gesture of impatience. "I told you once I
could not read it, nor do I know what I have written. Read it aloud."

Although I hastened to comply, I did it with a
decided air of incredulity as to the belief that he
did not already know every word of it, and even
closed with the gratuitous comment that I felt assured the quotation was perfect in every particular.

"Quotation!" repeated the old man, commiser-
atively; "quotation! Were you as well versed in
such works, my son, as you led me at first to presume, you would know at once that not a single
line of that occurs in 'Don Quixote,' although I do
grant that I am the humble instrument through

which the great Cervantes has just spoken." With this remark, delivered in a half-rebuking, half-compassionate tone, he stood milking his beard and blinking at the chandelier.

I acknowledged my error, and asked pardon for the insinuation, which I begged he would believe was not intended to offend; and that, upon second thought, I was satisfied that no such matter did exist in the printed history, which fact I have since proved by a thorough investigation.

It required, however, considerable inventive tact and show of admiration to counteract the effect of my indiscreet remark; and this was not effectually accomplished until I had incidentally discovered a marked resemblance of his brow to Shakespeare's, which, by actual measurement, I found to correspond to a fraction with the measurement of the mask of that illustrious bard, as furnished by an exhaustive article I had seen a short time previous in one of our magazines.

This happily brought about the result I so much longed for, as I was extremely desirous of a further opportunity in which to study the character of this remarkable man. "Ah, Shakespeare!" said he, in a burst of genuine eloquence,—"there was a mind the gods endowed with wisdom ages have yet to learn; for bright and lustrous as it shines to-day—the Morning Star of human intellect—its glittering purity has yet a million million dawns, each brighter than the last. Its chastened rays are yet to blaze and radiate the darkened ways— Hold! My pencil! Quick—quick!"

He snatched at the paper wildly, and bending over it, began writing with a vindictiveness of effort that was alarming. He slashed the *t*'s and stabbed the punctuation-points savagely. The writing continued, interspersed occasionally with a pause in which he would flourish his pencil like a dripping sword, only to plunge it again and again into the quivering breast of its victim. Finally he dashed it down, pushed the paper from him as one would spurn a vanquished enemy, and sank, limp and exhausted, into a chair. I snatched up the paper eagerly, and read:

*Falstaff.* I call him dog, forsooth, because he snarls—
Snarls, d'ye hear?—and laves his rabid fangs
In slobber-froth that drips in slimy gouts
Of venomous slander. Out upon the cur!
He sets his mangy foot upon the sod,
And grass grows rank and withers at the touch,
And tangles into wiry thatch for snakes
To spawn beneath. The very air he breathes
Becomes a poison gas, and generates
Disease and pestilence. Would he were here,
That I might whet my sword against his ribs,
Although his rotten, putrid soul unhoused
Would breed a stench worse than my barber's breath.
The dog! The damnable—

*Pistol.* Hist! here he comes!
God's body! master, has he overheard,
'Tis cock-crow with thy ghost!

*Poins* (*entering*). How now, my Jack—
Prince ass of Jacks, methought I heard thee bray.

*Falstaff*. Ay, well and marry! for this varlet here
Deserves more brays than praise, the scurvy dog!
Good lack! thou might'st have heard me call him dog
A pebble's toss from this; but now that thou art come,
My dagger-points of wrath do melt away
Before thy genial smile as icicles
Might ooze to nothingness at summer noon.
That other flask, you dog! and have a care
Thou handle it more gently than the first,
Lest I, as thou didst it, thy noddle burst."

Although expecting something after the Shakespearian school, I was not prepared for this, and in reading it aloud I actually found myself endeavoring to imitate the stage manner of Hackett, whom years ago I had seen in "King Henry IV" at the old Metropolitan, Indianapolis. "Ah!" said the old man, "you are more familiar with that, I see. Tell me, have you ever seen those lines in Shakespeare?" There was such a look of conscious triumph in his face, so self-satisfied an expression, that I—although half believing I was in some way being duped—could but reply that I was most thoroughly convinced the lines did not occur in any of the works of that great master.

"They do not," said the old man briefly.

"But how," said I, "is it possible for you to imitate his style so perfectly, not only in language, but theme, expression, force, character, grotesqueness—"

"Stop, my son; stop!" he broke in. "Must I again remind you that it is not imitation: I take no credit to myself—how dare I, when in writing thus my individual mind is gone, simply chaotic? It is not imitation; it is Shakespeare."

I could venture no further comment without fear of offending, and he already stood as though hesitating to depart.

"Stay, then," said I, "until I see a further exercise of this marvelous power you possess. Here, sit down, rest a while; you seem almost exhausted."

"I am nearly so," he replied, "but there is no rest for me until this influence is entirely subsided. No rest for me yet; no rest! no rest!"

He was again pacing his old walk, now like a weary sentinel, and I thought as I gazed upon him, "What riddle of the human kind is this?" Over and over again came the question; and over and over an old rhyme I had somewhere read, mockingly responded—

> "Rain, rain, and sun! a rainbow in the sky!
> A young man will be wiser by and by;
> An old man's wit may wander ere he die."

And lulled by the mild monotony of this, I was fast drifting into a dreamy train of thought, when the old man halted suddenly, and with one elbow leaning on the counter and his head resting on his hand, he began humming a tune—a strangely sweet and tender air; low, and just a little harsh at first and indistinct, but welling softly into cadence wonderfully rich and pure; then quavering again in minor swoons of melody so delicately beautiful I can but liken the effect produced to that ethereal mystery of sound unraveled from the zithern by a master hand,—

"A slender thread of song in saddest tune."

I had leaned forward with my own head resting in my hand, that I might listen the better, and was not aware, until the song abruptly ended, that the old man had been writing as he sang.

"There," said he, handing me the scrap, "you have heard the tune; here are the words, perhaps."

It may have been a very foolish thing, it may have been weak and womanish, yet as my eyes bent over it and read, the lines grew curiously blurred toward the last; nor did I guess the cause until a tear—a great ripe tear-drop—fell upon my hand. And, reader, could I present the song to you just as it came to me, with all the strange surroundings—the stranger experience of the hour; the solemn silence of the group; the wailing of the wind outside as though the world, weary of itself, could only sigh, sigh, sigh!—could I prelude it with that low, sweet murmuring of melody that haunts me even now, your own eyes needs must moisten as you read:

## THE HARP OF THE MINSTREL

The harp of the minstrel has never a tone
    As sad as the song in his bosom to-night,
For the magical touch of his fingers alone
    Can not waken the echoes that breathe it aright;

But oh! as the smile of the moon may impart
  A sorrow to one in an alien clime,
Let the light of the melody fall on the heart,
  And cadence his grief into musical rhyme.

The faces have faded, the eyes have grown dim
  That once were his passionate love and his pride;
And alas! all the smiles that once blossomed for him
  Have fallen away as the flowers have died.
The hands that entwined him the laureate's wreath
  And crowned him with fame in the long, long ago,
Like the laurels are withered and folded beneath
  The grass and the stubble—the frost and the snow.

Then sigh, if thou wilt, as the whispering strings
  Strive ever in vain for the utterance clear,
And think of the sorrowful spirit that sings,
  And jewel the song with the gem of a tear.
For the harp of the minstrel has never a tone
  As sad as the song in his bosom to-night,
And the magical touch of his fingers alone
  Can not waken the echoes that breathe it aright.

I had read the lines over to myself, and although recognizing many touches decidedly like those of the famous author of "Lalla Rookh," I was not wholly satisfied with the production; and it struck me with peculiar force that an ethereal composition would surely not be so lavishly tinctured with unutterable sorrow—aside from being far inferior to a hundred earthly songs of Moore's. So, with this argument for my weapon, I determined to conquer the superstition that had almost overpowered me. I had noticed, too, in both former instances a singular fact: The old man, though so ready to fend off all comment that might reflect a single ray of praise upon himself, listened with more of the air of a critic than one whose interest was merely that of curiosity, and still when the fragmentary productions were read aloud, a look of more than ordinary satisfaction would lighten up his eyes. The facts, hastily reviewed, determined me upon a course of action I had instant opportunity to adopt.

"Read it aloud," said the old man, impatiently; "read it aloud!"

I complied with more than usual enthusiasm, reading verbatim from the copy, until I came to the repetition of the first four lines, which I thus transposed, or, rather, paraphrased.

"The harp of the minstrel has never a *note*
  As sad as the song in his bosom *expressed,*
And the magical touch of his fingers *afloat*
  *Drifts over the echoes that sleep in the breast.*"

This I was careful to deliver without emphasis or mark of any kind by which he might discover any imposition on my part. As I closed I stole a hasty glance at his face, and was gratified to find it wearing a rather startled expression: not only did his features betray a puzzled and questioning air, but his hand was mechanically extended, as though reaching for the paper in my own.

"Do you want to see it?" I asked suddenly, handing him the scrap.

"Yes, I—Oh, no—no," he broke in, dropping his

hand, and his face colored vividly. But turning
again as quickly, he added: "Yes, give it to me.
Where are the others? I must be going."

"Why must you go?" I asked, still retaining the
scrap; "I had hoped—"

"I am going!" he interrupted bruskly, snatching
up the scraps that lay upon the counter, and reaching for the one I still held. "Give me the poem. I
will trouble you no longer."

"Allow me to retain it, I beg of you," said I, with
a significant smile, and the slightest tinge of sar-
casm in my voice. "Let me keep it as a befitting
memento of the 'inspiration' I have seen so po-
tently exercised."

His face was pale with anger as he replied:

"I will not. When you want rhyme write it
yourself. You can at least write *doggerel.*"

"Very neat," said I, laughing. "We understand
each other, so let's be friends. Here is my hand
and a dollar besides. Give me the other scraps—I
want them all."

I took them from him as he clutched at the bill,
which he smothered in his palm, and then turned
away without a word.

"Here, Charley," called one of the bystanders,
"half of that's enough for you to-night."

The door slammed violently and he was gone.

"Old Cain will have that dollar in just five minutes," continued the man.

"And who's Old Cain?" I asked.

"Keeps the doggery just over the line."

"Old Charley" M—— is a well-known character in Union City—his home, in fact, although he often disappears for long periods, but, as my informant remarked, "always turns up again like a bad penny."

His story of his early life is at least based upon the truth, but now so highly colored it is a decidedly difficult matter to detect that simple element.

Originally he was a printer, but he early abandoned that vocation for another, and that in turn for another, and so on, until by easy gradations he had become, as the old saw has it, "Jack of all trades and master of none."

Among his many accomplishments he is a musician of considerable skill—plays the flute, violin, and guitar—all quite passably; is a great reader, a fine conversationalist—which accomplishment I personally vouch for. But chief of all his accomplishments is that of writing clever imitations of the old authors and poets. These productions he prepares with great care, commits to memory, and is ready to dispose of by as ingenious a method.

And yet, although he be a vagabond; although his friends—such as they are—are first to call him sot; although the selfish world that hurries past may jostle him unnoticed from the path; and although he styles himself a "graceless dog,"—in all candor, and in justice to my true belief, I call him a remarkable man.

## AN ADJUSTABLE LUNATIC

" A N 'adjustable lunatic'?"
"Yes, sir, an adjustable lunatic—you may
know I don't make a business of insanity, or I
wouldn't be running at large here in the streets of
the city."

It was on the morning of St. Patrick's Day. I
had been drifting aimlessly around the city for
hours, tossed about by the restless tide of humanity
that ebbed and flowed in true sea-fashion at the
Washington and Illinois street crossing. The few
friends I had been fortunate enough to fall in with
prior to the parade I had been unfortunate enough
to lose in the flurry and excitement attending that
event; and, brought to a sudden anchorage at the
Bates House landing, I found myself at the mercy
of a boundless throng that held not one familiar
face. It was a literal jam at that juncture, and
anxious and impatient as I was to break away, I
was forced into a bondage which, though not exactly agreeable, was at least the source of an experience that will linger in my memory fresh and clear
when every other feature of the day shall have
faded.

I had been crowded into a position on a step of

the stairway that gave me a lean upon the balustrade and placed me head and shoulders above the crowd; and although I comprehended the helplessness of my position, I was, in a manner, thankful for the opportunity it afforded me to study the unsuspecting subjects just below. As my hungry eyes went foraging about from face to face they fell upon the features of an individual so singularly abstracted in appearance and so apparently oblivious to his surroundings, that I mentally congratulated him upon his enviable disposition.

He was a slender man, of thirty years, perhaps; not tall, but something over medium height; he had dark hair and eyes, with a complexion much too fair to correspond; was not richly dressed, but neatly, and in good taste.

Instinctively I wondered who and what he was; and my speculative fancy went to work and made a lawyer of him—then a minister—an artist—a musician—an actor—and a dancing-master. Suddenly I found my stare returned with equal fervor, and tried to look away, but something held me. He was elbowing his way to where I stood, and smiling as he came.

"I don't know you," he said, when, after an almost superhuman effort, he had gained my side, to the discomfiture of a brace of mangy little bootblacks that occupied the step below—"I don't know you personally, but you look bored. I'm troubled with the same disease and want company—as the poet of the Sierras wails, 'How all alone a man may

be in crowds!'" Something in the utterance made
me offer him my hand.

He grasped it warmly. "It's curious," he said,
"how friends are made and where true fellowship
begins. Now we've known each other all our lives
and never met before. What d'ye say?"

I smiled approval at the odd assertion.

"But tell me," he continued, "what conclusion you
have arrived at in your study of me; come, now, be
frank—what do you make of me?"

Although I found myself considerably startled, I
feigned composure and acknowledged that I had
been speculating as to who and what he was, but
found myself unable to define a special character.

"I thought so," he said. "No one ever reads my
character—no one ever will. Why, I've had phre-
nologists groping around among my bumps by the
hour to no purpose, and physiognomists driving
themselves cross-eyed; but they never found it, and
they never will. The very things of which I am
capable they invariably place beyond my capacity;
and, with like sageness, the very things I can't do
they declare me to be a master hand at. But
I like to worry them; it's fun for me. Why,
old Fowler himself, here the other night, thumbed
my head as mellow as a May-apple, and never came
within a mile of it! Some characters are readable
enough, I'm willing to admit. Your face, for instance, is a bulletin-board to me, but you can't read
mine, for I'm neither a doctor, lawyer, artist, actor,
musician, nor anything else you may have in your

mind. You might guess your way all through the dictionary and then not get it. It's simply an impossibility, that's all."

I laughed uneasily, for although amused at the quaint humor of his language, a nervous fluttering of the eyes and a spasmodic twitching of the corners of his mouth made me think his manner merely an affectation. But I was interested, and as his conversation seemed to invite the interrogation, I flatly asked him to indulge my curiosity and tell me what he was.

"Wait till the crowd thins, and maybe I will. In the meantime here's a cigar and here's a light—as Mr. Quilp playfully remarks to Tom Scott—'Smoke away, you dog you!'"

"Well, you're a character," said I, dubiously.

"Yes," he replied, "but you can't tell what kind, and I can tell you the very trade you work at."

I smiled incredulously.

"Now don't look lofty and assume a professional air, for you're only a mechanic, and a sign-painter at that."

Although he spoke with little courtesy of address, there was a subtle something in his eye that drew me magnet-like and held me. I was silent.

"Want to know how I became aware of that fact?" he went on, with a quick, sharp glance at my bewildered face. "There's nothing wonderful about my knowing that; I've had my eye on you for two hours, and you stare at every sign-board you pass, worse than a country-jake; and once or twice I saw

you stop and study carefully some fresh design, or
some new style of letter. You're a stranger here in
the city, too. Want to know how I can tell? Because you walk like you were actually going some
place; but I notice that you never get there, for
continually crossing and recrossing streets, and
back-tracking past show-windows, and congratulating yourself, doubtless, upon the thorough business
air of your reflection in the plate glass. Come, we
can get through now; let's walk."

I followed him unhesitatingly. To say that I was
simply curious would be too mild; I was fascinated,
and to that degree I actually fastened on his arm,
and clung there till we had quite escaped the crowd.
"I like you, some way," he said, "but you're too
impulsive; you let your fancy get away with your
better judgment. Now, you don't know me, and
I'm even pondering whether to frankly unbosom
to you, or give you the slip; and I'll not leave the
proposition to you to decide, for I know you'd say
'unbosom'; so I'll think about it quietly for a while
yet and give you an unbiased verdict."

We walked on in silence for the distance, perhaps, of half a dozen blocks, turning and angling
about till we came upon an open stairway in an old
unpainted brick building, where my strange companion seemed to pause mechanically.

"Do you live here?" I asked.

"I stay here," he replied, "for I don't call it living
to be fastened up in this old sepulcher. I like it well
enough at night, for then I feast and fatten on the

gloom and glower that infest it; but in the normal atmosphere of day my own room looks repellent, and I only visit it, as now, out of sheer desperation."

If I had at first been mystified with this curious being, I was by this time thoroughly bewildered. The more I studied him the more at a loss I was to fathom him; and as I stood staring blankly in his face, he exclaimed almost derisively: "You give it up, don't you?"

I nodded.

"Well," he continued, "that's a good sign, and I've concluded to 'unbosom':—I'm an adjustable lunatic."

"An 'adjustable lunatic'!" I repeated, blankly. And after the remarkable proposition that ushers in the story, he continued smilingly:

"Don't be alarmed, now, for I'm glad to assure you of the fact that I'm as harmless as a baby-butterfly. Nobody knows I'm crazy, nobody ever dreams of such a thing—and why?—Because the faculty is adjustable, don't you see, and self-controlling. I never allow it to interfere with business matters, and only let it on at leisure intervals for the amusement it affords me in the pleasurable break it makes in the monotony of a matter-of-fact existence. I'm off duty to-day—in fact, I've been off duty for a week; or, to be franker still, I lost my situation ten days ago, and I've been humoring this propensity in the meanwhile; and now, if you're inclined to go up to my room with me—the

windows are both raised, you see, and you can call
for help should occasion require; people are con-
stantly passing—if you feel inclined, I say, to go
up with me, I'll do my best to entertain you. I
like you, as I said before, and you can trust me, I
assure you. Come."

If I were to attempt a description of the feelings
that possessed me as I followed my strange acquaintance up the stairway, I should fail as utterly
as one who would attempt to portray the experience
of lying in a nine-days' trance, so I leave the reader's fancy to befriend me, and hasten on to more
tangible matters.

We paused at the first landing, my companion
unlocking a door on the right, and handing me the
key with the remark: "You may feel safer with it.
And don't be frightened," he continued, "when I
open the door, for it always whines like somebody
had stepped on its knob," and I laughed at the odd
figure as he threw the door open and motioned me
to enter.

It was a queer apartment, filled with a jumbled
array of old chairs and stands; old trunks, a lounge,
and a stack of odd-shaped packages. A frowzy
carpet thrown over the floor like a blanket, and a
candle-box spittoon with a broken lamp-chimney
in it. A little swinging shelf of dusty books, with
a railroad map pasted just above it. A narrow
table with a telegraph instrument attached, and
wires like ivy-vines running all about the walls;
and scattered around the instrument was an end-

less array of zinc and copper scraps, and bits of
brass, spiral springs, and queer-shaped little tools.
A flute propped up one window, and near it, on
another stand, were a cornet and an old guitar, a
pencil sketch half finished, and a stuffed glove with
a pencil in its fingers lying on it, a spirit-lamp, a
lump of beeswax, and a hundred other odds and
ends, betokening the presence of some mechanical,
musical, scientific genius.

"It's a bachelor's room," said the host, noting my
inquisitive air.—"It's a bachelor's room, so you'll
expect no apologies. Sit down when you're through
with the industrial, and turn your attention to the
art department."

I followed the direction of his hand, and my eyes
fell upon a painted face of such ineffable sweetness
and beauty I was fairly dazed. It was not an
earthly form, at least in coloring, for the features
seemed to glow with beatific light. The eyes were
large, dark, and dewy, thrown upward with a longing look, and filled with such intensity of tenderness
one could but sigh to see them. The hair, swept
negligently back, fell down the gleaming shoulders
like a silken robe, and nestled in its glossy waves
the ears peeped shyly out like lily-blooms. The lips
were parted with an utterance that one could almost
hear, and weep for because the blessed voice was
mute. The hands were folded on a crumpled letter
and pressed close against the heart, and a curl of
golden hair was coiled around the fingers.

"Is it a creation of the fancy?" I asked.

"Well, yes," he answered, with a dreamy drawl. "I call it fancy, when in a normal state; but now," he continued, in a fainter tone, "I will designate it as a portrait." And oh, so sad, so hopeless and despairing was the utterance, it seemed to well up from the fountain of his heart like a spray of purest sorrow.

"Who painted it?" I asked.

" 'Who painted it?' " he repeated, drowsily—" 'who painted it?' Oh, no; I mustn't tell you that; for if I answered you with 'Raphael,' you'd say, 'Ah, no! the paint's too fresh for that, and he's been dead for ages.' 'Who painted it? No, no, I mustn't tell you that!'"

"But are you not an artist?—I see an easel in the corner there, and here's a mahlstick lying on the mantel."

"I an artist? Why, man, what ails you? I told you not ten minutes since that I was an adjustable lunatic; and don't you see I am?—You can't mislead me nor throw me off my guard. When it comes to reason or solid logic, don't you find me there? And here again, to show the clearness of my judgment, I remove the cause of our little dissension, and our friendly equanimity is restored—" and he turned the picture to the wall.

I could but smile at the gravity and adroitness of his language and demeanor.

"There," said he, smiling in return; "your face is brighter than the day outside; let's change the topic. Do you like music?"

"Passionately," I responded.  "Will you play?"

"No; I will sing."

He took the guitar from the table, and, with a prelude wilder than the "Witches' Dance," he sang a song he called "The Dream of Death," a grievously sad song, so full of minor tones and wailing words, the burden of it still lingers in my ears:

"O gentle death, bow down and sip
The soul that lingers on my lip;
O gentle death, bow down and keep
Eternal vigil o'er my sleep;
For I am weary and would rest
Forever on your loving breast."

His voice, as plaintive as a dove's, went trailing through the rondel like weariness itself; and when at last it died away in one long quaver of ecstatic melody, though I felt within my heart an echoing of grief

"Too sweetly sad to name as pain,"

I broke the silence following to remind him of his having told me he was not a musician.

"Only a novice," he responded.—"One may twang a lute and yet not be a troubadour. By the way," he broke off abruptly, "is that expression original with me, or have I picked it up in some old book of rhyme?—Oh, yes! How do you like poetry?"

He sprang to his feet as he spoke, and without

awaiting an answer to his query went diving about
in a huge waste-basket standing near the table.

"It's a thing I dislike to acknowledge," he went
on, "but I don't mind telling you. The fact is, I'm
a follower of Wegg and sometimes 'drop into
poetry—as a friend,' you understand; and if you'll
'lend me your ears,' I'll give you a specimen of my
versification."

He had drawn up a roll of paper from the débris
of the basket, and unrolling it with a flourish, and a
mock-heroic air of inspiration, he read as follows:

> "A fantasy that came to me
>   As wild and wantonly designed
> As ever any dream might be
>   Unraveled from a madman's mind,—
> A tangle-work of tissue, wrought
>   By cunning of the spider-brain,
>   And woven, in an hour of pain,
> To trap the giddy flies of thought——."

He paused, and with a look of almost wild entreaty he pleaded: "You understand it, don't you?"

I nodded hesitatingly.

"Why, certainly you do. The meaning's the
plainest thing in it. What's your idea of its meaning? tell me!—Why don't you tell me!"

"Read it again that I may note it carefully."

He repeated it.

"Why," said I, "it appears to me to be the introduction to a poem written under peculiar circumstances, and containing, perhaps, some strange ideas

that the author would excuse for the reason of their coming in the way they did."

"Right!" he exclaimed, joyously; "and now if you'll give me your most critical attention, and promise not to interrupt, I'll read the poem entire."

"Go on," I said, for I was far more eager to listen than I would have him know.

"And will you excuse any little wildness of gesture or expression that I may see fit to introduce in the rendition?"

"Certainly," said I, "certainly; go on!"

"And you won't interrupt or get excited? Light another cigar; and here's a chair to throw your feet across. Now, unbutton your coat and lean back. Are you thoroughly comfortable?"

"Thoroughly," said I, impatiently—"a thousand thoroughlies."

"All right," he said; "I'm glad to hear you say it; but before I proceed I desire to call your attention to the fact that this poem is a literary orphan —a foundling, you understand?"

"I understand; go on."

And with a manner all too wild to be described, he read, or rather recited, the following monstrosity of rhyme:

> "I stood beneath a summer moon
>     All swollen to uncanny girth,
> And hanging, like the sun at noon,
>     Above the center of the earth;
>     But with a sad and sallow light,
>     As it had sickened of the night

And fallen in a pallid swoon.
Around me I could hear the rush
    Of sullen winds, and feel the whir
Of unseen wings apast me brush
    Like phantoms round a sepulcher;
And, like a carpeting of plush,
    A lawn unrolled beneath my feet,
    Bespangled o'er with flowers as sweet
To look upon as those that nod
Within the garden-fields of God,
    But odorless as those that blow
    In ashes in the shades below.

"And on my hearing fell a storm
    Of gusty music, sadder yet
    Than every whimper of regret
That sobbing utterance could form,
    And patched with scraps of sound that seemed
    Torn out of tunes that demons dreamed,
    And pitched to such a piercing key,
    It stabbed the ear with agony;
    And when at last it lulled and died,
    I stood aghast and terrified.
I shuddered and I shut my eyes,
    And still could see, and feel aware
    Some mystic presence waited there;
And staring, with a dazed surprise,
    I saw a creature so divine
    That never subtle thought of mine
    May reproduce to inner sight
    So fair a vision of delight.

"A syllable of dew that drips
From out a lily's laughing lips
Could not be sweeter than the word
I listened to, yet never heard.—
For, oh, the woman hiding there
Within the shadows of her hair,

Spake to me in an undertone
So delicate, my soul alone
But understood it as a moan
Of some weak melody of wind
A heavenward breeze had left behind.

"A tracery of trees, grotesque
　　Against the sky, behind her seen,
Like shapeless shapes of arabesque
　　Wrought in an oriental screen;
And tall, austere and statuesque
　　She loomed before it—e'en as though
　　The spirit-hand of Angelo
　　Had chiseled her to life complete,
　　With chips of moonshine round her feet.
And I grew jealous of the dusk,
　　To see it softly touch her face,
　　As lover-like, with fond embrace,
It folded round her like a husk:
But when the glitter of her hand,
　　Like wasted glory, beckoned me,
　　My eyes grew blurred and dull and dim—
　　My vision failed—I could not see—
I could not stir—I could but stand,
　　Till, quivering in every limb,
　　I flung me prone, as though to swim
　　The tide of grass whose waves of green
　　Went rolling ocean-wide between
　　My helpless shipwrecked heart and her
　　Who claimed me for a worshiper.

"And writhing thus in my despair,
　　I heard a weird, unearthly sound,
　　That seemed to lift me from the ground
And hold me floating in the air.
I looked, and lo! I saw her bow
　　Above a harp within her hands;
A crown of blossoms bound her brow,

> And on her harp were twisted strands
> Of silken starlight, rippling o'er
> With music never heard before
> By mortal ears; and, at the strain,
> I felt my Spirit snap its chain
> And break away,—and I could see
> It as it turned and fled from me
> To greet its mistress, where she smiled
> To see the phantom dancing wild
> And wizard-like before the spell
> Her mystic fingers knew so well."

I sat throughout it all as though under the strange influence of an Eastern drug. My fancy was so wrought upon I only saw the reader mistily, and clothed, as it were, in a bedragoned costume of the Orient. My mind seemed idle—steeped in drowse and languor, and yet peopled with a thousand shadowy fancies that came trooping from chaotic hiding-places, and mingling in a revelry of such riotous extravagance it seemed a holiday of elfish thought.

I shook my head, I rubbed my eyes, arose bewildered, and sat down again; arose again and walked across the room, my strange companion following every motion with an intensity of gaze almost mesmeric.

"You fail to comprehend it?" he queried.

I shook my head.

"You can almost grasp it, can't you?"

"Yes," I answered.

"But not quite?"

"Not quite."

"Does it worry you?"

"Yes."

"Think it will cling to you, and fret you, vex you, haunt you?"

"I know it will."

"Think you'll ever fully comprehend it?"

"I can't say," I replied, thoughtfully.—"Perhaps I may in time.  Will you allow me to copy it?"

"What do you want with it?"

"I want to study it," I replied.

"And you're sure you don't understand it, and it worries you, and frets you, and vexes you, and haunts you?  Good!  I'll read you the final clause now; that may throw a light of some kind on it"; and, opening the scroll, again he read:

> "What is it?  Who will rightly guess
> If it be aught but nothingness
> That dribbles from a wayward pen
> To spatter in the eyes of men?
> What matter!  I will call it mine,
>     And I will take the changeling home
> And bathe its face with morning-shine,
>     And comb it with a golden comb
>     Till every tangled tress of rhyme
>     Will fairer be than summer-time:
> And I will nurse it on my knee,
>     And dandle it beyond the clasp
>     Of hands that grip and hands that grasp,
> Through life and all eternity!"

"Now what do you think of it?" he asked with a savageness that startled me.

"I am more at sea than ever," I replied.

"Well, I wish you a prosperous voyage! Here's the poem; I've another copy. 'Read and reflect,' as the railroad poster says, but don't you publish it—at least while I'm alive, for I've no thirst for literary fame—I only write for home-use; but you're a good fellow, and I like you for all your weak points, and I trust the confidence I repose will not be disregarded. Come!"

He had opened the door and was holding out his hand for the key.

I gave it to him and followed out mechanically. He left the door ajar and followed to the bottom of the stairs.

"And now if you'll pardon me," he said, "I'll say good-by to you here; I've some packing to do and ought to be at it."

"Why, you're not going to leave the city?" I asked.

"Well, no, not to-day; but the jig's up with me here, and it's only a question of time—I can't hold out much longer—as our rural friend remarks, 'Money matters is mighty sceerce'; and if I don't pull out shortly I'll have to 'fold my tent like the Bedouin and silently plagiarize away!'"

"If I could be of any assistance to you—" I began, but he checked me abruptly with, "Oh, no, I don't require it, I assure you; I've two dollars to your one, doubtless. Thank you just the same, and good-by. Here's my card; it's not my name, however, but it'll answer; I'll not see you again, though you should live to be as bald as a brickyard, for, my dear young friend, I'm going away. Good-by, and may all good things overtake you!"

He gripped my hand like a vise, and turning quickly, went skipping up the stairway two steps at a time.

"Good-by!" I called to him, sorrowfully; then turned reluctantly away, examining the card he had given me, which, to my astonishment, was not his card at all, but a railroad ticket entitling the bearer to a ride from Danville, Illinois, to York, Pennsylvania; this fact I remember quite distinctly, as I read it over and over, revolving in my mind the impression that this was but another instance of his eccentricity, or perhaps a trick by which I might be victimized in some undreamed-of way. But upon second thought I concluded it to be simply a mistake, and so turned back and called him to the window above and explained.

He came down and begged my pardon for the trouble he had given me, took the ticket, thanked me, and said good-by again.

"But," said I, "you haven't given me your real card in exchange."

"Oh, no matter!" he said smilingly. "Call me Smith, Jones or Robinson, it's all the same; good-by, and don't forget your old friend and well-wisher, the Adjustable Lunatic." And even thus he vanished from my sight forever.

The remainder of the day and half of the night I spent in studious contemplation of the curious composition, but without arriving at any tangible conclusion. I am still engaged with my investigation. Sometimes the meaning seems almost within my mental grasp; but, balancing, adjusting, and comparing its many curious bearings, I find my judgment persistently at fault. It has puzzled and bewildered me for weeks. No line of it but canters through my brain like a fractious nightmare; no syllable but fastens on my fancy like a leech, and sucks away the life-blood of my every thought. I am troubled, worried, fretted, vexed, and haunted; and I write this now in the earnest hope that wiser minds may have an opportunity of making it a subject of investigation, and because one week ago to-day my eyes fell upon the following special telegram to *The Indianapolis Journal:*

PERU, IND., April 12.—An unknown man committed suicide in the eastward-bound train on the Wabash road, just below Waverly, at about 11 o'clock this morning. He had in his possession, besides the revolver with which he shot himself, a ticket from Danville, Illinois, to York, Pennsylvania, a gold watch, $19 in money, a small valise, and some letters and other papers which indicated his name to be George S. Clofling.

He was shot twice in the region of the heart, and his revolver showed that between the first and last shots two cartridges missed fire.

# TWIGGS AND TUDENS

IF my old school-chum and roommate John
Skinner is alive to-day—and no doubt he *is*
alive, and quite so, being, when last heard from,
the very alert and effective train despatcher at
Butler, Indiana,—he will not have forgotten a certain night, that of June the eighth, 1870, in "Old
Number 'Leven" of the Dunbar House, Greenfield,
when he and I sat the long night through, getting
ready a famous issue of our old school-paper, "The
Criterion." And he will remember, too, the queer
old man who occupied, but that one night, the room
just opposite our own, "Number 13." For reasons
wholly aside from any superstitious dread connected
with the numerals, Thirteen was not a desirable
room; its locality was alien to all accommodations,
and its comforts, like its furnishings, were extremely meager. In fact, it was the room usually
assigned to the tramp-printer, who, in those days,
was an institution; or again, it was the local habita-
tion of the oft-recurring transient customer who
was too incapacitated to select a room himself
when he retired—or rather, when he was personally retired by "the hostler," as the gentlemanly
night clerk of that era was habitually designated.

As both Skinner and myself—between fitful
terms of school—had respectively served as "printer's devil" in the two rival newspaper offices of the
town, it was natural for us to find a ready interest
in anything pertaining to the newspaper business;
and so it was, perhaps, that we had been selected,
by our own approval and that of our fellow students of the graded schools, to fill the rather
exalted office of editing "The Criterion." Certain
it is that the rather abrupt rise from the lowly
duties of the "roller" to the editorial management
of a paper of our own (even if issued in handwriting) we accepted as a natural right; and, vested in
our new power of office, we were largely "shaping
the whisper of the throne" about our way.

And upon this particular evening it was, as John
and I had fairly squared ourselves for the work of
the night, that we heard the clatter and shuffle of
feet on the side stairs, and, an instant later, the
hostler establishing some poor unfortunate in Thirteen, just across the hall.

"Listen!" said John, as we heard an old man's
voice through the open transom of our door,—
"listen at that!"

It was an utterance peculiarly refined, in language
as well as intonation. A low, mild, rather apologetic voice, gently assuring the hostler that "everything was very snug and comfortable indeed—so
far as the *compartment* was concerned—but would
not the *attendant* kindly supply a better light, together with pen-and-ink—and just a sheet or two

of paper,—if he would be so very good as to find a
pardon for so very troublesome a guest."

"Hain't no writin'-paper," said the hostler,
briefly,—"and the big lamps is all in use. These
fellers here in 'Leven might let you have some
paper and—Hain't *you* got a lead-pencil?"

"Oh, no matter!" came the impatient yet kindly
answer of the old voice—"no matter at all, my good
fellow!—Good night—good night!"

We waited till the sullen, clumpy footsteps down
the hall and stair had died away.

Then Skinner, with a handful of foolscap, opened
our door; and, with an indorsing smile from me,
crossed the hall and tapped at Thirteen—was ad-
mitted—entered, and very quietly closed the door
behind him, evidently that I might not be disturbed.

I wrote on in silence for quite a time. It was, in
fact, a full half-hour before John had returned,—
and with a face and eye absolutely blazing with
delight.

"An old printer," whispered John, answering my
look,—"and we're in luck:—He's a *genius,* 'y God!
and an Englishman, and knows Dickens *personally*
—used to write races with him, and's got a manuscript of his in his 'portmanteau,' as he calls an old
oil-cloth knapsack with one lung clean gone. Excuse this extra light.—Old man's lamp's like a sore
eye, and he's going to touch up the Dickens sketch
for *us! Hear?—For us*—for "The Criterion." Says
he can't sleep—he's in distress—has a presentiment

—some dear friend is dying—or dead now—and he must write—*write!"*

This is, in briefest outline, the curious history of the subjoined sketch, especially curious for the reason that the following morning's cablegram announced that the great novelist, Charles Dickens, had been stricken suddenly and seriously the night previous. On the day of this announcement—even as "The Criterion" was being read to perfunctorily interested visitors of the Greenfield graded schools —came the further announcement of Mr. Dickens' death. The old printer's manuscript, here reproduced, is, as originally, captioned—

### TWIGGS AND TUDENS

"Now who'd want a more cozier little home than me and Tude's got here?" asked Mr. Twiggs, as his twinkling eyes swept caressingly around the cheery little room in which he, alone, stood one chill December evening as the great Saint Paul's was drawling six.

"This ain't no princely hall with all its gorgeous paraphanaly, as the play-bills says; but it's what I calls a' 'interior,' which for meller comfort and cheerful surroundin's ain't to be ekalled by no other 'flat' on the boundless, never-endin' stage of this existence!" And as the exuberant Mr. Twiggs rendered this observation, he felt called upon to smile and bow most graciously to an invisible audience, whose wild approval he in turn interpreted by an

enthusiastic clapping of his hands and the cry of
"Ongcore!" in a dozen different keys—this strange
acclamation being made the more grotesque by a
great green parrot perched upon the mantel, which,
in a voice less musical than penetrating, chimed in
with "Hooray for Twiggs and Tudens!" a very
great number of times.

"Tude's a queer girl," said Mr. Twiggs, subsid-
ing into a reflective calm, broken only by the puf-
fing of his pipe, and the occasional articulation of
a thought, as it loitered through his mind. "Tude's
a queer girl!—a werry queer girl!" repeated Mr.
Twiggs, pausing again, with a long whiff at his pipe,
and marking the graceful swoop the smoke made
as it dipped and disappeared up the wide, black-
throated chimney; and then, as though dropping
into confidence with the great fat kettle on the coals,
that steamed and bubbled with some inner paroxysm, he added, "And queer and nothink short,
is the lines for Tude, eh?

"Now s'posin'," he continued, leaning forward
and speaking in a tone whose careful intonation
might have suggested a more than ordinary depth
of wisdom and sagacity,—"s'posin' a pore chap
like me, as ain't no property only this-'ere 'little
crooked house,' as Tude calls it, and some o' the
properties I 'andles at the Drury—as I was a-sayin',—s'posin' now a' old rough chap like me was
jest to tell her all about herself, and who she is and
all, and not no kith or kin o' mine, let alone a
daughter, as *she* thinks—What do you reckon now

'ud be the upshot, eh?" And as Mr. Twiggs propounded this mysterious query he jabbed the poker
prankishly in the short-ribs of the grate, at which
the pot, as though humoring a joke it failed to comprehend wholly, set up a chuckling of such asth-
matic violence that its smothered cachinnations
tilted its copper lid till Mr. Twiggs was obliged to
dash a cup of water in its face.

"And Tude's a-comin' of a' age, too," continued
Mr. Twiggs, "when a more tenderer pertecter than
a father, so to speak, wouldn't be out o' keepin'
with the nat'ral order o' things, seein' as how she's
sort o' startin' for herself-like now. And it's a question in my mind, if it ain't my bounden duty as
her father—or ruther, who has been a father to her
all her life—to kind o' tell her jest how things is,
and all—and how *I* am, and everythink,—and how
I feel as though I ort'o stand by her, as I allus have,
and allus *have* had her welfare in view, and kind o'
feel as how I allus—ort'o kind o'—ort'o kind o'"—
and here Mr. Twiggs' voice fell into silence so
abruptly that the drowsy parrot started from its
trance-like quiet and cried "Ortokindo! Ortokindo!" with such a strength of seeming mockery
that it was brushed violently to the floor by the
angry hand of Mr. Twiggs and went backing awkwardly beneath the table.

"Blow me," said Mr. Twiggs, "if the knowin'
impidence of that-'ere bird ain't astonishin'!" And
then, after a serious controversy with the draught
of his pipe, he went on with his deliberations.

"Lor'! it were jest scrumptious to see Tude in 'The Iron Chest' last night! Now, I ain't no actur myself,—I've been on, of course, a thousand times as 'fillin',' 'sogers' and 'peasants' and the like, where I never had no lines, on'y in the 'choruses'; but if I don't know nothin' but 'All hail!—All hail!' I've had the experience of bein' under the baleful hin-fluence of the hoppery-glass, and I'm free to say it air a ticklish position and no mistake. But *Tude!* w'y, bless you, she warn't the first bit flustered, was she? 'Peared-like she jest felt perfectly at home-like—like her mother afore her! And I'm dashed if I didn't feel the cold chills a-creepin' and a-crawl-in' when she was a-singin' 'Down by the river there grows a green willer and a-weepin' all night with the bank for her piller'; and when she come to the part about wantin' to be buried there 'while the winds was a-blowin' close by the stream where her tears was a-flowin', and over her corpse to keep the green willers growin',' I'm d—d if I didn't blubber right out!" And as the highly sympathetic Mr. Twiggs delivered this acknowledgment, he stroked the inner corners of his eyes, and rubbed his thumb and finger on his trousers.

"It were a tryin' thing, though," he went on, his mellow features settling into a look not at all in keeping with his shiny complexion—"it were a tryin' thing, and it *air* a tryin' thing to see them lovely arms o' hern a-twinin' so lovin'-like around that-'ere Stanley's neck and a-kissin' of him—as she's obleeged to do, of course—as the 'properties' of the

play demands; but I'm blowed if she wouldn't do it
quite as nat'ral-like I'd feel easier. Blow me!" he
broke off savagely, starting up and flinging his pipe
in the ashes, "I'm about a-comin' to the conclusion
I ain't got no more courage'n a blasted schoolboy!
Here I am old enough to be her father—mighty
nigh it—and yet I'm actually afeard to speak up
and tell her jest how things is, and all, and how I
feel like I—like I—ort'o—ort'o—"

*"Ortokindo! Ortokindo!"* shrieked the parrot,
clinging in a reversed position to the under round of
a chair.—*"Ortokindo! Ortokindo! Tude's come
home!—Tude's come home!"* And as though in
happy proof of this latter assertion, the gentle Mr.
Twiggs found his chubby neck encircled by a pair
of rosy arms, and felt upon his cheek the sudden
pressure of a pair of lips that thrilled his old heart
to the core. And then the noisy bird dropped from
its perch and marched pompously from its place
of concealment, trailing its rusty wings and shriek-
ing, "Tude's come home!" at the top of its brazen
voice.

"Shet up!" screamed Mr. Twiggs, with a pre-
tended gust of rage, kicking lamely at the feathered
oracle; "I'll 'Tude's-come-home' ye! W'y, a feller
can't hear his *ears* for your infernal squawkin'!"
And then, turning toward the serious eyes that
peered rebukingly into his own, his voice fell gentle as a woman's: "Well, there, Tudens, I beg pard-
ing; I do indeed. Don't look at me thataway. I
know I'm a great, rough, good-for—" But a warm,

swift kiss cut short the utterance; and as the girl drew back, still holding the bright old face between her tender palms, he said simply, "You're a queer girl, Tudens; a queer girl."

"Ha! am I?" said the girl, in quite evident heroics and quotation, starting back with a theatrical flourish and falling into a fantastic attitude.— " 'Troth, I am sorry for it; me poor father's heart is bursting with gratichude, and he would fain ease it by pouring out his thanks to his benefactor.' "

"Werry good! Werry good, indeed!" said Mr. Twiggs, gazing wistfully upon the graceful figure of the girl. "You're a-growin' more wonderful' clever in your 'presence' every day, Tude. You don't think o' nothink else but your actin', do ye, now?" And, as Mr. Twiggs concluded his observations, a something very like a sigh came faltering from his lips.

"Why, listen there! Ah-ha!" laughed Tude, clapping her hands and dancing gaily around his chair. —"Why, you old melancholy Dane, you!—are you actually *sighing?*" Then, dropping into a tragic air of deep contrition, she continued: " 'But, believe me, I would not question you, but to console you, Wilford. I would scorn to pry into any one's grief, much more yours, Wilford, to satisfy a busy curiosity.' "

"Oh, don't, Tude; don't *rehearse* like that at me! —I can't a-bear it." And the serious Mr. Twiggs held out his hand as though warding off a blow.

At this appeal the girl's demeanor changed to one of tenderest solicitude.

"Why, Pop'm," she said, laying her hand on his shoulder, "I did not mean to vex you—forgive me. I was only trying to be happy, as I ought, although my own heart is this very minute heavy—very heavy—very.—No, no; I don't mean that—but, Father, Father, I have not been dutiful."

"W'y, yes, you have," broke in Mr. Twiggs, smothering the heavy exclamation in his handkerchief. "You ain't been undutiful, nor nothink else. You're jest all and everythink that heart could wish. It's all my own fault, Tudens; it's all my fault. You see, I git to thinkin' sometimes like I was a-goin' to *lose* you; and now that you are a-comin' on in years, and gittin' such a fine start, and all, and position and everythink.—Yes-sir! *position,* 'cause everybody likes you, Tudens. You know that; and I'm that proud of you and all, and that selfish, that its onpossible I could ever, ever give you up;—never, never, *ever* give you up!" And Mr. Twiggs again stifled his voice in his handkerchief and blew his nose with prolonged violence.

It may have been the melancholy ticking of the clock, as it grated on the silence following, it may have been the gathering darkness of the room, or the plaintive sighing of the rising wind without, that caused the girl to shudder as she stooped to kiss the kind old face bent forward in the shadows, and turned with feigned gaiety to the simple task of

arranging supper. But when, a few minutes later,
she announced that Twiggs' and Tudens' tea was
waiting, the two smilingly sat down, Mr. Twiggs
remarking that if he only knew a blessing, he'd
ask it upon that occasion most certainly.

"—For on'y look at these-'ere 'am and eggs,"
he said, admiringly: "I'd like to know if the Queen
herself could cook 'em to a nicer turn, or serve 'em
up more tantaliz-in'er to the palate. And this-'ere
soup,—or whatever it is, is rich as gravy; and these
boughten rolls ain't a bad thing either, split in two
and toasted as you do 'em, air they, Tude?" And
as Mr. Twiggs glanced inquiringly at his companion,
he found her staring vacantly at her plate. "I was
jest a-sayin', Tudens—" he went on, pretending
to blow his tea and glancing cautiously across his
saucer.

"Yes, Pop'm, I heard you;—we really *ought* to
have a blessing, by all means."

Mr. Twiggs put down his tea without tasting it.
"Tudens," he said, after a long pause, in which he
carefully buttered a piece of toast for the second
time,—"Tudens, I'm most afeard you didn't grasp
that last remark of mine: I was a-sayin'—"

"Well—" said Tudens, attentively.

"I was a-sayin'," said Mr. Twiggs, averting his
face and staring stoically at his toast—"I was
a-sayin' that you was a-gittin' now to be quite a
young woman."

"Oh, so you were," said Tudens, with charming
naïveté.

"Well," said Mr. Twiggs, repentantly, but with a humorous twinkle, "if I wasn't a-sayin' of it, I was *a-thinkin'* it."—And then, running along hurriedly, "And I've been a-thinkin' it for days and days—ever sence you left the 'balley' and went in 'chambermaids,' and last in leadin' rôles. Maybe *you* ain't noticed it, but I've had my eyes on you from the 'flies' and the 'wings'; and jest betwixt us, Tudens, and not for me as ort to know better, and does know better, to go a-flatterin', at my time o'—or to go a-flatterin' anybody, as I said, after you're a-gittin' to be a young woman—and what's more, a werry *'andsome* young woman!"

"*Why, Pop'm!*" exclaimed Tudens, blushing.

"Yes, you are, Tudens, and I mean it, every word of it; and as I was a-goin' on to say, I've been a-watchin' of you, and a-layin' off a long time jest to tell you sommat that will make your eyes open wider 'an that! What I mean," said Mr. Twiggs, coughing vehemently and pushing his chair back from the table—"what I mean is, you'll soon be old enough to be a-settin' up for yourself-like, and a-marry'—W'y, Tudens, what *ails* you?" The girl had risen to her feet, and, with a face dead white and lips all tremulous, stood clinging to her chair for support. "What ails you, Tudens?" repeated Mr. Twiggs, rising to his feet and gazing on her with a curious expression of alarm and tenderness.

"Nothing serious, dear Pop'm," said Tudens, with a flighty little laugh,—"only it just flashed on me all at once that I'd clean forgotten poor Dick's supper." And as she turned abruptly to the parrot, cooing and clucking to him playfully,—up, up from some hitherto undreamed-of depth within the yearning heart of Mr. Twiggs mutely welled the old utterance, "Tude's a queer girl!"

"Whatever made you think of such a thing, Father?" called Tudens, gaily; and then, without waiting for an answer, went on cooing to the parrot,—"Hey, old dicky-bird! do *you* think Tudens is a handsome young woman? and do *you* think Tudens is old enough to marry, eh?" This query delivered, she broke into a fit of merriment which so wrought upon the susceptibilities of the bird that he was heard repeatedly to declare and affirm, in most positive and unequivocal terms, that Tude had actually come home.

"Yes—*sir,* Tudens!" broke in Mr. Twiggs at last, lighting a fresh churchwarden and settling into his old position at the grate; "have your laugh out over it now, but it's a werry serious fact, for all that."

"I know it, Father," said the girl, recovering her gravity, turning her large eyes lovingly upon him and speaking very tenderly. "I know it—oh, I know it; and many, many times when I have thought of it, and then again of your old kindly faith; all the warm wealth of your love; and our old home here, and all the happiness it ever held for me and you alike—oh, I have tried hard—indeed, indeed I have—to put all other thought away and live for you alone! But, Pop'm! dear old Pop'm—" And even as the great strong breast made shelter for her own, the woman's heart within her flowed away in mists of gracious tears.

"Couldn't live without old Pop'm, could her?" half cried and laughed the happy Mr. Twiggs, tangling his clumsy fingers in the long dark hair that fell across his arm, and bending till his glad face touched her own.—"Couldn't live without old Pop'm?"

"Never! never!" sobbed the girl, lifting her brimming eyes and gazing in the kind old face. "Oh, may I always live with you, Pop'm? Always?—Forever?—"

"—And a day!" said Mr. Twiggs, emphatically.

"Even after I'm—" and she hid her face again.

"Even after—*what,* Tudens?"

"After I'm—after I'm—married?" murmured Tudens, with a longing pressure.

"Nothink short!" said Mr. Twiggs;—"perwidin'," he added, releasing one hand and smoothing back his scanty hair—"perwidin', of course, that your man is a' honest, straitforrerd feller, as ain't no lordly notions nor nothink o' that sort."

"Nor rich?"

"Well, I ain't so p'ticklar about his bein' *pore,* adzackly.—Say a feller as works for his livin', and knows how to 'usband his earnin's thrifty-like, and allus 'as a hextry crown or two laid up against a rainy day—and a good perwider, of course," said

Mr. Twiggs, with a comfortable glance around the room.—"'Ll blow me if I didn't see a face there a-peerin' in the winder!"

"Oh, no, you didn't," said the girl, without raising her head. "Go on—'and a good provider—'"

"—A good perwider," continued Mr. Twiggs; "and a feller, of course, as has a' eye out for the substantials of this life, and ain't afeard o' work— that's the idear! that's the idear!" said Mr. Twiggs, by way of sweeping conclusion.

"And that's all old Pop'm asks, after all?" queried the girl, with her radiant face wistful as his own.

"W'y, certainly!" said Mr. Twiggs, with heartiness. "Ain't that all and everythink to make home happy?"—catching her face between his great brown hands and kissing her triumphantly.

"Hooray for Twiggs-and Twiggs-and Twiggs-and—" cootered the drowsy bird, disjointedly.

The girl had risen.—"And you'll forgive me for marrying such a man?"

"Won't I?" said Mr. Twiggs, with a rapturous twinkle.

As he spoke, she flung her arms about his neck and pressed her lips close, close against his cheek, her own glad face now fronting the little window. . . . She heard the clicking of the latch, the opening of the door, and the step of the intruder ere she loosed her hold.

"God bless you, Pop'm, and forgive me!—This is my husband."

The newcomer, Mr. Stanley, reached and grasped the hand of Mr. Twiggs, eagerly, fervidly, albeit the face he looked on then will haunt him to the hour of his death.—Yet haply, some day, when the Master takes the selfsame hand within his own and whispers, "Tude's come home," the old smile will return.

# AN OLD SETTLER'S STORY

WILLIAM WILLIAMS his name was—er so
he said;—Bill Williams they called him, and
them 'at knowed him best called him Bill Bills.

The first I seed o' Bills was about two weeks
after he got here. The Settlement wasn't nothin'
but a baby in them days, fer I mind 'at old Ezry
Sturgiss had jest got his saw and griss-mill a-goin',
and Bills had come along and claimed to know all
about millin', and got a job with him; and millers
in them times was wanted worse'n congerssmen, and
I reckon got better wages; fer afore Ezry built,
there wasn't a dust o' meal er flour to be had short
o' the White Water, better'n sixty mil'd from here,
the way we had to fetch it. And they used to come
to Ezry's fer their grindin' as fur as that; and one
feller I knowed to come from what used to be the
old South Fork, over eighty mil'd from here, and
in the wettest, rainyest weather; and mud! *Law!*

Well, this-here Bills was a-workin' fer Ezry at
the time—part the time a-grindin', and part the
time a-lookin' after the sawin', and gittin' out tim-
ber and the like. Bills was a queer-lookin' feller,
shore: About as tall a build man as Tom Carter—
but of course you don't know nothin' o' Tom Car-

ter. A great big hulk of a feller, Tom was; and as
fur back as Fifty-eight used to make his brags that
he could cut and putt up his seven cord a day.

Well, what give Bills this queer look, as I was
a-goin' on to say, was a great big ugly scar a-runnin'
from the corner o' one eye clean down his face and
neck, and I don't know how fur down his breast—
awful lookin'; and he never shaved, and there wasn't
a hair a-growin' in that scar, and it looked like a—
some kind o' pizen snake er somepin' a-crawlin' in
the grass and weeds. I never seed sich a' out-and-
out ornry-lookin' chap, and I'll never fergit the first
time I set eyes on him.

Steve and me—Steve was my youngest brother;
Steve's be'n in Californy now fer, le' me see,—well,
anyways, I rickon, over thirty year.—Steve was a-
drivin' the team at the time—I allus let Steve drive;
'peared like Steve was made a-purpose fer hosses.
The beatin'est hand with hosses 'at ever you *did*
see and-I-know! W'y, a hoss, after he got kind o'
used to Steve a-handlin' of him, would do anything
fer *him!* And I've knowed that boy to swap fer
hosses 'at couldn't hardly make a shadder; and,
afore you knowed it, Steve would have 'em a-ca-
vortin' around a-lookin' as peert and fat and slick!

Well, we'd come over to Ezry's fer some grindin'
that day; and Steve wanted to price some lumber fer
a house, intendin' to marry that fall—and would
a-married, I reckon, ef the girl hadn't a-died jest as
she'd got her weddin' clothes done—and that set
hard on Steve fer a while. Yit he rallied, you know,

as a youngster will; but he never married, someway
—never married. Reckon he never found no other
woman he could love well enough—'less it was—
well, no odds.—The Good Bein's jedge o' what's
best fer each and all.

We lived *then* about eight mil'd from Ezry's and
it tuck about a day to make the trip; so you kin
kind o' git an idy o' how the roads was in them days.

Well, on the way over I noticed Steve was mighty
quiet-like, but I didn't think nothin' of it, tel at
last he says, says he, "Ben, I want you to kind o'
keep an eye out fer Ezry's new hand"—meanin'
Bills. And then I kind o' suspicioned somepin' o'
nother was up betwixt 'em; and shore enough there
was, as I found out afore the day was over.

I knowed 'at Bills was a mean sort of a man, from
what I'd heerd. His name was all over the neighberhood afore he'd be'n here two weeks.

In the first place, he come in a suspicious sort o'
way: Him and his wife, and a little baby on'y a
few months old, come through in a kivvered wagon
with a fambly a-goin' some'eres in The Illinoy; and
they stopped at the mill, fer some meal er somepin',
and Bills got to talkin' with Ezry 'bout millin', and
one thing o' nother, and said he was expeerenced
some 'bout a mill hisse'f, and told Ezry ef he'd give
him work he'd stop; said his wife and baby wasn't
strong enough to stand trav'lin', and ef Ezry'd give
him work he was ready to lick into it then and
there; said his woman could pay her board by sewin'
and the like, tel they got ahead a little; and then,

ef he liked the neighberhood, he said he'd as lif settle there as anywheres; he was huntin' a home, he said, and the outlook kind o' struck him, and his woman railly needed rest, and wasn't strong enough to go much furder. And old Ezry kind o' tuk pity on the feller; and havin' house-room to spare, and railly in need of a good hand at the mill, he said all right; and so the feller stopped and the wagon druv ahead and left 'em; and they didn't have no things ner nothin'—not even a cyarpet-satchel, ner a stitch o' clothes, on'y what they had on their backs. And I think it was the third er fourth day after Bills stopped 'at he whirped Tomps Burk, the bully o' here them days, tel you wouldn't 'a' knowed him!

Well, I'd heerd o' this, and the facts is I'd made up my mind 'at Bills was a bad stick, and the place wasn't none the better fer his bein' here. But, as I was a-goin' on to say,—as Steve and me driv up to the mill, I ketched sight o' Bills the first thing, a-lookin' out o' where some boards was knocked off, jest over the worter-wheel; and he knowed Steve—I could see that by his face; and he hollered somepin', too, but what it was I couldn't jest make out, fer the noise o' the wheel; but he looked to me as ef he'd hollered somepin' mean a-purpose so's Steve *wouldn't* hear it, and *he'd* have the consolation o' knowin' 'at he'd called Steve some ornry name 'thout givin' him a *chance* to take it up. Steve was allus quiet-like, but ef you raised his dander onc't—and you could do that 'thout much trouble, callin' him names er somepin', particular'

anything 'bout his mother. Steve loved his mother—
allus loved his mother, and would fight fer her at
the drap o' the hat. And he was her favo-*rite*—allus
a-talkin' o' "her boy, Steven," as she used to call
him, and so proud of him, and so keerful of him
allus, when he'd be sick or anything; nuss him like
a baby, she would.

So when Bills hollered, Steve didn't pay no attention; and *I* said nothin', o' course, and didn't let
on like I noticed him. So we druv round to the
south side and hitched and Steve 'lowed he'd better
feed; so I left him with the hosses and went into
the mill.

They was jest a-stoppin' fer dinner. Most of 'em
brought their dinners—lived so fur away, you know.
The two Smith boys lived on what used to be the
old Warrick farm, five er six mil'd, anyhow, from
where the mill stood. Great stout fellers, they was;
and little Jake, the father of 'em, wasn't no man
at all—not much bigger'n you, I rickon. Le' me see,
now:—There was Tomps Burk, Wade Elwood, and
Joe and Ben Carter; and Wesley Morris, John Coke
—wiry little cuss, he was, afore he got his leg sawed
off;—and Ezry, and—Well, I don't jest mind *all*
the boys—'s a long time ago, and I never was much
of a hand fer names.—Now, some folks'll hear a
name and never fergit it, but I can't boast of a good
rickollection, 'specially o' names; and fer the last
thirty year my mem'ry's be'n a-failin' me, ever
sence a spell o' fever 'at I brought on onc't—fever
and rheumatiz together:—You see, I went a-sainin'

with a passel o' the boys, fool-like, and let my clothes freeze on me a-comin' home. W'y, my breeches was like stove-pipes when I pulled 'em off. 'Ll, ef I didn't pay fer *that* spree! Rheumatiz got a holt o' me and helt me there flat o' my back fer eight weeks, and couldn't move hand er foot 'thout a-hollerin' like a' Injun.

And I'd 'a' be'n there yit, I rickon, ef it hadn't 'a' be'n fer a' old hoss-doctor, name o' Jones; and he gits a lot o' sod and steeps it in hot whisky and pops it on me,—and I'll-be-switched-to-death ef it didn't cuore me up, fer all I laughed and told him I'd better take the whisky in'ardly and let him keep the grass fer his doctor bill. But that's nuther here ner there! —As I was a-sayin' 'bout the mill: As I went in, the boys had stopped work and was a-gittin' down their dinners, and Bills amongst 'em, and old Ezry a chattin' away—great hand, he was, fer his joke, and allus a-cuttin' up and a-gittin' off his odd-come-shorts on the boys. And that day he was in particular good humor. He'd brought some liquor down fer the boys, and he'd be'n drinkin' a little hisse'f, enough to feel it. He didn't drink much—that is to say, he didn't git drunk adzactly; but he tuk his dram, you understand. You see, they made their own whisky in them days, and it wasn't nothin' like the bilin' stuff you git now. Old Ezry had a little still, and allus made his own whisky, enough fer fambly use, and jest as puore as worter, and as harmless. But nowadays the liquor you git's rank pizen. They say they putt tobacker in it, and strychnine, and the

Lord knows what; ner I never knowed why, 'less it
was to give it a richer-lookin' flavor, like. Well,
Ezry he'd brought up a jug, and the boys had be'n
a-takin' it purty free; I seed that as quick as I
went in.

And old Ezry called out to *me* to come and take
some, the first thing. Told him I didn't b'lieve I
keered about it; but nothin' would do but I must
take a drink with the boys; and I was tired anyhow and I thought a little wouldn't hurt; so I takes
a swig; and as I set the jug down *Bills* spoke up
and says, "You're a stranger to me, and I'm a
stranger to you, but I rickon we can drink to our
better acquaintance,"—er somepin' to that amount,
and poured out another snifter in a gourd he'd be'n
a-drinkin' coffee in, and handed it to me. Well, I
couldn't well refuse, of course; so I says "Here's
to us," and drunk her down—mighty nigh a half
pint, I rickon. Now, I railly didn't want it, but,
as I tell you, I was obleeged to take it, and I downed
her at a swaller and never batted an eye, fer, to
tell the fact about it, I liked the taste o' liquor; and
I do *yit*, on'y I know when I' got enough. Jest then
I didn't want to drink on account o' Steve. Steve
couldn't abide liquor in no shape ner form—fer
medicine ner nothin', and I've allus thought it was
his mother's doin's.

Now, a few months afore this I'd be'n to Vin-
cennes, and I was jest a-tellin' Ezry what they was
a-astin' fer their liquor there—fer I'd fetched a
couple o' gallon home with me 'at I'd paid six bits

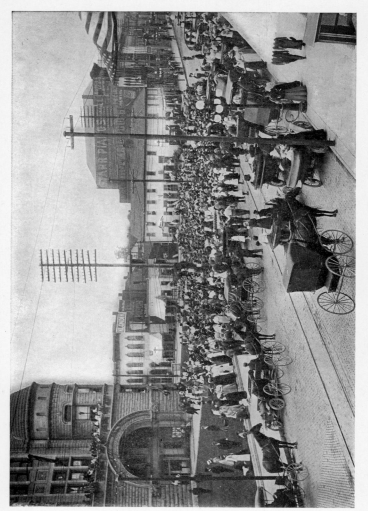

Riley in Greenfield, October 9th, 1912

fer, and pore liquor at that: And I was a-tellin'
about it, and old Ezry was a-sayin' what an oudaci-
ous figger that was, and how he could make money
a-sellin' it fer half that price, and was a-goin' on
a-braggin' about his liquor—and it was a good
article—fer new whisky,—and jest then Steve
comes in, jest as Bills was a-sayin' 'at a man 'at
wouldn't drink *that* whisky wasn't no man at all!
So, of course, when they ast *Steve* to take some and
he told 'em no, 'at he was much obleeged, Bills was
kind o' tuk down, you understand, and had to say
somepin'; and says he, "I reckon you ain't no better'n the rest of us, and *we've* be'n a-drinkin' of it."
But Steve didn't let on like he noticed Bills at all,
and retch and shuk hands with the other boys and
ast how they was all a-comin' on.

I seed Bills was riled, and more'n likely wanted
trouble; and shore enough, he went on to say, kind o'
snarlin'-like, 'at "he'd knowed o' men in his day 'at
had be'n licked fer refusin' to drink when their bet-
ters ast 'em"; and said furder at "a lickin' wasn't
none too good fer anybody 'at would refuse liquor
like that o' Ezry's, and in his own house too"—er
*buildin'*, ruther. Ezry shuk his head at him, but I
seed 'at Bills was bound fer a quarrel, and I winks
at Steve, as much as to say, "Don't you let him
bully you; you'll find your brother here to see you
have fair play!" *I* was a-feelin' my oats some about
then, and Steve seed I was, and looked so sorry-
like, and like his mother, 'at I jest thought, "I *kin*
fight fer *you,* and *die* fer you, 'cause you're wuth

it !"—And I didn't someway feel like it would
amount to much ef I *did* die er git killed er somepin' on *his* account. I seed Steve was mighty white
around the mouth, and his eyes was a-glitterin' like
a snake's ; yit Bills didn't seem to take warnin', but
went on to say 'at "he'd knowed boys 'at loved their
mothers so well they couldn't drink nothin' strong-
er'n milk."

And then you'd ort o' seed Steve's coat fly
off, jest like it wanted to git out of his way and
give the boy room accordin' to his stren'th. I
seed Bills grab a piece o' scantlin' jest in time to
ketch his arm as he struck at Steve,—fer Steve was
a-comin' fer him danger's. But they'd ketched
Steve from behind jest then; and Bills turned fer
me. I seed him draw back, and I seed Steve a-scufflin' to ketch his arm ; but he didn't reach it quite in
time to do me no good. It must 'a' come awful suddent. The first I rickollect was a roarin' and a buzzin' in my ears, and when I kind o' come a little
better to, and crawled up and peeked over the saw-
log I was a-layin' the other side of, I seed a couple
clinched and a-rollin' over and over and a-makin'
the chips and sawdust fly, now I *tell* you! Bills and
Steve it was—head and tail, tooth and toe-nail, and
a-bleedin' like good fellers! I seed a gash o' some
kind in Bills's head, and Steve was purty well
tuckered and a-pantin' like a lizard; and I made a
rush in, and one o' the Carter boys grabbed me and
told me to jest keep cool—'at *Steve* didn't need no
he'p, and they might need me to keep Bills's friends

off ef *they* made a rush. By this time Steve had
whirlt Bills, and was a-jest a-gittin' in a fair way
to finish him up in good style, when Wesley Morris run in—I seed him do it—run in, and afore we
could ketch him he struck Steve a deadener in the
butt o' the ear and knocked him as limber as a rag.
And then Bills whirlt Steve and got him by the
th'oat, and Ben Carter and me and old Ezry closed
in.—Carter tackled Morris, and Ezry and me grabs
Bills—and as old Ezry grabbed him to pull him off,
Bills kind o' give him a side swipe o' some kind and
knocked him—I don't know *how* fur! And jest then
Carter and Morris come a-scufflin' back'ards right
amongst us, and Carter th'owed him right acrost
Bills and Steve.

Well, it ain't fair, and I don't like to tell it,
but I seed it was the last chance and I tuk advantage if it:—As Wesley and Ben fell it pulled
Bills down in a kind o' twist, don't you understand,
so's he couldn't he'p hisse'f, yit still a-clinchin' Steve
by the th'oat, and him black in the face.—Well, as
they fell I grabbed up a little hick'ry limb, not big-
ger'n my two thumbs, and I struck Bills a little tap
kind o' over the back of his head like, and, blame
me! ef he didn't keel over like a stuck pig—and
not any too soon, nuther,—fer he had Steve's chunk
as nigh putt out as you ever seed a man's, to come
to ag'in. But he was up th'reckly and ready to 'a'
went at it ef Bills could 'a' come to the scratch but
Mister Bills he wasn't in no fix to try it over! After
a-waitin' a while fer him to come to, and him not

a-comin' to, we concluded 'at we'd better he'p him,
maybe. And we worked with him, and warshed him,
and drenched him with whisky, but it 'peared like
it wasn't no use.—He jest laid there with his eyes
about half shet, and a-breathin' like a hoss when
he's bad sceart; and I'll be dad-limbed ef I don't
believe he'd 'a' *died* on our hands ef it hadn't a-hap-
pened old Doc Zions come a-ridin' past on his way
home from the Murdock neighberhood, where they
was a-havin' sich a time with the milk-sick. And he
examined Bills, and had him laid on a plank and
carried down to the house—'bout a mil'd, I reckon,
from the mill. Looked kind o' cur'ous to see Steve
a-he'ppin' pack the feller, after his nearly chokin'
him to death. Oh, it was a bloody fight, I tell you!
W'y, they wasn't a man in the mill 'at didn't have
a black eye er somepin'; and old Ezry, where Bills
hit him, had his nose broke, and was as bloody as a
butcher. And you'd ort 'a' seed the women-folks
when our p'session come a-bringin' Bills in. I never
seed anybody take on like Bills's woman.—It was
distressin'; it was, indeed.—Went into hysterics, she
did; and we thought fer a while she'd gone plum
crazy, fer she cried so pitiful over him, and called
him "Charley! Charley!" stid of his right name, and
went on, clean out of her head, tel she finally jest
fainted clean away.

Fer three weeks Bills laid betwixt life and death,
and that woman set by him night and day, and
tended him as patient as a' angel—and she *was* a'
angel, too; and he'd 'a' never lived to bother nobody

ag'in ef it hadn't 'a' be'n fer Annie, as he called her. Zions said there was a 'brazure of the—some kind o' p'tuber'nce, and ef he'd 'a' be'n struck jest a quarter of a' inch below—jist a quarter of a' inch—he'd 'a' be'n a dead man. And I've sence wished—not 'at I want the life of a human bein' to account fer— on'y,—well, no odds—I've sence wished 'at I *had* 'a' hit him jest a quarter of a' inch below!

Well, of course, them days they wasn't no law o' no account, and nothin' was ever done about it. So Steve and me got our grindin', and talked the matter over with Ezry and the boys. Ezry said he was a-goin' to do all he could fer Bills, 'cause he was a good hand, and when he wasn't drinkin' they wasn't no peaceabler man in the Settlement. I kind o' suspicioned what was up, but I said nothin' then. And Ezry said furder, as we was about drivin' off, that Bills was a despert feller, and it was best to kind o' humor him a little. "And you must kind o' be on your guard," he says, "and I'll watch him, and ef anything happens 'at I git wind of I'll let you know," he says; and so we putt out fer home.

Mother tuk on awful about it. You see, she thought she'd be'n the whole blame of it, 'cause the Sund'y afore that her and Steve had went to meetin', and they got there late, and the house was crowded, and Steve had ast Bills to give up his seat to mother, and he wouldn't do it, and said somepin' at disturbed the prayin', and the preacher prayed 'at the feller 'at was a-makin' the disturbance might be forgive'; and that riled Bills so he got up and left, and hung around till it broke up, so's he could git a chance at Steve to pick a fight. And he did *try* it, and dared Steve and double-dared him fer a fight, but mother begged so hard 'at she kep' him out of it. Steve said 'at he'd 'a' told me all about it on the way to Ezry's, on'y he'd promised mother, you know, not to say nothin' to me.

Ezry was over at our house about six weeks after the fight, apparently as happy as you please. We ast him how him and Bills was a-makin' it, and he said first-rate; said 'at Bills was jest a-doing splendid; said he'd got moved in his new house 'at he'd fixed up fer him, and ever'thing was a-goin' on as smooth as could be; and Bills and the boys was on better terms'n ever; and says he, "As fur as you and Steve's concerned, Bills don't 'pear to bear you no ill feelin's, and says as fur as he's concerned the thing's settled." "Well," says I, "Ezry, I hope so; but I can't he'p but think they's somepin' at the bottom of all this"; and says I, "I don't think it's in Bills to ever amount to anything good"; and says I, "It's my opinion they's a dog in the well, and now you mark it!"

Well, he said he *wasn't* jest easy, but maybe he'd come out all right; said he couldn't turn the feller off—he hadn't the heart to do that, with that-air pore, dilicate woman o' his, and the baby. And then he went on to tell what a smart sort o' woman Bills' wife was,—one of the nicest little women he'd ever laid eyes on, said she was; said she was the kindest thing, and the sweetest-tempered, and all—and the handiest woman 'bout the house, and 'bout sewin', and cookin', and the like, and all kinds o' house-work; and so good to the childern, and all; and how they all got along so well; and how proud she was of her baby, and allus a-goin' on about it and a-cryin' over it and a-carryin' on, and wouldn't leave it out of her sight a minute. And Ezry said 'at she could write so purty, and made sich purty pic-tur's fer the childern; and how they all liked her better'n their own mother. And, sence she'd moved, he said it seemed so lonesome-like 'thout *her* about the house—like they'd lost one o' their own fambly; said they didn't git to see her much now, on'y sometimes, when her man would be at work, she'd run over fer a while, and kiss all the childern and women-folks about the place,—the greatest hand fer the childern, she was; tell 'em all sorts o' little stories, you know, and sing fer 'em; said 'at she could sing so sweet-like, 'at time and time ag'in she'd break clean down in some song o' nother, and her voice would trimble so mournful-like 'at you'd find yourse'f a-cryin' afore you knowed it. And she used to coax Ezry's woman to let her take the childern home with her; and they used to allus want to go, tel Bills come onc't while they was there, and they said he got to jawin' her fer a-makin' some to-do over the baby, and swore at her and tuk it away from her and whirped it fer cryin', and *she* cried and told him to whirp her and not little Annie, and he said that was jest what he *was* a-doin'. And the childern was allus afeard to go there any more after that—'feard he'd come home and whirp little Annie ag'in. Ezry said he jest done that to skeer 'em away—'cause he didn't want a passel o' childern a-whoopin' and a-howlin' and a-trackin' round the house all the time.

But, shore enough, Bills, after the fight, 'peared like he'd settled down, and went 'bout his business so stiddy-like, and worked so well, the neighbers begin to think he was all right after all, and railly *some* got to *likin' him*. But fer *me*,—well, I was a leetle slow to argy 'at the feller wasn't "a-possum-in'." But the next time I went over to the mill— and Steve went with me—old Ezry come and met us, and said 'at Bills didn't have no hard feelin's ef *we* didn't, and 'at he wanted us to fergive him; said 'at Bills wanted him to tell us 'at he was sorry the way he'd acted, and wanted us to fergive him. Well, I looked at Ezry, and we both looked at him, jest perfectly tuk back—the idee o' Bills a-wantin' anybody to *fergive him!* And says I, "Ezry, what in the name o' common sense do you mean?" And says he, "I mean jest what I say; Bills jined meetin' last night and had 'em all a-prayin' fer him; and we all had *a glorious time*," says old Ezry; "and his woman was there and jined, too, and prayed and shouted and tuk on to beat all; and Bills got up and spoke and give in his experience, and said he'd be'n a bad man, but, glory to God, them times was past and gone; said 'at he wanted all of 'em to pray fer him, and he wanted to prove faithful, and wanted

all his inemies to fergive him; and prayed 'at you
and Steve and your folks would fergive him, and
ever'body 'at he ever wronged anyway." And old
Ezry was a-goin' on, and his eyes a-sparklin', and
a-rubbin' his hands, he was so excited and tickled
over it, 'at Steve and me we jest stood there a-gawk-
in' like, tel Bills hisse'f come up and retch out one
hand to Steve and one to me; and Steve shuk with
him kind o' oneasy-like, and I—well, sir, I never felt
cur'oser in my born days than I did that minute.

The cold chills crep' over me, and I shuk as ef I
had the agur, and I folded my hands behind me and
I looked that feller square in the eye, and I tried
to speak three or four times afore I could make it,
and when I did, my voice wasn't natchurl—sounded
like a feller a-whisperin' through a tin horn er
somepin'.—And I says, says I, "You're a liar," slow
and delibert. That was all. His eyes blazed a minute, and drapped; and he turned, 'thout a word, and
walked off. And Ezry says, "He's in airnest; I
know he's in airnest, er he'd 'a' never 'a' tuk that!"
And so he went on, tel finally Steve jined in, and
betwixt 'em they p'suaded me 'at I was in the
wrong and the best thing to do was to make it all
up, which I finally did. And Bills said 'at he'd
'a' never 'a' felt jest right 'thout *my* friendship, fer
he'd wronged me, he said, and he'd wronged Steve
and mother, too, and he wanted a chance, he said,
o' makin' things straight ag'in.

Well, a-goin' home, I don't think Steve and me
talked o' nothin' else but Bills—how airnest the fel-

ler acted 'bout it, and how, ef he *wasn't* in airnest,
he'd 'a' never 'a' swallered that "lie," you see. That's
what walked my log, fer he could 'a' jest as easy
'a' knocked me higher'n Kilgore's kite as he could to
walk away 'thout a-doin' of it.

Mother was awful tickled when she heerd about
it, fer she'd had an idee 'at we'd have trouble afore
we got back, and a-gittin' home safe, and a-bringin'
the news 'bout Bills a-jinin' church and all, tickled
her so 'at she mighty nigh shouted fer joy. You see,
mother was a' old church-member all her life; and
I don't think she ever missed a sermont er a prayer-
meetin' 'at she could possibly git to—rain er shine,
wet er dry. When they was a meetin' of any kind
a-goin' on, go she would, and nothin' short o' sickness in the fambly, er knowin' nothin' of it, would
stop *her!* And clean up to her dyin' day she was a
God-fearin' and consistent Christian ef they ever
was one. I mind now when she was tuk with her
last spell and laid bedfast fer eighteen months, she
used to tell the preacher, when he'd come to see her
and pray and go on, 'at she could die happy ef she
could on'y be with 'em all ag'in in their love-feasts
and revivals. She was purty low then, and had be'n
a-failin' fast fer a day er two; and that day they'd
be'n a-holdin' service at the house. It was her request, you know, and the neighbers had congergated
and was a-prayin' and a-singin' her favorite hymns
—one in p'tickler, "God moves in a myster'ous way
his wunders to p'form," and 'bout his "Walkin' on
the sea and a-ridin' of the storm."

Well, anyway, they'd be'n a-singin' that hymn fer her—she used to sing that'n so much, I rickollect as fur back as I kin remember; and I mind how it used to make me feel so lonesome-like and solemn, don't you know,—when I'd be a-knockin' round the place along o' evenings, and she'd be a-milkin', and I'd hear her, at my feedin', way off by myse'f, and it allus somehow made me feel like a feller'd ort 'o try and live as nigh right as the law allows, and that's about my doctern yit. Well, as I was a-goin' on to say, they'd jest finished that old hymn, and Granny Lowry was jest a-goin' to lead in prayer, when I noticed mother kind o' tried to turn herse'f in bed, and smiled so weak and faint-like, and looked at me, with her lips a-kind o' movin'; and I thought maybe she wanted another dos't of her sirup 'at Ezry's woman had fixed up fer her, and I kind o' stooped down over her and ast her ef she wanted anything.

"Yes," she says, and nodded, and her voice sounded so low and solemn and so fur-away-like 'at I knowed she'd never take no more medicine on this airth. And I tried to ast her what it was she wanted, but I couldn't say nothin'; my throat hurt me, and I felt the warm tears a-boolgin' up, and her kind old face a-glimmerin' away so pale-like afore my eyes, and still a-smilin' up so lovin' and forgivin' and so good 'at it made me think so fur back in the past I seemed to be a little boy ag'in; and seemed like her thin gray hair was brown and a-shinin' in the sun as it used to do when

she helt me on her shoulder in the open door, when
father was a-livin' and we used to go to meet him
at the bars; seemed like her face was young ag'in,
and a-smilin' like it allus used to be, and her eyes
as full o' hope and happiness as afore they ever
looked on grief er ever shed a tear. And I thought
of all the trouble they had saw on my account, and
of all the lovin' words her lips had said, and of all
the thousand things her pore old hands had done fer
me 'at I never even thanked her fer; and how I
loved her better'n all the world besides, and would
be so lonesome ef she went away.—Lord! I can't
tell you what I *didn't* think and feel and see. And
I knelt down by her, and she whispered then fer
Steven, and he come, and we kissed her—and she
died—a-smilin' like a child—jest like a child.

Well—well! 'Pears like I'm allus a-runnin' into
somepin' else. I wisht I *could* tell a story 'thout
driftin' off in matters 'at hain't no livin' thing to do
with what I started out with. I try to keep from
thinkin' of afflictions and the like, 'cause sich is
bound to come to the best of us; but feller's rickollection will bring 'em up, and I reckon it'd ort'o
be er it wouldn't be; and I've thought, sometimes,
it was done maybe to kind o' admonish a feller, as
the Good Book says, of how good a world'd be
'thout no sorrow in it.

Where was I? Oh, yes, I rickollect;—about Bills
a-jinin' church. Well, sir, they wasn't a better-
actin' feller and more religious-like in all the neighberhood. Spoke in meetin's, he did, and tuk a' ac-

tive part in all religious doin's, and, in fact, was jest
as square a man, appearantly, as the preacher hisse'f.
And about six er eight weeks after he'd jined, they
got up another revival, and things run high. They
was a big excitement, and ever'body was a'tendin'
from fur and near. Bills and Ezry got the mill-
hands to go, and didn't talk o' nothin' *but* religion.
People thought a while 'at old Ezry'd turn preacher
he got so interested 'bout church matters. He was
easy excited 'bout anything; and when he went into
a thing it was in dead airnest, shore!—"jest flew
off the handle," as I heerd a comical feller git off
onc't. And him and Bills was up and at it ever'
night—prayin' and shoutin' at the top o' their voice.
Them railly did seem like good times—when ever'-
body jined together, and prayed and shouted "Ho-
sanner," and danced around together, and hugged
each other like they was so full o' glory they jest
couldn't he'p theirse'v's!—That's the reason *I* jined;
it looked so kind o' whole-souled-like and good, you
understand. But law! I didn't hold out—on'y fer a
little while, and no wunder!

Well, about them times Bills was tuk down with
the agur; first got to chillin' ever'-other-day, then
*ever'* day, and harder and harder, tel sometimes he'd
be obleeged to stay away from meetin' on account
of it. And onc't I was at meetin' when he told about
it, and how when he couldn't be with 'em he allus
prayed at home, and he said 'at he believed his
prayers was answered, fer onc't he'd prayed fer a
new outpourin' of the Holy Sperit, and that very

night they was three new jiners. And another time
he said 'at he'd prayed 'at Wesley Morris would
jine, and lo and behold you! he *did* jine, and the
very night 'at he *prayed* he would.

Well, the night I'm a-speakin' of he'd had a chill
the day afore and couldn't go that night, and was
in bed when Ezry druv past fer him; said he'd like
to go, but had a high fever and couldn't. And then
Ezry's woman ast him ef he was too sick to spare
Annie; and he said no, they could take her and the
baby: and told her to fix his medicine so's he could
reach it 'thout gittin' out o' bed, and he'd git along
'thout her. And so she tuk the baby and went along
with Ezry and his folks.

I was at meetin' that night and rickollect 'em
comin' in. Annie got a seat jest behind me—Steve
give her his'n and stood up; and I rickollect a-astin'
her how Bills was a-gittin' along with the agur;
and little Annie, the baby, kep' a-pullin' my hair
and a-crowin' tel finally she went to sleep; and Steve
ast her mother to let *him* hold her—cutest little
thing you ever laid eyes on, and the very pictur'
*of* her mother.

Old Daddy Barker preached that night, and a
mighty good sermont. His text, ef I rickollect right,
was "workin' out your own salvation"; and when I
listen to preachers nowadays in their big churches
and their fine pulpits, I allus think o' Daddy Barker,
and kind o' some way wisht the old times could come
ag'in, with the old log meetin'-house with its pun-
cheon-floor, and the chinkin' in the walls, and old

Daddy Barker in the pulpit. He'd make you feel 'at the Lord could make Hisse'f at home there, and find jest as abundant comfort in the old log house as He could in any of your fine-furnished churches 'at you can't set down in 'thout payin' fer the privilege, like it was a theater.

Ezry had his two little girls jine that night, and I rickollect the preacher made sich a purty prayer about the Savior a-cotin' from the Bible 'bout "Suffer little childern to come unto Me"—and all; and talked so purty 'bout the jedgment day, and mothers a-meetin' their little ones there—and all; and went on tel they wasn't a dry eye in the house— And jest as he was a-windin' up, Abe Riggers stuck his head in at the door and hollered "Fire!" loud as he could yell. We all rushed out, a-thinkin' it was the meetin'-house; but he hollered it was the mill; and shore enough, away off to the south'ards we could see the light acrost the woods, and see the blaze a-lickin' up above the trees. I seed old Ezry as he come a-scufflin' through the crowd; and we putt out together fer it. Well, it was two mil'd to the mill, but by the time we'd half-way got there, we could tell it wasn't the mill a-burnin', 'at the fire was furder to the left, and that was Ezry's house; and by the time we got there it wasn't much use. We pitched into the household goods, and got out the beddin', and the furnitur' and cheers, and the like o' that; saved the clock and a bedstid, and got the bureau purt' nigh out when they hollered to us 'at the roof was a-cavin' in, and we had to leave it;

well, we'd tuk the drawers out, all but the big one,
and that was locked; and it and all in it went with
the buildin'; and that was a big loss: All the money
'at Ezry was a-layin' by was in that-air drawer, and
a lot o' keepsakes and trinkets 'at Ezry's woman
said she wouldn't 'a' parted with fer the world and
all.

I never seed a troubleder fambly than they was.
It jest 'peared like old Ezry give clean down, and the
women and childern a-cryin' and a-takin' on. It
looked jest awful—shore's you're born!—Losin'
ever'thing they'd worked so hard fer—and there
it was, purt' nigh midnight, and a fambly, jest a little while ago all so happy, and now with no home
to go to, ner nothin'!

It was arranged fer Ezry's to move in with Bills—
that was about the on'y chance—on'y one room and
a loft; but Bills said they could manage *some* way,
fer a while anyhow.

Bills said he seed the fire when it first started,
and could a-putt it out ef he'd on'y be'n strong
enough to git there; said he started twic't to go, but
was too weak and had to go back to bed ag'in; said
it was a-blazin' in the kitchen roof when he first
seed it. So the gineral conclusion 'at we all come
to was—it must a-ketched from the flue.

It was too late in the fall then to think o' buildin' even the ornriest kind of shanty, and so Ezry
moved in with Bills. And Bills used to say ef it
hadn't 'a' be'n fer Ezry *he'd* 'a' never 'a' had no

house, ner nothin' to putt in it, nuther! You see, all
the household goods 'at Bills had in the world he'd
got of Ezry, and he 'lowed he'd be a triflin' whelp ef
he didn't do all in *his* power to make *Ezry* perfeckly
at home's long as he wanted to stay there. And
together they managed to make room fer 'em all,
by a-buildin' a kind o' shed-like to the main house,
intendin' to build when spring come. And ever'-
thing went along first-rate, I guess; never heerd
no complaints—that is, p'tickler.

Ezry was kind o' down fer a long time, though;
didn't like to talk about his trouble much, and didn't
'tend meetin' much, like he used to; said it made
him think 'bout his house burnin', and he didn't
feel safe to lose sight o' the mill. And the meetin's
kind o' broke up altogether that winter. Almost
broke up religious doin's, it did. 'S long as I've
lived here I never seed jest sich a slack in religion
as they was that winter; and 'fore *then,* I kin mind
the time when they wasn't a night the whole en-
durin' winter when they didn't have preachin' er
prayer-meetin' o' some kind a-goin' on. W'y, I rickollect one night in p'tickler—the *coldest* night,
*whooh!* And somebody had stold the meetin'-house
door, and they was obleeged to preach 'thout it.
And the wind blowed in so they had to hold their
hats afore the candles, and then onc't-in-a-while
they'd git sluffed out. And the snow drifted in so it
was jest like settin' outdoors; and they had to stand
up when they prayed—yes-sir! stood up to pray. I
noticed that night they was a' oncommon lot o' jin-

ers, and I believe to this day 'at most of 'em jined jest to git up where the stove was. Lots o' folks had their feet froze right in meetin'; and Steve come home with his ears froze like they was whittled out o' bone; and he said 'at Mary Madaline Wells's feet was froze, and she had two pair o' socks on over her shoes. Oh, it *was* cold, now I *tell* you!

They run the mill part o' that winter—part they couldn't. And they didn't work to say stiddy tel along in Aprile, and then they was snow on the ground yit—in the shadders—and the ground froze, so you couldn't hardly dig a grave. But at last they got to kind o' jiggin' along ag'in. Plenty to do there was; and old Ezry was mighty tickled, too; 'peared to recruit right up like. Ezry was allus best tickled when things was a-stirrin', and then he was a-gittin' ready fer buildin', you know,—wanted a house of his own, he said.—And of course it wasn't adzactly like home, all cluttered up as they was there at Bills's.

They got along mighty well, though, together; and the women-folks and childern got along the best in the world. Ezry's woman used to say she never laid eyes on jest sich another woman as Annie was. Said it was jest as good as a winter's schoolin' fer the childern; said her two little girls had learnt to read, and didn't know their a-b abs afore Annie learnt 'em; well, the oldest one, Mary Patience, she *did* know her *letters,* I guess—fourteen year old, she was; but Mandy, the youngest, had never seed inside a book afore that winter; and

the way she learnt was jest su'prisin'. She was
puny-like and frail-lookin' allus, but ever'body
'lowed she was a heap smarter'n Mary Patience,
and she *was;* and in my opinion she railly had more
sense'n all the rest o' the childern putt together,
'bout books and cipherin' and 'rethmetic, and the
like; and John Wesley, the oldest of 'em, he got to
teachin' at last, when he growed up,—but, law! he
couldn't write his own name so's you could read it.
I allus thought they was a good 'eal of old Ezry in
John Wesley. Liked to romance 'round with the
youngsters 'most too well.—Spiled him fer teachin', I allus thought; fer instance, ef a scholard said
somepin' funny in school, John-Wes he'd jest have
to have his laugh out with the rest, and it was jest
fun fer the boys, you know, to go to school to *him.*
Allus in fer spellin'-matches and the like, and learn-
in' songs and sich. I rickollect he give a' exhibition
onc't, one winter, and I'll never fergit it, I rickon.

The schoolhouse would on'y hold 'bout forty,
comf'table, and that night they was up'ards of a
hunderd er more—jest crammed and jammed! And
the benches was piled back so's to make room fer
the platform they'd built to make their speeches and
dialogues on; and fellers a-settin' up on them back
seats, their heads was clean against the j'ist. It was
a low ceilin', anyhow, and o' course them 'at tuk
a part in the doin's was way up, too. Janey Thompson had to give up her part in a dialogue, 'cause
she looked so tall she was afeard the congergation
would laugh at her; and they couldn't git her to

come out and sing in the openin' song 'thout lettin'
her set down first and git ready 'fore they pulled
the curtain.  You see, they had sheets sewed together, and fixed on a string some way, to slide
back'ards and for'ards, don't you know.  But they
was a big bother to 'em—couldn't git 'em to work
like.  Ever' time they'd git 'em slid 'bout half-way
acrost somepin' would ketch, and they'd haf to stop
and fool with 'em a while 'fore they could git 'em
the balance o' the way acrost.  Well, finally, to'rds
the last, they jest kep' 'em drawed back all the time.

It was a pore affair, and spiled purt' nigh ever'
piece; but the scholards all wanted it fixed thataway,
the teacher said, in a few appropert remarks he
made when the thing was over.  Well, I was a-settin' in the back part o' the house on them high
benches, and my head was jest even with them on
the platform, and the lights was pore, and where
the string was stretched fer the curtain to slide on
it looked like the p'formers was strung on it.  And
when Lige Boyer's boy was a-speakin'—kind o'
mumbled it, you know, and you couldn't half hear
—it looked fer the world like he was a-chawin'
that-air string; and some devilish feller 'lowed ef
he'd chaw it clean in two it'd be a good thing fer the
balance.  After that they all sung a sleigh-ridin'
song, and it was right purty, the way they got it off.
Had a passel o' sleigh-bells they'd ring ever' onc't-
in-a-while, and it sounded purty—shore!

Then Hunicut's girl, Marindy, read a letter 'bout

winter, and what fun the youngsters allus had in winter-time, a-sleighin' and the like, and spellin'-matches, and huskin'-bees, and all. Purty good, it was, and made a feller think o' old times. Well, that was about the best thing they was done that night; but ever'body said the teacher wrote it fer her; and I wouldn't be su'prised much, fer they was married not long afterwards. I expect he wrote it fer her.—Wouldn't putt it past Wes!

Then had a dialogue, too, 'at was purty good. Little Bob Arnold was all fixed up—had on his pap's old bell-crowned hat, the one he was married in. Well, I jest thought die I would when I seed that old hat and called to mind the night his pap was married, and we all got him a little how-come-you-so on some left-handed cider 'at had be'n a-layin' in a whisky-bar'l tel it was strong enough to bear up a' egg. I kin rickollect now jest how he looked in that hat, when it was all new, you know, and a-settin' on the back o' his head, and his hair in his eyes; and sich hair!—as red as git-out—and his little black eyes a-shinin' like beads. Well-sir, you'd 'a' died to 'a' seed him a-dancin'. We danced all night that night, and would 'a' be'n a-dancin' yit, I rickon, ef the fiddler hadn't 'a' give out. Wash Lowry was a-fiddlin' fer us; and along to'rds three er four in the morning Wash was purty well fagged out. You see, Wash could never play fer a dance er nothin' 'thout a-drinkin' more er less, and when he got to a certain pitch you couldn't git nothin' out o' him but

"Barbary Allen"; so at last he struck up on that, and jest kep' it up and *kep'* it up, and nobody couldn't git nothin' else out of him!

Now, anybody 'at ever danced knows 'at "Barbary Allen" hain't no tune to dance by, *no* way you can fix it; and, o' course, the boys seed at onc't their fun was gone ef they couldn't git him on another tune.— And they'd coax and beg and plead with him, and maybe git him started on "The Wind Blows over the Barley," and 'bout the time they'd git to knockin' it down ag'in purty lively, he'd go to sawin' away on "Barbary Allen"—and I'll-be-switched-to-death ef that feller didn't set there and play hisse'f sound asleep on "Barbary Allen," and we had to wake him up afore he'd quit! Now, that's jest the plum facts.

And they wasn't a better fiddler nowheres than Wash Lowry, when he was at hisse'f. I've heerd a good many fiddlers in my day, and I never heerd one yit 'at could play my style o' fiddlin' ekal to Wash Lowry. You see, Wash didn't play none o' this-here newfangled music—nothin' but the old tunes, you understand, "The Forkèd Deer," and "Old Fat Gal," and "Gray Eagle," and the like. Now, them's music! Used to like to hear Wash play "Gray Eagle." He could come as nigh a-makin' that old tune talk as you ever heerd! Used to think a heap o' his fiddle—and he had a good one, shore. I've heerd him say, time and time ag'in, 'at a five-dollar gold-piece wouldn't buy it, and I knowed him myse'f to refuse a calf fer it onc't—yes-sir, a year-land calf—and the feller offered him a double-bar'l'd

pistol to boot, and blame ef he'd take it; said he'd
ruther part with anything else he owned than his
fiddle.—But here I am, clean out o' the furry ag'in!
. . . Oh, yes; I was a-tellin' 'bout little Bob, with
that old hat; and he had on a swaller-tail coat and
a lot o' fixin's, a-actin' like he was a squire; and he
had him a great long beard made out o' corn-silks,
and you wouldn't 'a' knowed him ef it wasn't fer his
voice. Well, he was a-p'tendin' he was a squire
a-tryin' some kind o' lawsuit, you see; and John
Wesley he was the defendunt, and Joney Wiles, I
believe it was, played like he was the plaintive. And
they'd had a fallin' out 'bout some land, and was
a-lawin' fer p'session, you understand. Well, Bob
he made out it was a mighty bad case when *John-
Wes* comes to consult him 'bout it, and tells *him* ef a
little p'int o' law was left out he thought he could git
the land fer him. And then John-Wes *bribes* him,
you understand, to leave out the p'int o' law, and the
squire says he'll do all he kin, and so John-Wes
goes out a-feelin' purty good. Then *Wiles* comes in
to consult the squire, don't you see. And the squire
tells *him* the same tale he told *John Wesley.* So
*Wiles* bribes him to leave out the p'int o' law in *his*
favor, don't you know. So when the case is tried he
decides in favor o' John-Wes, a-tellin' *Wiles* some
cock-and-bull story 'bout havin' to manage it thataway so's to git the case mixed so's he could git it
fer him shore; and posts *him* to sue fer a change
of venue er somepin',—anyway, Wiles gits a new
trial, and then the squire decides in *his* favor, and

tells John-Wes another trial will fix it in *his* favor, and so on.—And so it goes on tel, anyway, he gits holt o' the land hisse'f and all their money besides, and leaves them to hold the bag! Well-sir, it was purty well got up; and they said it was John-Wes's doin's, and I 'low it was—he was a good hand at anything o' that sort, and knowed how to make fun. —But I've be'n a-tellin' you purty much ever'thing but what I started out with, and I'll try and hurry through, 'cause I know you're tired.

'Long 'bout the beginnin' o' summer, things had got back to purty much the old way. The boys round was a-gittin' devilish, and o' nights 'specially they was a sight o' meanness a-goin' on. The mill-hands, most of 'em, was mixed up in it—Coke and Morris, and them 'at had jined meetin' 'long in the winter had all backslid, and was a-drinkin' and carousin' round worse'n ever.

People perdicted 'at *Bills* would backslide, but he helt on faithful, to all appearance; said he liked to see a feller when he made up his mind to do right, he liked to see him do it, and not go back on his word; and even went so fur as to tell Ezry ef they didn't putt a stop to it he'd quit the neighberhood and go some'eres else. And Bills was Ezry's head man then, and he couldn't 'a' got along 'thout him; and I b'lieve ef Bills had 'a' said the word old Ezry would 'a' turned off ever' hand he had.—He got so he jest left ever'thing to Bills. Ben Carter was turned off fer somepin', and nobody ever knowed what. Bills and him had never got along jest right sence the fight.

Ben was with this set I was a-tellin' you 'bout, and they'd got him to drinkin' and in trouble, o' course. I'd knowed Ben well enough to know he wouldn't do nothin' ornry ef he wasn't agged on, and ef he ever was mixed up in anything o' the kind Wes Morris and John Coke was at the bottom of it, and I take notice *they* wasn't turned off when Ben was.

One night the crowd was out, and Ben amongst 'em, o' course.—Sence he'd be'n turned off he'd be'n a-drinkin',—and I never blamed him much; he was so good-hearted like and easy led off, and I allus b'lieved it wasn't his own doin's.

Well, this night they cut up awful, and ef they was one fight they was a dozend; and when all the devilment was done they *could* do, they started on a stealin' expedition, and stol'd a lot o' chickens and tuk 'em to the mill to roast 'em; and, to make a long story short, that night the mill burnt clean to the ground. And the whole pack of 'em collogued to-gether aginst Carter to saddle it on to him; claimed 'at they left Ben there at the mill 'bout twelve o'clock—which was a fact, fer he was dead drunk and couldn't git away. Steve stumbled over him while the mill was a-burnin' and drug him out afore he knowed what was a-goin' on, and it was all plain enough to Steve 'at Ben didn't have no hand in the firin' of it. But I'll tell you he sobered up mighty suddent when he seed what was a-goin' on and heerd the neighbers a-hollerin', and a-threatenin' and a-goin' on!—fer it seemed to be the giner'l idee 'at the buildin' was fired a-purpose. And says Ben to Steve, says he, "I expect I'll haf to say good-by to you, fer they've got me in a ticklish place! I kin see through it all now, when it's too late!" And jest then Wesley Morris hollers out, "Where's Ben Carter?" and started to'ards where me and Ben and Steve was a-standin'; and Ben says, wild-like, "Don't you two fellers ever think it was *my* doin's," and whispers "Good-by," and started off; and when we turned, Wesley Morris was a-layin' flat of his back, and we heerd Carter yell to the crowd 'at "that man"—meanin' Morris—"needed lookin' after worse than *he* did," and another minute he plunged into the river and swum acrost; and we all stood and watched him in the flickerin' light tel he clum out on t'other bank; and 'at was the last anybody ever seed o' Ben Carter!

It must 'a' be'n about three o'clock in the morning by this time, and the mill then was jest a-smolderin' to ashes—fer it was as dry as tinder and burnt like a flash—and jest as a party was a-talkin' o' organizin' and follerin' Carter, we heerd a yell 'at I'll never fergit ef I'd live tel another flood. Old Ezry, it was, as white as a corpse, and with the blood a-streamin' out of a gash in his forred, and his clothes half on, come a-rushin' into the crowd and a-hollerin' fire and murder ever' jump. "My house is a-burnin', and my folks is all a-bein' murdered whilse you're a-standin' here! And Bills done it!

Bills done it!" he hollered, as he headed the crowd and started back fer home. "Bills done it! I caught him at it; and he would 'a' murdered me in cold blood ef it hadn't 'a' be'n fer his woman. He knocked me down, and had me tied to a bed-post in the kitchen afore I come to. And his woman cut me loose and told me to run fer he'p; and says I, 'Where's Bills?' and she says, 'He's after *me* by this time.' And jest then we heerd Bills holler, and we looked, and he was a-standin' out in the clearin' in front o' the house, with little Annie in his arms; and he hollered wouldn't she like to kiss the baby good-by. And she hollered 'My God!' fer me to save little Annie, and fainted clean dead away. And I heerd the roof a-crackin', and grabbed her up and packed her out jest in time. And when I looked up, Bills hollered out ag'in, and says, 'Ezry,' he says, 'you kin begin to kind o' git an idee o' what a good feller I am! And ef you hadn't 'a' caught me you'd 'a' never 'a' knowed it, and *"Brother Williams"* wouldn't 'a' be'n called away to another app'intment like he is.' And says he, 'Now, ef you foller me I'll finish you shore!— You're safe *now,* fer I hain't got time to waste on you furder.' And jest then his woman kind o' come to her senses ag'in and hollered fer little Annie, and the child heerd her and helt out its little arms to go to her, and hollered 'Mother! Mother!' And Bills says, 'Damn yer mother! ef it hadn't 'a' be'n fer *her* I'd 'a' be'n all right. And damn you, too!' he says to me.—'This'll pay you fer that lick you struck me; and fer you a-startin' reports, when I first come, 'at more'n likely I'd done somepin' mean over East and come out West to reform! And I wonder ef I *didn't* do somepin' mean afore I come here?' he went on; 'kill somebody er somepin'? And I wonder ef I ain't reformed enough to go back? Good-by, Annie!' he hollered; 'and you needn't fret about yer baby, I'll be the same indulgent father to it I've allus be'n!' And the baby was a-cryin' and a-reach-in' out its little arms to'rds its mother, when Bills he turned and struck off in the dark to'rds the river."

This was about the tale 'at Ezry told us, as nigh as I can rickollect: and by the time he finished, I never want to see jest sich another crowd o' men as was a-swarmin' there. Ain't it awful when sich a crowd gits together? I tell you it makes my flesh creep to think about it!

As Bills had gone in the direction of the river, we wasn't long in makin' our minds up 'at he'd haf to cross it, and ef he done *that* he'd haf to use the boat 'at was down below the mill, er wade it at the ford, a mil'd er more down. So we divided in three sections, like—one to go and look after the folks at the house, and another to the boat, and another to the ford. And Steve and me and Ezry was in the crowd 'at struck fer the boat: and we made time a-gittin' there! It was awful dark, and the sky was a-cloudin' up, like a storm; but we wasn't long a-git-tin' to the p'int where the boat was allus tied; but they wasn't no boat there! Steve kind o' tuk the lead, and we all talked in whispers. And Steve said

to kind o' lay low and maybe we could hear somepin'; and some feller said he thought he heerd
somepin' strange-like, but the wind was kind o'
raisin' and kep' up sich a moanin' through the trees
along the bank 'at we couldn't make out nothin'.

"Listen!" says Steve, suddent-like, "*I* hear somepin'!" We was all still ag'in—and we all heerd a
moanin' 'at was sadder'n the wind—sounded mourn-
fuller to *me*,—'cause I knowed it in a minute, and
I whispered, "Little Annie." And 'way out acrost
the river we could hear the little thing a-sobbin', and
we all was still's death; and we heerd a voice we
knowed was Bills's say, "Damn ye! Keep still, or I'll
drownd ye!" And the wind kind o' moaned ag'in,
and we could hear the trees a-screetchin' together
in the dark, and the leaves a-rustlin'; and when it
kind o' lulled ag'in, we heerd Bills make a kind o'
splash with the oars; and jest then Steve whispered
fer to lay low and be ready—he was a-goin' to
riconn'iter; and he tuk his coat and shoes off, and
slid over the bank and down into the worter as
slick as a' eel. Then ever'thing was still ag'in, 'cept
the moanin' o' the child, which kep' a-gittin' louder
and louder; and then a voice whispered to us, "He's
a-comin' back; the crowd below has sent scouts up,
and they're on t'other side. Now watch clos't, and
he's our meat." We could hear Bills, by the moanin' o' the baby, a-comin' nearer and nearer, tel
suddently he made a sort o' miss-lick with the oar,
I reckon, and must 'a' splashed the baby, fer she set
up a loud cryin'; and jest then old Ezry, who was

a-leanin' over the bank, kind o' lost his grip, some way o' nother, and fell kersplash in the worter like a' old chunk.  "Hello!" says Bills, through the dark, "you're there, too, air ye?" as old Ezry splashed up the bank ag'in.  And "Cuss you!" he says then, to the baby—"ef it hadn't be'n fer *your* infernal squawkin' I'd 'a' be'n all right; but you've brought the whole neighberhood out, and, damn you, I'll jest let you swim out to 'em!"  And we heerd a splash, then a kind o' gurglin', and then Steve's voice a-hollerin', "Close in on him, boys; I've got the baby!"

And about a dozent of us bobbed off the bank like so many bullfrogs, and I'll tell you the worter b'iled!  We could jest make out the shape o' the boat, and Bills a-standin' with a' oar drawed back to smash the first head 'at come in range.  It was a mean place to git at him.  We knowed he was despert, and fer a minute we kind o' helt back.  Fifteen foot o' worter's a mighty onhandy place to git hit over the head in!  And Bills says, "You hain't afeard, I rickon—twenty men ag'in' one!"  "You'd better give yourse'f up!" hollered Ezry from the shore.  "No, Brother Sturgiss," says Bills, "I can't say 'at I'm at all anxious 'bout bein' borned ag'in, jest yit a while," he says; "I see you kind o' 'pear to go in fer baptism; guess you'd better go home and git some dry clothes on; and, speakin' o' home, you'd ort 'o be there by all means—your house might catch afire and burn up whilse you're gone!"  And jest then the boat give a suddent shove under him— some feller'd div under and tilted it—and fer a minute it throwed him off his guard, and the boys closed in. Still he had the advantage, bein' in the boat: and as fast as a feller would climb in he'd git a whack o' the oar, tel finally they got to pilin' in a little too fast fer him to manage, and he hollered then 'at we'd have to come to the bottom ef we got him, and with that he div out o' the end o' the boat, and we lost sight of him; and I'll be blame' ef he didn't give us the slip after all!

Well sir, we watched fer him, and some o' the boys swum on down stream, expectin' he'd raise, but couldn't find hide ner hair of him; so we left the boat a-driftin' off down stream and swum ashore, a-thinkin' he'd jest drownded hisse'f a-purpose. But they was more su'prise waitin' fer us yit,—fer lo-and-behold-ye, when we got ashore they wasn't no trace o' Steve er the baby to be found. Ezry said he seed Steve when he fetched little Annie ashore, and she was all right, on'y she was purt' nigh past cryin'; he said Steve had lapped his coat around her and give her to him to take charge of, and he got so excited over the fight he laid her down be-twixt a couple o' logs and kind o' fergot about her tel the whole thing was over, and he went to look fer her, and she was gone. Couldn't 'a' be'n 'at she'd 'a' wundered off her-own-se'f; and it couldn't 'a' be'n 'at *Steve*'d take her, 'thout a-lettin' us know it. It was a mighty aggervatin' conclusion to come to, but we had to do it, and that was, *Bills* must 'a' got ashore unbeknownst to us and packed her off. Sich a thing wasn't hardly probable, yit it was a thing 'at

*might* be; and after a-talkin' it over we had to admit
'at *that* must 'a' be'n the way of it. But where was
*Steve?* W'y, we argied, he'd diskivvered she was
gone, and had putt out on track of her 'thout losin'
time to stop and explain the thing. The next question was, what did Bills want with her ag'in?—He'd
tried to drownd her onc't. We could ast questions
enough, but c'rect answers was mighty skearce, and
we jest concluded 'at the best thing to do was to putt
out fer the ford, fer that was the nighdest place
Bills could cross 'thout a boat, and ef it *was* him
tuk the child, he was still on our side o' the river, o'
course. So we struck out fer the ford, a-leavin' a
couple o' men to search *up* the river. A drizzlin'
sort o' rain had set in by this time, and with that and
the darkness and the moanin' of the wind, it made
'bout as lonesome a prospect as a feller ever wants
to go through ag'in.

It was jest a-gittin' a little gray-like in the morning by the time we reached the ford, but you
couldn't hardly see two rods afore you fer the mist
and the fog 'at had settled along the river. We
looked fer tracks, but couldn't make out nothin'.
Therectly old Ezry punched me and p'inted out
acrost the river. "What's that?" he whispers. Jest
'bout half-way acrost was somepin' white-like in
the worter—couldn't make out what—perfectly still
it was. And I whispered back and told him I guess
it wasn't nothin' but a sycamore snag. "Listen!"
says he; "sycamore snags don't make no noise like
that!" And, shore enough, it was the same moanin'

noise we'd heerd the baby makin' when we first got on the track. Sobbin' she was, as though nigh about dead. "Well, ef that's *Bills,*" says I—"and I reckon they hain't no doubt but it is—what in the name o' all that's good and bad's the feller a-standin' there fer?" And a-creepin' clos'ter, we could make him out plainer and plainer. It *was* him; and there he stood breast-high in the worter, a-holdin' the baby on his shoulder like, and a-lookin' up stream, and a-waitin'.

"What do you make out of it?" says Ezry. "What's he waitin' fer?"

And, a-strainin' my eyes in the direction *he* was a-lookin', I seed somepin' a-movin' down the river, and a minute later I'd made out the old boat a-driftin' down stream; and then of course ever'-thing was plain enough: He was waitin' fer the boat, and ef he got *that* he'd have the same advantage on us he had afore.

"Boys," says I, "he mustn't git that boat ag'in! Foller me, and don't let him git to the shore alive!" And in we plunged. He seed us, but he never budged, on'y to grab the baby by its little legs, and swing it out at arm's len'th. "Stop, there!" he hollered.—"Stop jest where ye air! Move another inch and I'll drownd this damn' young-un afore yer eyes!" he says.—And he'd 'a' done it. "Boys," says I, "he's got us. Don't move! This thing'll have to rest with a higher power'n our'n! Ef any of you kin *pray,*" says I, "now's a good time to do it!"

Jest then the boat swung up, and Bills grabbed it

and retch 'round and set the baby in it, never a-takin' his eye off us, though, fer a minute. "Now," says he, with a sort o' snarlin' laugh, "I've on'y got a little while to stay with you, and I want to say a few words afore I go. I want to tell you fellers, in the first place, 'at you've be'n *fooled* in me: I *hain't* a good feller—now, honest! And ef you're a little worse fer findin' it out so late in the day, you hain't none the worse fer losin' me so soon —fer I'm a-goin' away now, and any interference with my arrangements'll on'y give you more trouble; so it's better all around to let me go peaceable and jest while I'm in the notion. I expect it'll be a disapp'intment to some o' you that my name hain't Williams, but it hain't. And maybe you won't think nigh as much o' me when I tell you furder 'at I was obleeged to 'dopt the name o' Williams onc't to keep from bein' strung up to a lamp-post, but sich is the facts. I was so extremely unfortunit onc't as to kill a p'tickler friend o' mine, and he forgive me with his dyin' breath, and told me to run whilse I could, and be a better man. But he'd spotted me with a' ugly mark 'at made it kind o' onhandy *to* git away, but I did at last; and jest as I was a-gittin' reformed-like, you fellers had to kick in the traces, and I've made up my mind to hunt out a more moraler community, where they don't make such a fuss about trifles. And havin' nothin' more to say, on'y to send *Annie* word 'at I'll still be a father to her young-un here, I'll bid you all good-by." And with that he turned and clum in the boat

—or ruther *fell* in,—fer somepin' black-like had riz
up in it, with a' awful lick—my—God!—And, a
minute later, boat and baggage was a-gratin' on the
shore, and a crowd came thrashin' 'crost from
t'other side to jine us,—and 'peared like wasn't a
*second* longer tel a feller was a-swingin' by his neck
to the limb of a scrub-oak, his feet clean off the
ground and his legs a-jerkin' up and down like a
lumber-jack's.

And Steve it was a-layin' in the boat, and he'd rid
a mil'd er more 'thout knowin' it. Bills had struck
and stunt him as he clum in whilse the rumpus was
a-goin' on, and he'd on'y come to in time to hear
Bills's farewell address to us there at the ford.

Steve tuk charge o' little Annie ag'in, and ef she'd
'a' be'n his own child he wouldn't 'a' went on more
over her than he did; and said nobody but her
mother would git her out o' his hands ag'in. And
he was as good as his word; and ef you could 'a' seen
him a half hour after that, when he *did* give her to
her mother—all lapped up in his coat and as drip-
pin'-wet as a little drownded angel—it would
'a' made you wish't you was him to see that little
woman a-caperin' round him, and a-thankin' him,
and a-cryin' and a-laughin', and almost a-huggin'
him, she was so tickled,—well, I thought in my soul
she'd die! And Steve blushed like a girl to see her
a-takin' on, and a-thankin' him, and a-cryin', and
a-kissin' little Annie, and a-goin' on. And when
she inquired 'bout Bills, which she did all suddent-
like, with a burst o' tears, we jest didn't have the

heart to tell her—on'y we said he'd crossed the river
and got away. And he had!

And now comes a part o' this thing 'at'll more'n
like tax you to believe it: Williams and her wasn't
man and wife—and you needn't look su'prised,
nuther, and I'll tell you fer why:—They was own
brother and sister; and that brings me to *her* part
of the story, which you'll haf to admit beats anything 'at you ever read about in books.

Her and Williams—that *wasn't* his name, like he
acknowledged, hisse'f, you rickollect—ner *she*
didn't want to tell his right name; and we forgive
her fer that. Her and "Williams" was own brother
and sister, and their parunts lived in Ohio some'eres.
Their mother had be'n dead five year' and better—
grieved to death over her onnatchur'l son's reck-
lessness, which Annie hinted had broke her father
up in some way, in tryin' to shield him from the
law. And the secret of her bein' with him was this:
She had married a man o' the name of Curtis or
Custer, I don't mind which, adzactly—but no matter; she'd married to a well-to-do young feller 'at
her brother helt a' old grudge ag'in', she never
knowed what; and, sence her marriage, her brother
had went on from bad to worse, tel finally her
father jest give him up and told him to go it his
own way—he'd killed his *mother* and ruined *him,*
and he'd jest give up all hopes! But Annie—you
know how a sister is—she still clung to him and
done ever'thing fer him, tel finally, one night, about
three years after she was married, she got word

some way that he was in trouble ag'in, and sent her
husband to he'p him; and a half hour after he'd
gone, her brother come in, all excited and bloody,
and told her to git the baby and come with him, 'at
her husband had got in a quarrel with a friend o'
his and was bad hurt. And she went with him, of
course, and he tuk her in a buggy, and lit out with
her as tight as he could go all night; and then told
her 'at *he* was the feller 'at had quarreled with her
husband, and the officers was after him, and he was
obleeged to leave the country, and fer fear he hadn't
made shore work o' him, he was a-takin' her along
to make shore of his gittin' his revenge; and he
swore he'd kill her and the baby too ef she dared to
whimper.

And so it was, through a hunderd hardships
he'd made his way at last to our section o' the
country, givin' out 'at they was man and wife,
and keepin' her from denyin' of it by threats, and
promises of the time a-comin' when he'd send her
home to her man ag'in in case he hadn't killed him.
And so it run on tel you'd 'a' cried to hear her tell it,
and still see her sister's love fer the feller a-breakin'
out by a-declarin' how kind he was to her *at times,*
and how he wasn't railly bad at heart, on'y fer his
ungov'nable temper. But I couldn't he'p but notice,
when she was a-tellin' of her hist'ry, what a quiet
sort o' look o' satisfaction settled on the face o'
Steve and the rest of 'em, don't you understand.

And now they was on'y one thing she wanted to
ast, she said; and that was,—could she still make

her home with us tel she could git word to her
friends?—and there she broke down ag'in, not
knowin', of course, whether *they* was dead er alive;
fer time and time ag'in she said somepin' told her
she'd never see her husband ag'in on this airth; and
then the women-folks would cry with her and console her, and the boys would speak hopeful—all but
Steve; some way o' nother Steve was never like hisse'f from that time on.

And so things went fer a month and better. Ever'-
thing had quieted down, and Ezry and a lot o'
hands, and me and Steve amongst 'em, was a-workin' on the framework of another mill. It was purty
weather, and we was all in good sperits, and it
'peared like the whole neighberhood was int*erest*ed
—and they *was*, too—women-folks and ever'body.
And that day Ezry's woman and amongst 'em was
a-gittin' up a big dinner to fetch down to us from
the house; and along about noon a spruce-lookin'
young feller, with a pale face and a black beard,
like, come a-ridin' by and hitched his hoss, and
comin' into the crowd, said "Howdy," pleasant-like,
and we all stopped work as he went on to say 'at
he was on the track of a feller o' the name o' "Williams," and wanted to know ef we could give him
any information 'bout sich a man. Told him maybe,
—'at a feller bearin' that name desappeared kind o'
myster'ous from our neighberhood 'bout five weeks
afore that.

"My God!" says he, a-turnin' paler'n ever, "am
I too late? Where did he go, and was his sis-

ter and her baby with him?" Jest then I ketched
sight o' the women-folks a-comin' with the baskets,
and Annie with 'em, with a jug o' worter in her
hand; so I spoke up quick to the stranger, and says
I, "I guess 'his sister and her baby' wasn't along,"
says I, "but his *wife* and *baby's* some'eres here in
the neighberhood yit." And then a-watchin' him
clos't, I says, suddent, a-p'intin' over his shoulder,
"There his woman is now—that one with the jug,
there." Well, Annie had jest stooped to lift up one
o' the little girls, when the feller turned, and their
eyes met. "Annie! My wife!" he says; and Annie
she kind o' give a little yelp like and came a-flutterin'
down in his arms; and the jug o' worter rolled clean
acrost the road, and turned a somerset and knocked
the cob out of its mouth and jest laid back and hollered "Good—good—good—good—good!" like as ef
it knowed what was up and was jest as glad and
tickled as the rest of us.

# JAMESY

ONE week ago this Christmas day, in the little
back office that adjoins the counting-room of
the "Daily Journal," I sat in genial conversation
with two friends. I do not now recall the theme of
our discussion, but the general trend of it—suggested, doubtless, by the busy scene upon the streets
—I remember most distinctly savored of the mellowing influences of the coming holidays, with perhaps
an acrid tang of irony as we dwelt upon the great
needs of the poor at such a time, and the chariness
with which the hand of opulence was wont to dole
out alms. But for all that we were merry, and as
from time to time our glances fell upon the ever-
shifting scene outside, our hearts grew warmer, and
within the eyes the old dreams glimmered into fuller dawn. It was during a lull of conversation, and
while the philanthropic mind, perchance, was
wandering amid the outer throng, and doubtless
quoting to itself

"Whene'er I take my walks abroad,"

that our privacy was abruptly broken into by
the grimy apparition of a boy of ten; a ragged

120

little fellow—not the stereotyped edition of the street waif, but a cross between the bootblack and the infantine Italian with the violin. Where he had entered, and how, would have puzzled us to answer; but there he stood before us, as it were, in a majesty of insignificance. I have never had the features of a boy impress me as did his, and as I stole a covert glance at my companions I was pleased to find the evidence of more than ordinary interest in their faces. They gazed in attentive silence on the little fellow, as, with uncovered, frowzy head, he stepped forward boldly, yet with an air of deference as unlooked for as becoming.

"I don't want to bother you gentlemens," he began, in a frank but hesitating tone that rippled hurriedly along as he marked a general nod of indulgence for the interruption. "I don't want to bother nobody, but if I can raise fifty cents—and I've got a nickel—and if I can raise the rest—and it ain't much, you know—on'y forty-five—and if I can raise the rest—I tell you, gentlemens," he broke off abruptly, and speaking with italicized sincerity, "I want jist fifty cents, 'cause I can git a blackin'-box fer that, and brush and ever'thing, and you can bet if I had *that* I wouldn't haf to ast nobody fer nothin'! And I ain't got no father ner mother, ner brother ner—ner—no sisters, neether; but that don't make no difference, 'cause I'll work—at *anything*—yes, sir—when I can git anything to do—and I sleep jist any place—and I ain't had no breakfast—and, honest, gentlemens, I'm a good boy—I don't

swear ner smoke ner chew—but that's all right—
on'y if you'll—jist make up forty-five between you
—and that's on'y fifteen cents apiece—I'll thank you,
I will, and I'll jist do anything—and it's coming
Christmas, and I'll roll in the nickels, don't you
fergit—if I on'y got a box—'cause I throw up a
'bad' shine!—and I can git the box fer fifty cents
if you gentlemens'll on'y make up forty-five between
you." At the conclusion of this long and rambling
appeal, the little fellow stood waiting with an eager
face for a response.

A look of stoical deliberation played about the
features of the oldest member of the group, as with
an air of seriousness, which, I think, even the boy
recognized as affected, he asked:

"And you couldn't get a box like that for—say
forty cents? Fifty cents looks like a lot of money
to lay out in the purchase of a blacking-box."

The boy smiled wisely as he answered:

"Yes, it might look big to a feller that ain't up
on prices, but *I* think it's *cheap,* 'cause it's a second-
hand box, and a *new* one would cost seventy-five
cents anyhow—'thout no brushes ner nothin'!"

In the meantime I had dropped into the little
fellow's palm the only coin I had in my possession,
and we all laughed as he closed his thanks with:
"Oh, come, Cap, go the *other* nickel, er I won't
git out o' here with *half* enough!" and at that he
turned to the former speaker.

"Well, really," said that gentleman, fumbling in

his pockets, "I don't believe I've got a dime with me."

"A *dime,*" said the little fellow, with a look of feigned compassion. "Ain't got a dime? Maybe I'd loan you *this* one!" And we all laughed again.

"Tell you what do now," said the boy, taking advantage of the moment, and looking coaxingly into the smiling eyes of the gentleman still fumbling vainly in his pockets.—"Tell you what do: you borry twenty cents of the man that stays behind the counter there, and then we'll go the other fifteen, and that'll make it, and I'll skip out o' here a little the flyest boy you ever see! What do ye soy?" And the little fellow struck a Pat Rooney attitude that would have driven the original inventor mad with envy.

"Give him a quarter!" laughed the gentleman appealed to.

"And here's the other dime," and as the little fellow clutched the money eagerly, he turned; and in a tone of curious gravity, he said:

"Now, honest, gentlemens, I ain't a-givin' you no *game* about the box—'cause a new one costs seventy-five cents, and the one I've got—I mean the one I'm a-goin' to git—is jist as *good* as a new one, on'y it's *second-hand;* and I'm much oblige', gentlemens—honest, I am—and if ever I give you a shine you can jist bet it don't cost you nothin'!"

And with this expression of his gratitude, the little fellow vanished as mysteriously as he had at first appeared.

"That boy hasn't a bad face," said the first speaker—"wide between the eyes—full forehead—good mouth, denoting firmness—altogether, a good, square face."

"And a noble one," said I, perhaps inspired to that rather lofty assertion by the rehearsal of the good points noted by my more observant companion.

"Yes, and an honest, straightforward way of talking, I would say," continued that gentleman. "I only noted one thing to shake my faith in that particular, and that was in his latest reference to the box. You'll remember his saying he was 'giving us no game' about it, whereas he had not been accused of such a thing."

"Oh, he meant about the price, don't you remember?" said I.

"No," said the gentleman at the counter, "you're both wrong. He only threw in that remark because he thought I suspected him, for he recognized me just the instant before that speech, and it confused him, and with some reason, as you will see:—On my way to supper only last night, I overtook that same little fellow in charge of an old man who was in a deplorable state of drunkenness; and you know how slippery the streets were. I think if that old man fell a single time he fell a dozen, and once so violently that I ran to his assistance and helped him to his feet. I thought him badly hurt at first, for he gashed his forehead as he fell, and I helped the little fellow to take him into a drug-store, where the

wound, upon examination, proved to be nothing
more serious than to require a strip of plaster. I
got a good look at the boy, there, however, and
questioned him a little; and he said the man was his
father, and he was taking him home; and I gathered
further from his talk that the man was a confirmed
inebriate. Now you'll remember the boy told us
here a while ago he had no father, and when he
recognized me a moment since and found himself
caught in one 'yarn,' at least, he very naturally sup-
posed I would think his entire story a fabrication,
hence the suspicious nature of his last remarks, and
the sudden transition of his manner from that of real
delight to gravity, which change, in my opinion,
rather denotes lying to be a new thing to him. I
can't be mistaken in the boy, for I noticed, as he
turned to go, a bald place on the back of his head,
the left side, a 'trade-mark,' first discovered last
evening, as he bent over the prostrate form of his
father."

"I noticed a thin spot in his hair," said I, "and
wondered at the time what caused it."

"And don't you know?"

I shook my head.

"Coal-bins and entry floors.—That little fellow
hasn't slept within a bed for years, perhaps."

"But he told you, as you say, last night, he was
taking the old man home?"

"Yes, home! I can imagine that boy's home. There
are myriads like it in the city here—a cellar or a

shed—a box-car or a loft in some old shop, with a father to chase him from it in his sober interludes, and to hold him from it in unconscious shame when helplessly drunk. 'Home, Sweet Home!' That boy has heard it on the hand-organ, perhaps, but never in his heart—you couldn't grind it out of there with a thousand cranks."

The remainder of that day eluded me somehow; I don't know how or where it passed. I suppose it just dropped into a comatose condition, and so slipped away "unknelled, uncoffined, and unknown."

But one clear memory survives—an experience so vividly imprinted on my mind that I now recall its every detail: Entering the Union Depot that evening to meet the train that was to carry me away at six o'clock, muffled closely in my overcoat, yet more closely muffled in my gloomy thoughts, I was rather abruptly stopped by a small boy with a cry of: "Here, you man with the cigar; don't you want them boots blacked? Shine 'em fer ten cents! Shine 'em fer a nickel—on'y you mustn't give me away on that," he added, dropping on his knees near the entrance, and motioning me to set my foot upon the box.

It was then too dark for me to see his face clearly, but I had recognized the voice the instant he had spoken, and had paused and looked around.

"Oh, you'll have plenty o' time," he urged, guessing at the cause of my apparent hesitation. "None o' the trains on time to-night—on'y the Panhandle, and she's jist a-backin' in—won't start fer thirty minutes," and he again beckoned, and rattled a seductive tattoo on the side of his box.

"Well," said I, with a compromising air, "come inside, then, out of the cold."

"'G'inst the rules—cops won't have it. They jist fired me out o' there not ten minutes ago. Oh, come, Cap; step out here; it won't take two minutes," and the little fellow spat professionally upon his brush, with a covert glance of pleasure as he noted the apparent success of the maneuver. "You don't *live* here, I'll bet," said the boy, setting the first boot on the box, and pausing to blow his hands.

"How do you know that? Did you never see me here before?"

"No, I never *see* you here before, but that ain't no reason. I can tell you don't live here by them shoes—'cause they've been put up in some little pennyroyal shop,—that's how. When you want a fly shoe you want to git her put up som'er's where they know somepin' about style. They's good enough *metal* in that shoe, on'y she's about two years off in *style*."

"You're posted, then, in shoes," said I, with a laugh.

"I ort to be," he went on, pantingly, a brush in either hand gyrating with a velocity that jostled his hat over his eyes, leaving most plainly exposed to my investigative eye the trade-mark before alluded to; "I ort to be posted in shoes, 'cause I ain't done nothin' but black 'em fer five years."

"You're an old hand, then, at the business," said

I. "I didn't know but maybe you were just starting
out. What's an outfit like that worth?"

"Thinkin' o' startin' up?" he asked, facetiously.

"Oh, no," said I, good-humoredly. "I just asked
out of idle curiosity. That's a new box, ain't it?"

"*New!*" he repeated with a laugh. "Put up that
other hoof. *New?* W'y, if that box had ever had
eyes like a human it would 'a' been a-wearin' specs
by this time; that's a old, bald-headed box, with one
foot in the grave."

"And what did the old fellow cost you?" I asked,
highly amused at the quaint expressions of the boy.

"Cost? Cost nothin'—on'y about a' hour's work.
I made that box myse'f, 'bout four year ago."

"Ah!" said I.

"Yes," he went on, "they don't cost nothin'; the
boys makes 'em out o' other boxes, you know. Some
of 'em gits 'em made, but they ain't no good—ain't
no better'n this kind."

"So that didn't cost you anything?" said I,
"though I suspect you wouldn't like to part with it
for less than—well, I don't know how much money
to say—seventy-five cents maybe—would anything
less than seventy-five cents buy it?" I craftily in-
terrogated.

"Seventy-five cents! W'y, what's the matter with
you, man? I could git a cart-load of 'em fer seventy-five cents. I'll take yer measure fer one like
it fer fifteen, too quick!" and the little fellow leaned
back from his work and laughed up in my face with
absolute derision.

I pulled my hat more closely down for fear of recognition, but was reassured a moment later as he went on:

"Wisht you lived here; you'd be old fruit fer us fellows. I can see you now a-takin' wind—and we'd give it to you mighty slick now, don't you fergit!" and as the boy renewed his work, I think his little, ragged body shook less with industry than mirth.

"Wisht I'd struck you 'bout ten o'clock this morning!" and, as he spoke, he paused again and looked up in my face with real regret. "Oh, you'd 'a' been the loveliest sucker of 'em all! W'y, you'd 'a' went the whole pot yerse'f!"

"How do you mean?" said I, dropping the cigar I held.

"How do I mean? Oh, you don't want to smoke this thing again after its a-rollin' round in the dirt!"

"Why, you don't smoke," said I, reaching for the cigar he held behind him.

"*Me?* Oh, what you givin' me?"

"Come, let me have it," I said, sharply, drawing a case from my pocket and taking out another cigar.

"Oh, you want a *light*," he said, handing me the stub and watching me wistfully. "Couldn't give us a fresh cigar, could you, Cap?"

"I don't know," said I, as though deliberating on the matter. "What was that you were going to tell me just now? You started to tell me what a 'lovely sucker' I'd have been had you met me this morning. How did you mean?"

"Give me a cigar and I'll tell you. Oh, come, now, Cap; give me a smoker and I'll give you the whole game. I will, now, honest!"

I held out the open case.

"Nothin' mean about you, is they?" he said, eagerly taking a fresh cigar in one hand and the stub in the other. "A ten-center, too—*oh, I guess not!*" But, to my surprise, he took the stub between his lips, and began opening his coat. "Guess I'll jist fat this daisy, and save 'er up for Christmas. No, I won't either," he broke in suddenly, with a bright, keen flash of second thought. "Tell you what I'll do," holding up the cigar and gazing at it admiringly; "she's a ten-center all right, ain't she?"

I nodded.

"And worth every cent of it, too, ain't she?"

"Every cent of it," I repeated.

"Then give me a nickel, and she's yourn—'cause if you can afford to *give* this to me fer nothin', looks like I ort to let you have it fer half-price"; and as I laughingly dropped the nickel in his hand he concluded, "And they's nothin' mean about me, neither!"

"Now, go on with your story," said I. "How about that 'game' you were 'giving,' this morning?"

"Well, I'll tell you, Cap. Us fellers has got to lay fer ever' nickel, 'cause none of us is bondholders; and they's days and days together when we don't make enough to even starve on.—What I mean is, we on'y make enough to pay fer aggervatin' our ap-

petites with jist about enough chuck to keep us starv-
in'-hungry. So, you see, when a feller ain't got
nothin' else to do, and his appetite won't sleep in
the same bunk with him, he's bound to git on to
somepin' crooked and git up all sorts o' dodges to
git along. Some gives 'em one thing, and some another, but you bet they got to be mighty slick now,
'cause people won't have 'orphans,' and 'fits,' and
'cripples,' and 'drunk fathers,' and 'mothers that
eats morphine,' and 'white-swellin',' and 'consump-
tion,' and all that sort o' taffy! Got to git 'er down
finer'n that! But *I* been a-gittin' in my work all
the same, don't you fergit! You won't ever blow,
now?"

"How could I 'blow,' and what if I did?—I don't
live here," I replied.

"Well, you better never blow, anyhow; 'cause if
ever us duffers would git on to it you'd be a sp'iled
oyster!"

"Go on," said I, with an assuring tone.

"The lay I'm on jist now," he continued, dropping his voice and looking cautiously around, "is
a-hidin' my box and a-rushin' in, suddent-like,
where they's a crowd o' nobs a-talkin' politics er
somepin', and a-jist startin' in, and 'fore they know
*what's* a-comin' I'm a-flashin' up a nickel er a dime,
and a-tellin' 'em if I on'y had enough more to make
fifty cents I could buy a blackin'-box, and wouldn't
have to ast no boot o' my grandmother! And two
minutes chinnin' does it, don't you see, cause *they*
**don't know nothin' 'bout blackin'-boxes; they're jist**

as soft as *you* air. They got an idy, maybe, that blackin'-boxes comes all the way from Chiny, with cokeynut whiskers packed 'round 'em; and I make it solid by a-sayin' I'm on'y goin' to git a *second-hand* box—see? But *that* ain't the p'int—it's the Mr. Nickel I' already *got*. Oh! it'll paralyze 'em ever' time! *Some*times fellers'll make up seventy-five cents er a dollar, and tell me to 'git a *new* box, and go into the business right.' That's a thing that always rattles me. Now, if they'd on'y growl a little and look like they was jist a-puttin' up 'cause the first one did, I can stand it; but when they go to pattin' me on the head, and a-tellin' me 'that's right,' and 'not to be afeard o' work,' and I'll 'come out all right,' and a-tellin' me to 'git a good substantial box while I'm a-gittin',' and a-ponyin' up handsome, there's where I weaken—I do, honest!'' And never so plainly as at that moment did I see within his face and in his eyes the light of true nobility.

"You see," he went on, in a tone of voice half courage, half apology, "I' got a family on my hands, and I' jist *got* to git along somehow! I could git along on the square deal as long as *mother* was alive—'cause she'd *work*—but ever sence *she* died —and that was winter 'fore last—I've kind o' had to double on the old thing all sorts o' ways. But Sis don't know it. Sis, *she* thinks I'm the squarest muldoon in the business," and even side by side with the homely utterance a great sigh faltered from his lips.

"And who is Sis?" I inquired with new interest.

"Sis?" he repeated, knocking my foot from the box, and leaning back, still in the old position, his hat now lying on the ground beside him, and his frowzy hair tossed backward from the full, broad brow—"Who's Sis?" he repeated with an upward smile that almost dazzled me—"W'y, Sis is—is—w'y, Sis is the boss girl—and don't you fergit it!"

No need had he to tell me more than this. I knew who "Sis" was by the light of pride in the uplifted eyes; I knew who "Sis" was by the exultation in the broken voice, and the half-defiant tossing of the frowzy head; I knew who "Sis" was by the little, naked hands thrown upward openly; I knew who "Sis" was by the tear that dared to trickle through the dirt upon her ragged brother's face. And don't *you* forget it!

O that boy down there upon his knees!—there in the cinders and the dirt—so far, far down beneath us that we trample on his breast and grind our heels into his very heart; O that boy there, with his lifted eyes, and God's own glory shining in his face, has taught me, with an eloquence beyond the trick of mellow-sounding words and metaphor, that love may find a purer home beneath the rags of poverty and vice than in all the great warm heart of Charity.

I hardly knew what impulse prompted me, but as the boy rose to his feet and held his hand out for the compensation for his work, I caught the little dingy palm close, close within my own, and wrung it as I would have wrung the hand of some great conqueror.

The little fellow stared at me in wonderment, and although his lips were silent, I can but believe that had they parted with the utterance within his heart my feelings had received no higher recognition than the old contemptuous phrase, "Oh, what you givin' me?"

"And so you've got a family on your hands?" I inquired, recovering an air of simple curiosity, and toying in my pocket with some bits of change. "How much of a family?"

"On'y three of us now."

"Only three of you, eh?  Yourself, and Sis, and —and—"

"The old man," said the boy, uneasily; and after a pause, in which he seemed to swallow an utterance more bitter, he added, "And he ain't no good on earth!"

"Can't work?" I queried.

"*Won't* work," said the boy, bitterly.  "He *won't* work—he won't do nothin'—on'y *budge!*  And I haf to steer him in ever' night, 'cause the cops won't pull him any more—they won't let him in the station-house more'n they'd let him in a parler, 'cause he's a plum' goner now, and liable to croak any minute."

"Liable to what?" said I.

"Liable to jist keel over—wink out, you know— 'cause he has fits—kind o' jimjams, I guess.  Had a fearful old matinée with him last night!  You

see he comes all sorts o' games on me, and I haf
to put up fer him—'cause he's *got* to have *whisky,*
and if we can on'y keep him about so full he's a
regular lamb; but he don't stand no monkeyin'
when he wants whisky, now you bet! Sis can
handle him better'n me, but *she's* been a-losin' her
grip on him lately—you see Sis ain't stout any
more, and been kind o' sick-like so long she humors
him, you know, more'n she'd ort. And he couldn't
git on his pins at all yisterday morning, and Sis
sent fer me, and I took him down a pint, and that
set him a-runnin' so that when I left he made Sis
give up a quarter he saw me slip her; and it jist
happened I run into him that evening and got him
in, or he'd 'a' froze to death. I guess he must
'a' kind o' had 'em last night, 'cause he was the wildest man you ever see—saw grasshoppers with
paper-collars on, and old sows with feather-duster
tails—the durndest program you ever heard of!
And he got so bad onc't he was a-goin' to *belt* Sis,
and did *try* it: and—and I had to chug him one
or he'd 'a' done it. And then he cried, and *Sis* cried,
and *I* cri—, I— *Dern him!* you can bet yer life *I*
didn't cry!" And as the boy spoke, the lips quiv-
ered into stern compression, the little hands gripped
closer at his side, but for all that the flashing eye
grew blurred and the lids dropped downward.

"That's a boss shine on them shoes."

I was mechanically telling over in my hand the
three small coins I had drawn from my pocket.

"That *is* a nice job!" said I, gazing with an unusual show of admiration at the work; "and I thought," continued I, with real regret, "that I had two dimes and a nickel here, and was thinking that, as these were Christmas times, I'd just give you a quarter for your work."

"Honest, Cap?"

"Honest!" I repeated, "but the fact is the two dimes, as I thought they were, are only two three-cent pieces, so I have only eleven cents in change, after all."

"Spect they'd change a bill fer you 'crost there at the lunch-counter," he suggested, with charming artlessness.

"Won't have time—there's my train just coupling.—But take this—I'll see you again sometime, perhaps."

"How big a bill is it you *want* changed?" asked the little fellow, with a most acquisitive expression, and a swift glance at our then lonely surroundings.

"I only have one bill with me," said I, nervously, "and that's a five."

"Well, here then," said the boy, hurriedly, with another and more scrutinizing glance about him— "guess I can 'commodate you." And as I turned in wonder, he drew from some mysterious recess in the lining of his coat a roll of bills, from which he hastily detached four in number, then returned the roll; and before I had recovered from my surprise, he had whisked the note from my fingers and left in my hand instead the proper change.

"This is on the dead, now, Cap. Don't you ever

cheep about me havin' wealth, you know; 'cause it ain't *mine*—that is, it *is* mine, but I'm a— There goes yer train. Ta-ta!"

"The day before Christmas," said I, snatching his hand, and speaking hurriedly—"the day before Christmas I'm coming back, and if you'll be here when the five-thirty train rolls in you'll find a man that wants his boots blacked—maybe to get married in, or something—anyway he'll want a shine like this, and he'll come prepared to pay the highest market price—do you understand?"

"You jist tell that feller fer me," said the boy, eclipsing the twinkle of one eye, and dropping his voice to an inflection of strictest confidence—"you jist tell that feller fer me that I'm his oyster!"

"And you'll meet him, sure?" said I.

"I will," said the boy. And he kept his word.

My ride home was an incoherent fluttering of the wings of time, in which travail one fretful hour was born, to gasp its first few minutes helplessly; then moan, roll over and kick out its legs and sprawl about; then crawl a little—stagger to its feet and totter on; then tumble down a time or two and knock its empty head against the floor and howl; then loom up awkwardly on gangling legs, too much in their own way to comprehend that they were in the way of everybody else; then limp a little as it worried on—drop down exhausted— moan again—toss up its hands—shriek out, and die in violent convulsions.

We have all had that experience of the car-wheels—had them enter into conversation with us as we gaily embarked upon some pleasant trip, perhaps; had them rattle off in scraps of song, or lightly twit us with some dear one's name, or even go so far as to laugh at us and mock us for some real or fancied dereliction of car-etiquette. I shall ever have good reason to remember how once upon a time a boy of fourteen, though greatly under-sized, told the conductor he was only ten, and although the unsuspecting official accepted the statement as a truth, with the proper reduction in the fare, the car-wheels called that boy a "liar" for twenty miles—and twenty miles as long and tedious as he has ever compassed in his journey through this vale of tears.

The car-wheels on this bitter winter evening were not at all communicative. They were sullen and morose. They didn't feel like singing, and they wouldn't laugh. They had no jokes, and if there was one peculiar quality of tone they possessed in any marked degree it was that of sneering. They had a harsh, discordant snarl, as it seemed, and were spiteful and insinuating.

The topic they had chosen for that night's consideration was evidently of a very complex and mysterious nature, and they gnawed and mumbled at it with such fierceness, and, withal, such selfishness, I could only catch a flying fragment of it now and then, and that, I noticed, was of the coarsest fiber of intelligence, and of slangy flavor. Listen-

ing with the most painful interest, I at last made
out the fact that the inflection seemed to be in the
interrogative, and, with anxiety the most intense,
I slowly came to comprehend that they were desirous of ascertaining the exact distance between
two given points, but the proposition seemed determined not to round into fuller significance than to
query mockingly, "How *fur* is it? How *fur* is it?
How *fur,* how *fur,* how *fur* is it?" and so on to a
most exasperating limit. As this senseless phrase
was repeated and reiterated in its growing harsh-
ness and unchanging intonation, the relentless per-
tinacity of the query grew simply agonizing, and
when at times the car door opened to admit a
brakeman, or the train-boy, who had everything to
sell but what I wanted, the emphasized refrain
would lift me from my seat and drag me up and
down the aisle. When the phrase did eventually
writhe round into form and shade more tangible,
my relief was such that I sat down, and in my
fancy framed a grim, unlovely tune that suited it,
and hummed with it, in an undertone of dismal
satisfaction:

> *"How fur—how fur*
> *Is it from here—*
> *From here to Happiness?"*

When I returned, that same refrain rode back
into the city with me! All the gay metropolis was
robing for the banquet and the ball. All the windows of the crowded thoroughfares were kindling

into splendor. Along the streets rode lordly carriages, so weighted down with costly silks, and furs, and twinkling gems, and unknown treasures in unnumbered packages, that one lone ounce of needed charity would have snapped their axles, and a feather's weight of pure benevolence would have splintered every spoke.

And the old refrain rode with me through it all—as stoical, relentless and unchangeable as fate—and in the same depraved and slangy tone in which it seemed to find an especial pride, it sang, and sang again:

> *"How fur—how fur*
> *Is it from here—*
> *From here to Happiness?"*

The train, that for five minutes had been lessening in speed, toiled painfully along, and as I arose impatiently and reached behind me for my overcoat, a cheery voice cried, "Hello, Cap! Want a lift? I'll he'p you with that benjamin"; and as I looked around I saw the grimy features of my little hero of the brush and box.

"Hello!" said I, as much delighted as surprised. "Where did you drop from?"

"Oh, I collared this old hearse a mile er so back yonder," said the little fellow, gaily, standing on the seat behind me and holding up the coat. "Been a-doin' circus-business on the steps out there fer half an hour. You bet I had my eye on *you,* all the same, though!"

"You had, eh?" I exclaimed, gladly, although I instinctively surmised his highest interest in me was centered in my pocketbook. "You had, eh?" I repeated with more earnestness—"Well, I'm glad of that, Charlie—or, what *is* your name?"

"Squatty," said the boy. Then noticing the look of surprise upon my face, he added soberly: "That ain't my sure-enough name, you know; that's what the *boys* calls me. *Sis* calls me Jamesy."

"Well, Jamesy," I continued, buttoning my collar and drawing on my gloves, "I'm mighty glad to see you, and if you don't believe it, just go down in that right-hand overcoat-pocket and you'll find out."

The little fellow needed no second invitation, and as he drew forth a closely folded package the look of curiosity upon his face deepened to one of blank bewilderment.

"Open it," said I, smiling at the puzzled little face; "open it—it's for you."

"Oh, here, Cap," said the boy, dropping the package on the seat, and holding up a rigid finger, "you're a-givin' me this, ain't you?"

"I'm giving you the package, certainly," said I, somewhat bewildered. "Open it—it's a Christmas present for you—open it!"

"What's your idy o' layin' fer me?" asked the boy, with a troubled and uneasy air. "I've been a-givin' you square business right along, ain't I?"

"Why, Jamesy," said I, as I vaguely comprehended the real drift of his thought, "the package *is* for you, and if you won't open it, I will," and as I

spoke I began unfolding it. "Here," said I, "is a
pair of gloves a little girl about your size told me
to give to you, because I was telling her about you,
over where I live, and it's 'a clear case,'" and I
laughed lightly to myself as I noticed a slow flush
creeping to his face. "And here," said I, "is a bang-
up pair of good old-fashioned socks, and, if they'll
fit you, there's an old woman that wears specs and
a mole on her nose, told me to tell you, for her, that
she knit them for your Christmas present, and if
you don't wear them she'll never forgive you. And
here," I continued, "is a cap, as fuzzy as a woolly-
worm, and as warm a cap, I reckon, as you ever
stood on your head in; it's a cheap cap, but I bought
it with my own money, and money that I worked
mighty hard to get, because I ain't rich; now, if I
was rich, I'd buy you a plug; but I've got an idea
that this little, old, woolly cap, with earbobs to it,
and a snapper to go under your chin, don't you see,
won't be a bad cap to knock around in, such weather
as this. What do you say now! Try her on once,"
and as I spoke I turned to place it on his head.

"Oomh-ooh!" he negatively murmured, putting
out his hand, his closed lips quivering—the little
frowzy head drooping forward, and the ragged
shoes shuffling on the floor.

"Come," said I, my own voice growing curiously
changed; "won't you take these presents? They are
yours; you must accept them, Jamesy, not because
they're worth so very much, or because they're very

fine," I continued, bending down and folding up the parcel, "but because, you know, I want you to, and—and—you must take them; you must!" and as I concluded, I thrust the tightly folded parcel beneath his arm, and pressed the little tattered elbow firmly over it.

"There you are," said I.—"Freeze on to it, and we'll skip off here at the avenue. Come."

I hardly dared to look behind me till I found myself upon the street, but as I threw an eager glance over my shoulder I saw the little fellow following, not bounding joyfully, but with a solemn step, the little parcel hugged closely to his side, and his eyes bent soberly upon the frozen ground.

"And how's Sis by this time?" I asked cheerily, flinging the question backward, and walking on more briskly.

"'Bout the same," said the boy, brightening a little, and skipping into a livelier pace.

"About the same, eh? and how's that?" I asked.

"Oh, she can't git around much like she used to, you know; but she's a-gittin' better all the time. She set up mighty nigh all day yesterday"; and as the boy spoke the eyes lifted with the old flash, and the little frowzy head tossed with the old defiance.

"Why, she's not down sick?" said I, a sudden ache of sorrow smiting me.

"Yes," replied the boy, "she's been bad a long time. You see," he broke in by way of explanation, "she didn't have no shoes ner nothin' when winter

come, and kind o' took cold, you know, and that
give her the whoopin'-cough so's she couldn't git
around much. You jist ort to see her now!—Oh,
she's a-gittin' all right *now,* you can bet! and she
said yesterday she'd be plum well Christmas, and
that's on'y to-morry.—*Guess not!"* and as the little
fellow concluded this exultant speech, he circled
round me, and then shot forward like a rocket.

"Hi! Jamesy!" I called after him, pausing at a
stairway and stepping in the door.

The little fellow joined me in an instant. "Want
that shine now?" he inquired with panting eagerness.

"Not now, Jamesy," said I, "for I'm going to be
quite busy for a while. This is my stopping-place
here—the second door on the right, up-stairs, remember—and I work there when I'm in the city,
and I sometimes sleep there, when I work late.
And now I want to ask a very special favor of
you," I continued, taking a little sealed packet from
my pocket : "here's a little box that you're to take to
Sis, with my compliments—the compliments of the
season, you understand,—and tell her I sent it, with
particular directions that she shouldn't break it open
till Christmas morning—not till Christmas morning,
understand! Then you tell her that I would like
very much to come and see her, and if she says all
right,—and you must give me a good 'send-off,' and
she'll say all right if 'Jamesy' says all right,—then
come back here, say two hours from now, or three

hours, or to-night, anyway, and we'll go down and
see Sis together—what do you say?"

The boy nodded dubiously. "Honest—must I do
all that, sure enough?"

"Will you?" said I; "that's what I want to
know"; and I pushed back the dusky little face and
looked into the bewildered eyes.

"*Solid?*" he queried, gravely.

"Solid," I repeated, handing him the box. "Will
you come?"

"W'y, 'course I will, on'y I was jist a-thinkin'—"

"Just thinking what?" said I, as the little fellow
paused abruptly and shook the box suspiciously at
his ear. "Just thinking what?" I repeated; "for I
must go now; good-by.—Just thinking what?"

"Oh, nothin'," said the boy, backing off and staring at me in a phase of wonder akin to awe.—
"Nothin', on'y I was jist a-thinkin' that you was a
little the curiousest rooster *I* ever see."

Three hours later, as I sat alone, he came in upon
me timidly to say he had not been home yet, having "run acrost the old man jist a-bilin', and had to
git him corralled 'fore he dropped down som'er's in
the snow; but I'm a-gittin 'long bully with him
*now*," he added with a deep sigh of relief, " 'cause
he's so full he'll haf to let go purty soon. Say
you'll be here?"

I nodded silently, and he was gone.

The merry peals of laughter rang up from the
streets like mockery. The jingling of bells, the clat-

ter and confusion of the swarming thoroughfares, flung up to me not one glad murmur of delight; the faint and far-off blaring of a dreamy waltz, blown breeze-like over the drowsy ear of night, had sounded sweeter to me had I stood amidst the band, with every bellowing horn about my ears, and the drums and clashing cymbals howling mad.

I couldn't work, I couldn't read, I couldn't rest; I could only pace about. I heard the clock strike ten, and strike it hard; I heard it strike eleven, viciously; and twelve it held out at arm's length, and struck it full between the eyes, and let it drop—stone dead. O I saw the blood ooze from its ears, and saw the white foam freeze upon its lips! I was alone—alone!

It was three o'clock before the boy returned.

"Been a long while," he began, "but I had a fearful time with the old man, and he went on so when I *did* git him in I was 'most afeard to leave him; but he kind o' went to sleep at last, and Molly *she* come over to see how Sis was a-gittin'; and Sis said she'd like to see *you* if you'd come *now,* you know, while they ain't no racket goin' on."

"Come, then," said I, buttoning my coat closely at the throat, "I am ready"; and a moment later we had stepped into the frosty night. We moved along in silence, the little fellow half running, half sliding along the frozen pavement in the lead; and I noted, with a pleasurable thrill, that he had donned the little fuzzy cap and mittens, and from time to

time was flinging, as he ran, admiring glances at
his shadow on the snow.

Our way veered but a little from the very center
of the city, but led mainly along through narrow
streets and alley-ways, where the rear ends of mas-
sive business blocks had dwindled down to insignificant proportions to leer grimly at us as we passed
little grated windows and low, scowling doors.  Occasionally we passed a clump of empty boxes, barrels, and such débris and merchandise as had been
crowded pell-mell from some inner storage by their
newer and more dignified companions; and now
and then we passed an empty bus, bulging up in the
darkness like a behemoth of the olden times; or,
jutting from still narrower passages, the sloping
ends of drays and carts innumerable.  And along
even as forbidding a defile as this we groped until
we came upon a low, square brick building that
might have served at one time as a wash-house, or,
less probably, perhaps, a dairy.  There was but one
window in the front, and that but little larger than
an ordinary pane of glass.  In the sides, however,
and higher up, was a row of gratings, evidently designed more to serve as ventilation than as open-
ings for light.  There was but one opening, an upright doorway, half above ground, half below, with
little narrow side-steps leading down to it.  A light
shone dimly from the little window, and as the
boy motioned me to pause and listen, a sound of
female voices talking in undertones was audible,

mingled with a sound like that of some one snoring heavily.

"Hear the old man a-gittin' in his work?" whispered the boy.

I nodded. "He's asleep?"

"You *bet* he's asleep!" said the boy, still in a whisper; "and he'll jist about stay with it thataway fer five hours, anyhow. What time you got now, Cap?"

"A quarter now till four," I replied, peering at my watch.

"W'y, it's *Christmas,* then!" he cried in muffled rapture of delight; but abruptly checking his emotion, he beckoned me a little farther from the door, and spoke in a confidential whisper.

"Cap, look here, now; 'fore we go in I want you to promise me one thing—'cause you can fix it and *she'll* never drop! Now, here, I want to put up a job on *Sis,* you understand!"

"What!" I exclaimed, starting back and staring at the boy in amazement. "Put up a job on Sis?"

"Oh, look here, now, Cap; you ain't a-goin' back on a feller like that!" broke in the little fellow, in a mingled tone of pleading and reproof; "and if you don't help a feller I'll haf to wait till broad daylight, 'cause we ain't got no clock."

"No clock!" I repeated with increased bewilderment.

"Oh, come, Cap, what do you say? It ain't no lie, you know; all you got to do'll be to jist tell Sis it's Christmas—as though you didn't want *me* to

hear, you know; and then she'll git my 'Christmas
gift!' *first,* you know;—and, oh, lordy! won't she
think she's played it fine!" And as I slowly comprehended the meaning of the little fellow's plot I
nodded my willingness to assist in "putting up the
job."

"Now, hold on a second!" continued the little fellow, in the wildest glee, darting through an opening
in a high board fence a dozen steps away, and in an
instant reappearing with a bulky parcel, which, as
he neared me, I discovered was a paper flour-sack
half filled, the other half lapped down and fastened
with a large twine string. "Now this stuff," he went
on excitedly, "you must juggle in without Sis seein'
it—here, shove it under your 'ben,' here—there—
that's business! Now when you go in, you're to set
down with the other side to'rds the bed, you see,
and when Sis *hollers 'Christmas gift,'* you know,
you jist kind o' let it slide down to the floor like, and
I'll nail it slick enough—though I'll p'tend, you
know, it *ain't* Christmas yet, and look sold out, and
say it wasn't fair fer you to tell her, and all that;
and then I'll open up suddent-like, and if you don't
see old Sis bug out them eyes of hern I don't want a
cent!" And as the gleeful boy concluded this
speech, he put his hands over his mouth and dragged
me down the little, narrow steps.

"Here's that feller come to see you, Sis!" he announced abruptly, opening the door and peering in.
"Come on," he said, turning to me. I followed,

closing the door, and looking curiously around. A squabby, red-faced woman, sitting on the edge of a low bed, leered upon me, but with no salutation. An old cook-stove, propped up with bricks, stood back against the wall directly opposite, and through the warped and broken doors in front sent out a dismal suggestion of the fire that burned within. At the side of this, prone upon the floor, lay the wretched figure of a man, evidently in the deepest stage of drunkenness, and thrown loosely over him was an old tattered piece of carpet and a little checkered shawl.

There was no furniture to speak of ; one chair— and that was serving as a stand—stood near the bed, a high hump-shouldered bottle sitting on it, a fruit-can full of water, and a little dim and smoky lamp that glared sulkily.

"Jamesy, can't you git the man a cheer er somepin'?" queried a thin voice from the bed; at which the red-faced woman rose reluctantly with the rather sullen words: "He can sit here, I reckon," while the boy looked at me significantly and took up a position near the "stand."

"So this is Sis?" I said, with reverence.

The little haggard face I bent above was beautiful. The eyes were dark and tender—very tender, and though deeply sunken were most childish in expression and star-pure and luminous. She reached a wasted little hand out to me, saying simply: "It was mighty good in you to give them things to Jamesy, and send me that mo—that—that little box,

you know—on'y I guess I—I won't need it." As
she spoke a smile of perfect sweetness rested on the
face, and the hand within my own nestled in dove-
like peace.

The boy bent over the white face from behind and
whispered something in her ear, trailing the little
laughing lips across her brow as he looked up.

"Not now, Jamesy; wait a while."

"Ah!" said I, shaking my head with feigned merriment, "don't you two go to plotting about me!"

"Oh, hello, no, Cap?" exclaimed the boy, assur-
ingly. "I was on'y jist a-tellin' Sis to ast you if she
mightn't open that box *now*—honest! And you
jist ask her if you don't believe me—*I* won't listen."
And the little fellow gave me a look of the most
penetrative suggestiveness; and when a moment
later the glad words, "Christmas gift! Jamesy,"
rang out quaveringly in the thin voice, the little fellow snatched the sack up, in a paroxysm of delight,
and before the girl had time to lift the long dark
lashes once upon his merry face, he had emptied its
contents out tumultuously upon the bed.

"You got it on to me, Sis!" cried the little fellow,
dancing wildly round the room; "got it on to me *this*
time! but I'm *game,* don't you fergit, and don't put
up nothin' snide! How'll them shoes there ketch
you? and how's this fer a cloak?—is them enough
beads to suit you? And how's this fer a hat—
feather and all? And how's this fer a dress—made
and ever'thing? and I'd 'a' got a *corsik* with it if he'd
on'y had any little enough. *You* won't look fly ner

nothin' when you throw all that style on you in the morning!—*Guess not!*" And the delighted boy went off upon another wild excursion round the room.

"Lean down here," said the girl, a great light in her eyes and the other slender hand sliding from beneath the covering. "Here is the box you sent me, and I've *opened* it—it wasn't *right* you know, but somepin' kind o' said to open it *'fore* morning—and —and I opened it." And the eyes seemed asking my forgiveness, yet were filled with great bewilderment. "You see," she went on, the thin voice falling in a fainter tone, "I *knowed* that money in the box—that is, the *bills*—I *knowed* them bills 'cause *one* of 'em had a ink-spot on it, and the other ones had been pinned with it—they *wasn't* pinned together when *you* sent 'em, but the holes was in where they *had been* pinned, and they was all pinned together when *Jamesy* had 'em—'cause Jamesy used to have them very bills—he didn't think *I* knowed,—but onc't when he was asleep, and *father* was a-goin' through his clothes, I happened to find 'em in his coat 'fore *he* did; and I *counted* 'em, and hid 'em back ag'in, and father didn't find 'em, and Jamesy never knowed it.—I never said nothin', 'cause somepin' kind o' said to me it was all right; and somepin' kind o' said I'd git all these things here, too—on'y I won't need 'em, ner the money, nor nothin'. How did *you* get the money? That's all!"

The boy had by this time approached the bed, and was gazing curiously upon the solemn little face.

"What's the *matter* with you, Sis?" he asked in wonderment; "ain't you glad?"

"I'm *mighty* glad, Jamesy," she said, the little, thin hands reaching for his own. "Guess I'm *too* glad, 'cause I can't do nothin' on'y jist *feel* glad; and somepin' kind o' says that that's the gladdest glad in all the world. Jamesy!"

"Oh, pshaw, Sis! Why don't you tell a feller what's the matter?" said the boy, uneasily.

The white hands linked more closely with the brown, and the pure face lifted to the grimy one till they were blent together in a kiss.

"Be good to father, fer you know he used to be so good to us."

"O Sis! Sis!"

"Molly!"

The squabby, red-faced woman threw herself upon her knees and kissed the thin hands wildly and with sobs.

"Molly, somepin' kind o' says that *you* must dress me in the morning—but I won't need the hat, and you must take it home for Nannie— Don't cry so loud; you'll wake father."

I bent my head down above the frowzy one and moaned—moaned.

"And you, sir," went on the failing voice, reaching for my hand, "you—you must take this money back—you must take it back, fer I don't need it. You must take it back and—and—give it—give it to the poor." And even with the utterance upon the gracious lips the glad soul leaped and fluttered through the open gates.

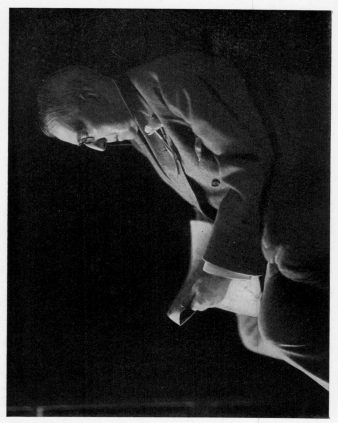

JAMES WHITCOMB RILEY
September, 1913

# TALE OF A SPIDER

FIRST—I want it most distinctly understood that I am superstitious, notwithstanding the best half of my life, up to the very present, has been spent in the emphatic denial of that fact. And I am painfully aware that this assertion at so late a date can but place my former character in a most unenviable light; yet for reasons *you* will never know, I have, with all due deliberation, determined to hold the truth up stark and naked to the world, with the just acknowledgment shorn of all attempt at palliation or excuse, that for the best half of my life I have been simply a coward and a liar.

Second—From a careful and impartial study of my fellow beings, I have arrived at the settled conviction that nine men of every ten are just as superstitious as myself; yet, with the difference, that, for reasons I know, they refuse to acknowledge it openly, many of them dodging the admission even within their own ever curious and questioning minds.

Third—Most firmly fixed in this belief and intuitively certain of at least the inner confidence and sympathy of a grand majority of those who read, I throw aside all personal considerations, defy all ridicule—all reason, if you like—in order to devote myself wholly to the narration of an actual experience that for three long weeks has been occurring with me nightly in this very room. You should hear me laugh about it in the daytime! Oh, I snap my fingers then, and whistle quite as carelessly and scornfully as you doubtless would; but at night—at night—and it's night now—I grow very, very serious somehow, and put all raillery aside, and here all in vain argue by the hour that it's nothing in the world but the baleful imaginings of a feverish mind, and the convulsive writhings of a dyspeptic fancy. But enough!—Even forced to admit that I'm a fool, I will tell my story.

Although by no means of a morbid or misanthropic disposition, the greater portion of my time I occupy in strict seclusion, here at my desk—for only when alone can I conscientiously indulge certain propensities of thinking aloud, talking to myself, leaping from my chair occasionally to dance a new thought round the room, or take it in my arms, and hug and hold and love it as I would a great, fat, laughing baby with a bunch of jingling keys.

Then there are times, too, when worn with work, and I find my pen dabbling by the wayside in sluggish blots of ink, that I delight to take up the old guitar which leans here in the corner, and twang among the waltzes that I used to know, or lift a most unlovely voice in half-forgotten songs whose withered notes of melody fall on me like dead

leaves, but whose crisp rustling still has power to
waken from "the dusty crypt of darkened forms
and faces" the glad convivial spirits that once
thronged about me in the wayward past, and made
my young life one long peal of empty merriment.
Someway, I've lost the knack of wholesome laughter now, and for this reason, maybe, I so often find
my fingers tangled in the strings of my guitar; for,
after all, there is an indefinable something in the
tone of a guitar that is not all of earth. I have
often fancied that departed friends came back to
hide themselves away in this old husk of song that
we might pluck them forth to live again in quavering tones of tenderness and love and minor voices of
remembrance that coax us on to Heaven. Pardon
my vagaries.—I'm practical enough at times; at
times I fail. But I must be clear to-night; I must
be, and I will.

This night three weeks ago I had worked late,
though on a task involving nothing that could possibly have warped my mind to an unnatural state,
other than that of peculiar wakefulness; for although physically needful of rest, I felt that it was
useless to retire; and so I wheeled my sofa in a
cozy position near the stove, lighted a cigar (my
chum Hays had left me four hours previous), and
flinging myself down in languid pose best suiting
the requirements of an aimless reverie, I resigned
all serious complexities of thought and was wholly
comfortable.

The silence of the night without was deep. Not

a footstep in the street below, and not a sound of any living earthly thing fell on the hearing, though that sense was whetted to such acuteness I could plainly hear the ticking of a clock somewhere across the street.

All things about the room were in their usual order. My letters on the desk were folded as I answered them, and filed away; my books were ranged in order, and my manuscripts tucked out of sight and mind, with no scrap of paper to remind me of my never-ended work, save the blank sheet that always lies in readiness for me to pounce upon with any vagrant thought that comes along, and close beside it the open inkstand and the idle pen.

I had reclined thus in utter passiveness of mind for half an hour perhaps, when suddenly I heard, or thought I heard, below me in the street, the sound of some stringed instrument. I rose on my elbow and listened. Some serenader, I guessed. Yes, I could hear it faintly, but—so far away it seemed, and indistinct. I arose, went to the window, raised it and leaned out; and as the sound grew fainter and failed entirely, I closed the window and sat down again; yet even as I did so the mysterious tones fell on my hearing plainer than before. I listened closely, and though little more than a ghost of sound, I still could hear, and quite audibly distinguish, the faint repeated twanging of the six open strings of a guitar—so plainly, indeed, that I instinctively recognized the irritating fact that both the "E" and "D" strings were slightly out of tune. I turned with some strange impulse to my own instrument, and I must leave the reader to imagine the cold thrill of surprise and fear that crept over me as the startling conviction slowly dawned upon my mind that the sounds came from that unlooked-for quarter. The guitar was leaning in its old position in the corner, the face turned to the wall, and although I confess it with reluctance, full five minutes elapsed before I found sufficient courage to approach and pick it up; then I nearly dropped it in abject terror as a great, fat, blowzy spider ran across my hand and went scampering up the wall. What do you think of spiders, anyhow? You say "Wooh!" I say you don't know anything about spiders.

I examined first the wall to see if there might not be some natural cause for the mysterious sounds—some open crevice for the wind, some loosened and vibrating edge of paper, or perhaps, a bristle protruding from the plaster—but I found no evidence that could in any way afford an answer to the perplexing query. An old umbrella and a broom stood in the corner, but in neither of these inanimate objects could I find the vaguest explanation of the problem that so wholly and entirely possessed me.

I could not have been mistaken. It was no trick of fancy—no hallucination. I had not only listened to the sounds repeated, over and over, a dozen times at least, but I had recognized and measured the respective values of the tones; and as I turned, half in awe, took up the instrument and lightly swept the strings, the positive proof, for the conviction jarred as discordantly upon my fancy as upon my ears—the two strings, "E" and "D," were out of tune.

I will no longer attempt the detail of my perturbed state of curiosity and the almost dazed condition of my mind; such an effort would at best be vain. But I sat down, doggedly, at last; and in a spirit of indifference the most defiant I could possibly assume, I ran the guitar up to a keen exultant key, and dashed off into a quickstep that made the dumb old echoes of the room leap up and laugh with melody. I was determined in my own mind to stave off the most unwholesome influence that seemed settling fog-like over me; and as the sharp twang of the strings rang out upon the night, and the rich vibrating chords welled up and overflowed the silence like a flood, the embers of old-time enthusiasm kindled in my heart and flamed up in a warmth of real delight. Suddenly, in the midst of this rapturous outburst, as with lifted face I stared ceilingward, my eyes again fell on that horrid spider, madly capering about the wall in a little circumference of a dozen inches, perhaps, wheeling and whirling up and down, and round and round again, as though laboring under some wild jubilant excitement.

I played on mechanically for a moment, my eyes riveted upon the grotesque antics of the insect, feeling instinctively that the music was producing this singular effect upon it. I was right; for, as I gradually paused, the gyrations of the insect assumed a milder phase, and as I ceased entirely, the great bloated thing ran far out overhead and dropped suddenly a yard below the ceiling, and, pendent by its unseen thread, hung sprawled in the empty air above my face, so near I could have touched it with the lifted instrument. And then, even as I shrank back fearfully, a new line of speculation was suggested to my mind: I arose abruptly, leaned the guitar back in the corner, took up a book, and sat down at the desk, leaving the silence of the room intensified till in my nervous state of mind I almost fancied I could hear that spider whispering to itself, as above the open pages of the book I watched the space between it and the ceiling slowly widening, till at last the ugly insect dropped and disappeared behind the sofa.

I had not long to wait; nor was my curious mind placed any more at ease, when, at last, faint and far-off sounding as at first, I heard the eery twanging of the guitar—though this time I could with some triumphant pleasure note the fact that the instrument was in perfect tune. But to assure myself thoroughly that I could in no way be mistaken as to the mysterious cause, I arose and crept cautiously across the carpet until within easy reach of the guitar. I paused again to listen and convince myself beyond all doubt that the sounds were there produced. There could be no possible mistake about it. Then suddenly I caught and whirled the instrument around, and as I did so the spider darted from the keyboard near the top, leaped to the broom-handle and fled up the wall.

I tried no more experiments that night, or rather morning—for it must have been three o'clock as I turned wearily away from the exasperating contemplation of the strange subject, turned down the lamp, then turned it up again, huddled myself into a shivering heap upon the sofa, and fell into an uneasy asleep, in which I dreamed that *I* was a spider—of Brobdingnagian proportions, and lived on men and women instead of flies, and had a web like a monster hammock, in which I swung myself out over the streets at night and fished up my prey with a hook and line—thought I caught more poets than anything else, and was just nibbling warily at my own bait, when the line was suddenly withdrawn, the hook catching me in the cheek, tearing out and letting me drop back with a sullen plunge into the great gulf of the night. And as I found myself, with wildly staring eyes, sitting bolt upright on the sofa, I saw the spider, just above my desk, lifted and flung upward by his magic line and thrown among the dusky shadows of the ceiling.

"Hays," said I to my chum in the early morning, as he came in on me, sitting at my desk and gazing abstractedly at an incoherent scrawl of ink upon the scrap of paper lying before me—"Hays," said I, "what's your opinion of spiders?"

"What's my opinion of spiders?" he queried, staring at me curiously.

"What's your opinion of spiders?" I repeated

with my first inflection—for Hays is a young man
in the medical profession, and likes point, fact and
brevity. "What I mean is this," I continued, "isn't
it generally conceded that the spider is endowed
with a higher order of intelligence than insects
commonly?"

"I believe so," he replied with the same curious
air, watching me narrowly; "I have a vague recol-
lection of some incident illustrative of that theory
in Goldsmith's 'Animated Nature,' or some equally
veracious chronicle," with suggestive emphasis on
the word "veracious." "Why do you ask?"

And, although half assured I would be sneered at
for my pains, I went into a minute recountal of my
strange experience of the night, winding up in a
high state of excitement, doubtless intensified by the
blandly smiling features of my auditor, who made
no interruption whatever, and only looked at me at
the conclusion of the dream with gratuitous compassion and concern. "Well!" said I uneasily, taking an impatient turn or two across the room. . . .
"Well!" I repeated, pausing abruptly and glaring at
the shrugged shoulders of my stoical companion,
"why don't you say something?"

"Nothing to say, I suppose," he answered, turning
on me with absolute severity. "You never listen to
advice. Two months ago I told you to quit this
night business—it would wreck you physically,
mentally, every way. Why, look at you!" he continued in pitiless reproof, as I flew off on another
nervous trip around the room. "Look at you! a

perfect crate of bones—no 'get-up' in your walk—
no color in your face—no appetite—no anything but
a wisp of shattered nerves, and a pair of howling-
hungry eyes that do nothing but stare."

"It wouldn't seem that you did have much to
say, upon the point, at least," I interrupted. "Never
mind my physical condition; what do you think of
my spider?"

"What do I think of your spider!" he repeated
contemptuously, "why, I think it's a little the thin-
nest piece of twaddle I ever listened to!—And I
think, further—"

"Hold on, now!" I exclaimed, a trifle warmed,
but smiling; "I knew you'd have to sweat a while
over that; but hold on—hold on! I have only told
you the minor facts of the strange occurrence;
the most startling and irrefutable portion yet remains. Now, listen! What I have already told you
I pledge you on my honor is pure truth. I can offer
nothing but my word for that. But I will close now
—don't interrupt me, if you please: As I awakened
from that dream, I saw that spider jerked from
above the desk here—just as a small boy might
whip up a fish-line—jerked by his own thread, of
course.—Well, and I got up at once—came to the
desk like this, feeling instinctively that that infernal spider had some object in lowering itself
among my letters; and I found this scrap of paper,
which I'll swear I left last night without one blot
or line of ink or pencil on it.—I found this scrap
of paper with this zigzag line—which you can see

was never made with human hand—scrawled across
it, and the ink was yet wet when I picked it up.
*Now,* what do you say?"

He took the scrap of paper in his hand half
curiously, and then, as though ashamed of having
betrayed so great a weakness, threw it back upon
the desk with scarce a look.

"What do you say?" I repeated, in a tone of triumph.

"Well," he replied, "it is barely possible you did
see a spider in this last instance, and I must confess
that it is a much easier matter for me to imagine
a spider dropping by accident into your inkstand
and leaving the trail of his salvation across your
writing-paper, than it is for me to fancy the fantastic insect plucking the strings of your guitar. In
fact, the first part of your story won't do at all. I
don't mean to intimate that your veracity is defective—not at all. But I do mean that you have
overworked yourself of late, and that your brain
needs rest."

"But," said I, pushing the scrap of paper toward
him again, "you don't seem to recognize the fact
that that ugly scrawl of ink means something. Look
at it carefully; it's writing."

He again took the paper in his hand, but this
time without a glance, and ere I could prevent him
he had torn it in a half dozen pieces and flung it
on the floor.

"What do you mean?" I cried resentfully, spring-
ing forward.

"Why, I mean that you're a babbling idiot," he answered in a tone half anger, half alarm; "and if you won't look after your own condition I'll do it for you, and in spite of you! You must quit this work—quit this room—quit everything, and come with me out in the fresh air, or you'll die; that's what I mean!"

Although he spoke with almost savage vehemence, I recognized, of course, the real promptings of his action, and smiled softly to myself as I gathered up the scattered scraps of paper from the carpet.

"Oh, we'll not quarrel," said I, seating myself patiently at the desk, and dipping my finger in the paste-cup—"we'll not quarrel about a little thing like this; only if you'll just wait a minute I'll show you that it does mean something."

I deftly joined the fragments in their proper places on a base of legal cap. "There!" said I good-naturedly, "now you can read it; but don't tear it again, please." I think I was very white when I said that, for my companion took the paper in his hand with at least a show of interest, and looked at it long and curiously.

"Well, what is it?" he asked, laying it back upon the desk before me: "I am really very sorry, but I am forced to acknowledge that I fail to find anything exactly tangible in it."

"Look," said I; "you see this capital that begins the line; the first letter?—It's a 'Y,' isn't it?"

"Yes; it looks a little like a 'Y'—or a 'G.'"

"No; it's a 'Y,'" said I, "and there's no more doubt about it than that this next one is an 'e.'"

"Well—"

"Well, this next letter is an 'S'—an old-fashioned 'S,' but it's an 'S' all the same, and you can't make anything else out of it; I've tried it, and it can't be done."

"Well, go on."

"This is a 'c,'" I continued.

"Go on; call it anything you like."

"No; but I want you to be thoroughly satisfied."

"Oh, do you? Well, it's a 'c,' then; go on."

"And this is an 'h.'"

"Go on."

"And this is an 'o'; you know that!"

"Yes; know it by the hole in it."

"Don't get funny. And this is an 'l.'"

"That's an 'l.'"

"This is an 'a.'"

"Close observer!"

"And that's an 'r'—and that's all."

"Well, you've got it all down to suit you; now, what does it spell?"

"What does it spell? Why, can't you read?" I exclaimed, flourishing the scrap triumphantly before his eyes. "It spells 'Ye Scholar!'—why, I could read it across the room!"

"Yes, or across the street," he answered caustically. "But come now!" he continued seriously, "throw it aside for the present at least, and let's go out in the sunshine for a while. Here, light a cigar, and come along"; and he moved toward the door.

"No," said I, turning to the mysterious scrawl, "I will hound this thing down while the inspiration's on me."

"Inspiration?—Bah!" The door slammed, but I never turned my head.

I had sat thus in dead silence for ten minutes, when suddenly I heard a quick impatient movement at my back, and then the sharp impetuous words— "In God's name! quit biting your nails like that! Don't you know it's an indication of madness!"

I think I need not enter into any explanation as to the reason which, from that moment, determined me upon a course that could afford no further conflict of opinion other than that already going on within my own mind. That of itself furnished all the exasperating controversy that I felt was well for my indulgence. But in one way I was grateful for the pointed suggestion of my friend regarding the questionable status of my mental faculties, for by it I was made most keenly alive to that peculiar sense of duty that made me look upon myself and question every individual act, entirely separated from my own personality; in fact, to look upon myself, as I did, clearly and distinctly defined in the light of a very suspicious and a very dangerous character, whose sole intent and purpose was to play and practise on me all unlooked-for and un-dreamed-of deceptions, and which, to combat suc-

cessfully, must needs require the most rigid and unwavering strength of reason.

In further justice to my honesty in this resolve, I
will say that I began at once the exercise of syste-
matic habits. Although by no means pleasant, I
took long rambles in the country; ate regularly of
wholesome food, regained my appetite, and retired
at night at seasonable hours. I will not say that
sleep came sooner to my eyes by reason of the
change, but anyway I wooed sleep—let this suffice.
I threw smoking aside entirely—not by any means
a hard trial for me, although an occasional cigar is
a great pleasure; but I threw it aside. Did not
study so intensely as had been by wont; read but
little, and wrote less—even neglecting my letters.
Yet, with all this revolution of reform, I am left
to confess that I never for one waking moment forgot the mystic legend, "Ye Scholar," or its equally
incomprehensible author; and how could I?

Since the first discovery of the strange insect
and its musical proclivities three evenings only
have passed that I have not been favored with its
most extraordinary performances on the guitar. In
this way has its presence been usually made known.
And noting carefully, as I have done, the peculiar
times and conditions of its coming, together with
such other suggestions as the surroundings have
afforded me, I have been led to believe that the
spider reasoned as a man would reason: In no instance yet has it ever touched the instrument when
I sat busy at my desk; and only when my pen was

idle in my hand or I had turned wearily away to
pace about the room, has it ever exhibited any inclination whatever to occupy my attention.   This
curious fact interpreted itself at last in the rather
startling proposition that it was simply an indication
on the part of the insect that it desired me to favor
it with music, since my time was not better occupied.—Virtually this is what it *did* mean; I *know*
it!  I would know and appreciate now any want the
insect might choose to express; only at first I was
very dull, as one naturally would be.   And I noticed, too, that when I first responded to this summons the spider would leap from the guitar to the
wall with every evidence of pleasure, and glide back
to its old position near the ceiling, indulging the
wildest tokens of glee and approval throughout my
performances.   And many times I have marched off
round and round the room simply thrumming the
time, the spider following along the upper margin
of the wall with the most fantastic caperings of
joy.

Other experiments followed, too numerous and
too foolish for recountal here, but each, in its way,
sufficient to establish more conclusively in my mind
the belief that the hideous little monster was endowed with an intelligence as wise and subtle in its
workings as it was within the power of my own to
recognize—even greater—for gradually, as we became more accustomed to each other, the ugly insect grew so tame it would come down the wall and
dance for me on a level with my face as I sat play-

ing, and even spring off upon the instrument if I held it out. At last I found my mind so baffled and bewildered that more than once the conviction was forced upon me that the spider was *not* a spider, but a— No, I'll not say that—not yet, not yet!

These experiments had progressed for perhaps half a dozen nights, when, as I sat, pen in hand at the desk here one evening, mechanically poring over the still incomprehensible meaning of the scrawl and writing and rewriting the two words over and over again upon an empty page before me, I became suddenly aware of a strange sensation of repose. A great cool quiet fell upon my brain, as when suddenly within some noisy foundry the clanging hammers cease to beat and all the brazen tumult drops like a plummet into silence fathomless. I felt a soothing languor flowing down and over me, and ebbing through and through my very being. It was not drowsiness; my eyelids were not heavy, nor did they droop the shadow of a shade. I saw everything about me as clearly as I do this very moment—only, I did not seem a part of my surroundings. My eyes, although conscious of all objects within range, were fixed upon the scrap of paper headed by the zigag scrawl and with an intensity of gaze that seemed to pierce the paper and to see through and beyond it; and I did not think it strange. I was dimly conscious, too, of being under the control of some influence hitherto undreamed, but I felt no thought of resistance—

rather courted the sensation. All was utter calm
with me; and I did not think it strange. I saw
my hand held out before me in this same position—
the forearm resting on the desk—the same pen
grasped lightly in my fingers.

Slowly—slowly—slowly—I saw the spider lowering itself above it, wavering and swaying in the air,
until, at last, I saw it reach its dangling legs and
clutch and cling to the penholder at the tip, and rest
there; and I did not think it strange. But I grew
duller then, and very chilly, though I vividly recall
seeing the hand moved—not of my own volition—
the pen dipped in the ink, and brought directly over
the old scrap whereon the scrawl was traced; and I
remember, too, that as I watched the motion of my
hand, I still saw beyond the surface of the paper,
and read the very words my pen traced afterward.
I say the words my pen traced—or my hand—either
—both—for the act was not my own, I swear! And
the spider still sat perched there at his post, rocked
lightly with the motion of the pen, with all his arms
hugged round him as though chuckling to himself;
and I say to you again, and yet again, I did not
think it strange.

Not until the page before me had been filled
did I regain my natural state of being, nor did it
seem that I then would, had not the spider quitted
his position and run down the penholder, leaning
from it for an instant, touching and pressing my
naked hand: then I was conscious of a keen exquisite sting; and with a quick spasmodic motion

I flung the hideous insect from it. As I lifted my white face and starting eyes, I saw the spider wildly clambering toward the ceiling on its invisible thread. Then, with a mingled sense of fear, bewilderment and admiration, as oppressive and strange as indescribable, I turned to the mysterious scrap and read, traced tremblingly, but plainly, in a dainty flowing hand, unlike any I had ever seen before, the lines I now copy from the original script before me, bearing the pedantic title of "Ye Scholar":

"Ho! ho! Ye Scholar recketh not how lean
  His lank frame waxeth in ye hectic gloom
  That smeareth o'er ye dim walls of his room
His wavering shadow! Shut is he, I ween,
Like as a withered nosegay, in between
  Ye musty, mildewed leaves of some volume
  Of ancient lore ye moth and he consume
In jointure. Yet a something in his mien
  Forbids all mockery, though quaint is he,
And eke fantastical in form and face
  As that Old Knight ye Tale of Chivalry
Made mad immortally, yet spared ye grace
  Of some rare virtue which we sigh to see,
  And pour our laughter out most tenderly."

Over and over I read the strange production to myself; and, as at last I started to my feet repeating it aloud, all suddenly the spider swooped on its flying thread before my upturned face, swung back upon the margin of the wall, and went scampering round and round above me as I read.

I did not sleep two hours of the night, but

mouthed and mouthed that sonnet—even in my
scrappy dreams—until when morning strained the
sunlight through the slatted window-blinds I turned
and dragged myself from the room like an old, old
man with childish summer fancies in his head and
bleak and barren winter in his bones.

The night following, and the next night, and the
next, I did not permit myself to enter my room
after dark—not from a sense of fear, but simply
because I felt my mind was becoming too entirely
engrossed with the contemplation of a theme that,
even yet at times, I feared was more chimera than
reality.

Throughout the day as usual with me, I worked
perhaps three hours at such trivial tasks as required
only the lightest mental effort; nor did I allow my
mind to wander from the matter-of-fact duties before me to the contemplation of the ever-present
topic that so confounded it when studiously dwelt
on.   Only once in this long abstinence from the
fascinating problem did I catch sight of the spider,
peering down upon me from behind the shoulder
of the little terra-cotta bust of Dickens that sits on
a dusty bracket just above my desk.   I looked up
at the little fellow with a smile, rose to my feet
and held out my hand, when, at the motion the insect cowered trembling for an instant, then sprang
up the wall beyond my reach.   But from that time
on I always felt its presence though unseen, intuitively conscious that at all hours my every act was
vigilantly scrutinized and guarded by the all-seeing

eye of that spider, and that every motion of my
pen was duly noted by it, and accepted as token
of the fact that I was busy and must not be disturbed. Indeed, I even allowed my vanity such
license that I came to believe that the spider was
not only interested in everything I did, but was
actually proud of my accomplishments. Certain it
is, I argued, that he likes my silence, my music and
my voice, and equally apparent from his actions that
he likes my society under any and all circumstances.
Nor shall it be the promptings of mere curiosity
on my part that shall make me endeavor to
strengthen and develop this curious bond of fellowship, but my serious and most courteous duty as
well.

So I went back to my night labors, greeted the
first evening, as I lit my lamp, by another mysterious
scrawl, which I readily interpreted in the one word
"Love."

I dashed the scrap down in a very spasm of revulsion and loathing. I can not describe nor will I
weaken the sense of utter abhorrence that fell upon
me by an attempt to set it forth in words; why, I
could taste it, and it sickened me soul-deep! I remember catching quick breaths through my clenched
and naked teeth; I remember snatching up the pen
as a despairing man grasps a dagger; I remember stabbing it in the ink, and drawing it back
in defiance; but as my hand once more rested on
the desk it was *my* hand no longer.—It was like
another man's, and that man my deadly foe. I

looked upon it vengefully, wishing that in my other
I but held an ax—an old ax, with a nicked and
rusty edge,—that I might hack and haggle the
traitor-member sheer off at the numb and pulseless
wrist. And then the spider! I tried to shrink back
as the hideous insect again dangled before my eyes,
but could not move. Once more it clutched the
holder of the pen, huddled its quivering limbs together, and squatted in its old position on the tip.
And then began the movement of the hand.

This time my eyes were fixed upon the insect. I
could not move them from it. I could see nothing
else; and but for the undulating motions of the
pen I felt that I might note its very breathings—and
I *did* see it *smile*. Oh, horrible! Why, I set my
teeth together till my inner sense of hearing pinged
like a bell, and said, away down among the twanging
fibers of my heart, "I will kill you for that smile! I
will kill you—kill you!" And when at last the motion of the hand had ceased, and the hideous insect
again ran down the penholder, leaning, and pressing
into my naked flesh that keen exquisite sting, I
snapped the thrall that bound me, flung the spider
violently against the desk, stabbed the pen wildly
at it with a dozen swift vindictive motions as the
abhorrent thing lay for the moment writhing on its
back. And I struck it, too, and pinioned it; but as
for an instant I turned away from the revolting
sight, my pen still quivering above it, sunken eye-
deep in the desk, my victim yet escaped me, for,
as I turned again, no sign remained to designate

my murderous deed but one poor severed limb,
twitching and trembling in ever-lessening throes
and convulsions.

I turned my eyes upon the mysterious scrap once
more, with the same unaccountable feeling of dread
and revulsion that had possesed me as I read the
scrawl.   Written in the same minute, tremulous
but legible hand in which the first was traced, I
read:

> "O, what strange tragedy is this of mine
>    That wars within, and will not let me cry?
>    My soul seems leaking from me sigh by sigh;
> And yet I dare not say—nor he divine—
> That I, so vile and loathsome in design,
>    Am brimmed with boiling love; but I must lie
>    Forever steeped in seething agony!
> If all these quivering arms might wreathe and twine,
>    And soak him up in one warm clasp of bliss—
> One long caress, when babbling wild with words
>    My voice were crushed and mangled with his kiss,—
> My soul would whistle sweeter than the birds.—
>    But now, my dry and husky heart in this
>    Pent heat of gasping passion can but hiss!"

Be patient! I am hurrying toward the end.  I am
very lonesome here alone.  For three long empty
nights have I sat thus, with nothing but the raspings
of my pen for company.  I can not sleep now; and
I would not if I could.  My head feels as if I wore
a very heavy hat, and I put up my hand at times
to see.  My head is feverish, that's all.  I have been
working too late again.  Last night I heard Hays
come up the steps—my window opens on an alley;

but at night the light shows from the street. Hays has a peculiar walk: I'd know it if I heard it in the grass above my grave. And he came up the stairs last night, and knocked and rattled at the door; but I was very still, and so he went away. Sometimes I think that fellow isn't right exactly in his mind. I never knew what silence was before. It will not even whisper to me now. Sometimes I stop and listen, and then it holds its breath and listens too— but we never hear a thing. The old guitar leans in the corner with its face turned to the wall. I know it's sorry, but it would be such a comfort to me if it would only moan or murmur as it used. I always tune it the first thing when I come in, and lean it back, just as it was when the spider first began to play it; but the spider won't go near it any more. Even the spider has deserted me, and gone away and left me here alone—all alone! One night, late, I heard it coming up the stairs; and it knocked and rattled at the door, and I wouldn't let it in, and so it went away—and do you know that I have often thought that that spider wasn't right— in its mind, you know? Oh, yes! I have often thought so—often! This hat bothers me, but I'll hurry on—I must hurry on.

When I came in to-night—no; *last* night it was— when I came to work last night, there was another of those scrawls the spider had left for me, and it was written in a very trembling hand. The letters were blotted and slurred together so I could hardly make the word out; but I did make it out, and it

was simply the one word, "Death"—just "Death."
I didn't like the looks of it, and I tried to make it
read something else; but it wouldn't. It was
"Death." And so I laid it gently on the desk and
walked about the room very softly for a long time.
And the night kept on getting stiller, and stiller, and
stiller, till it just stopped. But that didn't disturb
me; I was not sleepy, anyhow, and so I sat down
at the desk, took up my pen, and waited. I had
nothing else to do, and the guitar wouldn't play
any more, and I was lonesome; so I sat down at
the desk, and took up the pen, and waited.

Sometimes I think it's those spells the spider
gives me that make my head feel this way. It feels
as if I had a heavy hat on; but I haven't any hat on
at all, and if I had I wouldn't have it on here in the
room. I can't even sit in the cars with a hat on.

And so I waited, and waited; but it seemed as if
it wasn't still enough for the spider yet. It was
still enough for me; but I got to thinking about
why the spider didn't come, and concluded at last
that it wasn't still enough yet for the spider. So I
waited till it got so still I could see it; and then
the spider came sliding along down through it; and
when it touched the penholder, and I got a good
clear look at it, I flashed dead-numb clean to the
marrow.—It was so pale! Did you ever see a spider
after it has had a long spell of sickness? That's
the way this spider looked. I shuddered as it huddled its trembling legs together and sat down. And
then the pen moved off, with that pale, ghastly hag-

gard insect nodding away again as though it still
were victor of the field; and as, at last, I found
courage to peer closer into its face, I saw that same
accursed smile flung back at me. All pity and compassion fled away, and I felt my heart snarl rabidly
and champ its bloody jaws with deadly hate. And
when the spider hobbled down the penholder and
touched my hand again, the only sting I felt upon
that hand was the vengeful blow I smote it with the
other and I held and ground it there with an exultant cry that rang out upon the silence till the echoes
clapped their very hands and shouted with me,
"Dead! dead at last! Dead! dead! and I am free!"
Oh, how I reveled in my fancied triumph as I danced
about the room, crunching my hands together till I
thought that I could feel the clammy fragments of
the hateful thing gaumed and slimed about between
my palms and fingers! And what a fool I was!
for when at last I unclasped them and spread them
wide apart in utter loathing, they were as free from
taint or moisture as they are this very moment; and
then it all flashed on me that I was in some horrid
dream—some hideous baleful nightmare—some fell
delusion of a fevered sleep. But no! I could not
force that comfort on myself, for here the lamp sat
burning brightly as at this very moment, and I
reached and held my finger on the chimney till it
burned. I wheeled across the room, opened the
door, went to the window and raised it, and felt
the chill draft sweeping in upon my fevered face.
I took my hat from the sofa and dashed out into

the night.  I was not asleep; I had not been asleep; for not until broad daylight did I return, to find the window opened just as I had left it; the lamp still blazing at its fullest glare, and that grim scrawl, "Death," lying still upon the desk, with these lines traced legibly beneath it:

"And did you know our old friend Death is dead?
    Ah me! he died last night; my ghost was there,
    And all his phantom-friends from everywhere
Were sorrowfully grouped about his bed.
'I die; God help the living now!' he said
    With such a ghastly pathos, I declare
    The tears oozed from the blind eyes of the air
And spattered on his face in gouts of red.
And then he smiled—the dear old bony smile
    That glittered on us in that crazy whim
When first our daring feet leapt the defile
    Of life and ran so eagerly to him:
And so he smiled upon us, even while
    The kind old sockets grew forever dim."

I am almost through.  It is nearly morning as I write.  When daylight comes, and this is finished, I can sleep.

That last spider that appeared to me was not the real spider.  That last spider was not a spider, and I'll tell you how I know:  Four hours ago, as I sat writing here, I dipped and dragged a strange clot from the inkstand with my pen.  It is barely dry yet, and it is a drowned spider.  It is the real spider —the other spider was its ghost.  Listen: I know this is the real spider from the fact that it has one leg missing, and the leg that has been lying on my desk here, for three days and nights, I find, upon careful examination and adjustment, is the leg that originally supplied this deficiency.

Whatever theory it may please you to advance regarding the mysterious manifestations of the spider while in the flesh will doubtless be as near the correct one as my own. Certainly I shall not attempt to controvert any opinion you may choose to express. I simply reserve the right, in conclusion of my story, to say that I believe this spider met his death by suicide.

# DREAMS

"Do I sleep, do I dream,
Do I wonder and doubt—
Are things what they seem
Or is visions about?"

THERE has always been an inclination, or desire, rather, on my part to believe in the mystic
—even as far back as stretches the gum-elastic remembrance of my first "taffy-pullin' " given in honor
of my fifth birthday; and the ghost-stories, served
by way of ghastly dessert, by our hired girl. In
fancy I again live over all the scenes of that eventful night:—

The dingy kitchen, with its haunting odors of a
thousand feasts and wash-days; the old bench-leg-
ged stove, with its happy family of skillets, stew-
pans and round-bellied kettles crooning and blub-
bering about it. And how we children clustered
round the genial hearth, with the warm smiles
dying from our faces just as the embers dimmed
and died out in the open grate, as with bated breath
we listened to how some one's grandmother had said
that her first man went through a graveyard once,
one stormy night, "jest to show the neighbors that
he wasn't afeard o' nothin'," and how when he was

just passing the grave of his first wife "something
kind o' big and white-like, with great big eyes like
fire, raised up from behind the headboard, and
kind o' re'ched out for him"; and how he turned
and fled, "with that-air white thing after him as
tight as it could jump, and a hollerin' 'wough-yough-
yough!' till you could hear it furder'n you could a
bullgine," and how, at last, just as the brave and
daring intruder was clearing two graves and the
fence at one despairing leap, the "white thing," had
made a grab at him with its iron claws, and had
nicked him so close his second wife was occasioned
the onerous duty of affixing another patch in his
pantaloons. And in conclusion, our hired girl went
on to state that this blood-curdling incident had so
wrought upon the feelings of "the man that wasn't
afeard o' nothin'," and had given him such a
distaste for that particular graveyard, that he
never visited it again, and even entered a clause in
his will to the effect that he would ever remain
an unhappy corpse should his remains be interred
in the said graveyard.

I forgot my pop-corn that night; I forgot my
taffy; I forgot all earthly things; and I tossed about
so feverishly in my little bed, and withal so rest-
lessly, that more than once my father's admonition
above the foot-board of the big bed, of "Drat you! go
to sleep, there!" foreshadowed my impending doom.
And once he leaned over and made a vicious snatch
at me, and holding me out at arm's length by one

leg, demanded in thunder-tones, "what in the name o' flames and flashes I meant, anyhow!"

I was afraid to stir a muscle from that on, in consequence of which I at length straggled off in fitful dreams—and heavens! what dreams!—A very long and lank, and slim and slender old woman in white knocked at the door of my vision, and I let her in. She patted me on the head—and oh! how cold her hands were! And they were very hard hands, too, and very heavy—and, horror of horrors! —they were not hands—they were claws!—they were iron!—they were like the things I had seen the hardware man yank nails out of a keg with. I quailed and shivered till the long and slim and slender old woman jerked my head up and snarled spitefully, "What's the matter with you, bub," and I said, "Nawthin'!" and she said, "Don't you dare to lie to me!" I moaned.

"Don't you like me?" she asked.

I hesitated.

"And lie if you dare!" she said—"Don't you like me?"

"Oomh-oomh!" said I.

"Why?" said she.

"Cos, you're too long—and slim—an' "—

"Go on!" said she.

"—And tall!" said I.

"Ah, ha!" said she,—"and that's it, hey?"

And then she began to grow shorter and thicker, and fatter and squattier.

"And how do I suit you now?" she wheezed at length, when she had wilted down to about the size of a large loaf of bread.

I shook more violently than ever at the fearful spectacle.

"How do you like me now?" she yelped again,— "And don't you lie to me neither, or I'll swaller you whole!"

I writhed and hid my face.

"Do you like me?"

"No-o-oh!" I moaned.

She made another snatch at my hair. I felt her jagged claws sink into my very brain. I struggled and she laughed hideously.

"You don't, hey?"

"Yes, yes, I do. I love you!" said I.

"You lie! You lie!" She shrieked derisively. "You know you lie!" and as I felt the iron talons sinking and gritting in my very brain, with one wild, despairing effort, I awoke.

I saw the fire gleaming in the grate, and by the light it made I dimly saw the outline of the old mantelpiece that straddled it, holding the old clock high upon its shoulders. I was awake then, and the little squatty woman with her iron talons was a dream! I felt an oily gladness stealing over me, and yet I shuddered to be all alone.

If only some one were awake, I thought, whose blessed company would drown all recollections of that fearful dream; but I dared not stir or make a noise. I could only hear the ticking of the clock, and my father's sullen snore. I tried to compose my thoughts to pleasant themes, but that telescopic old woman in white would rise up and mock my vain appeals, until in fancy I again saw her altitudinous proportions dwindling into that repulsive and revengeful figure with the iron claws, and I grew restless and attempted to sit up. Heavens! something yet held me by the hair. The chill sweat that betokens speedy dissolution gathered on by brow. I made another effort and arose, that deadly clutch yet fastened in my hair. Could it be possible! The short, white woman still held me in her vengeful grasp! I could see her white dress showing from behind either of my ears. She still clung to me, and with one wild, unearthly cry of "Pap!" I started round the room.

I remember nothing further, until as the glowing morn sifted through the maple at the window, powdering with gold the drear old room, and baptizing with its radiance the anxious group of old home-faces leaning o'er my bed, I heard my father's voice once more rasping on my senses—"Now get the booby up, and wash that infernal wax out of his hair!"

# THE OBJECT LESSON

BARELY a year ago I attended the Friday afternoon exercises of a country school. My mission there, as I remember, was to refresh my mind
with such material as might be gathered, for a
"valedictory," which, I regret to say, was to be
handed down to posterity under another signature
than my own.

There was present, among a host of visitors, a
pale young man of perhaps thirty years, with a tall
head and bulging brow and a highly-intellectual
pair of eyes and spectacles. He wore his hair without roach or "part" and the smile he beamed about
him was "a joy forever." He was an educator—
from the East, I think I heard it rumored—anyway
he was introduced to the school at last, and he
bowed, and smiled, and beamed upon us all, and
entertained us after the most delightfully edifying
manner imaginable. And although I may fail to
reproduce the exact substance of his remarks upon
that highly important occasion, I think I can at least
present his theme in all its coherency of detail.
Addressing more particularly the primary department of the school, he said:—

"As the little exercise I am about to introduce is

of recent origin, and the bright, intelligent faces of the pupils before me seem rife with eager and expectant interest, it will be well for me, perhaps, to offer by way of preparatory preface, a few terse words of explanation.

"The Object-Lesson is designed to fill a long-felt want, and is destined, as I think, to revolutionize, in a great degree, the educational systems of our land.—In my belief, the Object-Lesson will supply a want which I may safely say has heretofore left the most egregious and palpable traces of mental confusion and intellectual inadequacies stamped, as it were, upon the gleaming reasons of the most learned—the highest cultured, and the most eminently gifted and promising of our professors and scientists both at home and abroad.

"Now this deficiency—if it may be so termed—plainly has a beginning; and probing deeply with the bright, clean scalpel of experience we discover that—"As the twig is bent, the tree's inclined." To remedy, then, a deeply-seated error which for so long has rankled at the very root of educational progress throughout the land, many plausible, and we must admit, many helpful theories have been introduced to allay the painful errors resulting from the discrepancy of which we speak: but until now, nothing that seemed wholly to eradicate the defect has been discovered, and that, too, strange as it may seem, is, at last, found emanating, like the mighty river, from the simplest source, but broadening and gathering in force and power as it flows along, until, at last, its grand and mighty current sweeps on in majesty to the vast illimitable ocean of—of—of—Success! Ahem!

"And, now, little boys and girls, that we have had by implication, a clear and comprehensive explanation of the Object-Lesson and its mission, I trust you will give me your undivided attention while I endeavor—in my humble way—to direct your newly acquired knowledge through the proper channel. For instance:—

"This little object I hold in my hand—who will designate it by its proper name? Come, now, let us see who will be the first to answer. 'A peanut,' says the little boy here at my right. Very good—very good! I hold, then, in my hand, a peanut. And now who will tell me, what is the peanut? A very simple question—who will answer? 'Something good to eat,' says the little girl. Yes, 'something good to eat,' but would it not be better to say simply that the peanut is an edible? I think so, yes. The peanut, then, is—an edible—now, all together, an edible!

"To what kingdom does the peanut belong? The animal, vegetable or mineral kingdom? A very easy question. Come, let us have prompt answers. 'The animal kingdom,' does the little boy say? Oh, no! The peanut does not belong to the animal kingdom! Surely the little boy must be thinking of a larger object than the peanut—the elephant, perhaps. To what kingdom, then, does the peanut belong? The v-v-veg—'The vegetable kingdom,' says the bright-faced little girl on the back seat. Ah! that is better. We find then that the peanut belongs to the—what kingdom? The 'vegetable kingdom.' Very good, very good!

"And now who will tell us of what the peanut is composed. Let us have quick responses now. Time is fleeting! Of what is the peanut composed? 'The hull and the goody,' some one answers. Yes, 'the hull and the goody' in vulgar parlance, but how much better it would be to say simply, the shell and the kernel. Would not that sound better? Yes, I thought you would agree with me there!

"And now who will tell me the color of the peanut! And be careful now! for I shouldn't like to hear you make the very stupid blunder I once heard a little boy make in reply to the same question. Would you like to hear what color the stupid little boy said the peanut was? You would, eh? Well, now, how many of you would like to hear what color the stupid little boy said the peanut was? Come now, let's have an expression. All who would like to hear what color the stupid little boy said the peanut was, may hold up their right hands. Very good, very good—there, that will do.

"Well, it was during a professional visit I was once called upon to make to a neighboring city, where I was invited to address the children of a free school—Hands down, now, little boy—founded for the exclusive benefit of the little newsboys and bootblacks, who, it seems, had not the means to defray the expenses of the commonest educational accessories, and during an object lesson identical with the one before us now—for it is a favorite one of mine—I propounded the question, what is the color of the peanut? Many answers were given in response, but none as sufficiently succinct and apropos as I deemed the facts demanded; and so at last I personally addressed a ragged, but, as I then thought, a bright-eyed little fellow, when judge of my surprise, in reply to my question, what is the color of a peanut, the little fellow, without the slightest gleam of intelligence lighting up his face, answered, that 'if not scorched by roasting, the peanut was a blond.' Why, I was almost tempted to join in the general merriment his inapposite reply elicited. But I occupy your attention with trivial things; and as I notice the time allotted me has slipped away, we will drop the peanut for the present. Trusting the few facts gleaned from a topic so homely and unpromising will sink deep in your minds, in time to bloom and blossom in the fields of future usefulness—I—I——I thank you."

# EZ

"ORTENTER be a-fishin' on Sunday? That's all you know about it. Je-ru-sa-lem! what a bite! S'posin' a feller hain't got no other day to fish—S'posin' a feller sells papers ev'ry day and Sunday mornin', too, what then? 'Sides, the house ain't big enough to hold the whole fam'ly to-day."

The boy was not more than twelve years old. He was seated on the river bank under a clump of syca-mores about two hundred yards from the National Road bridge. Coatless, his one suspender ran over his shoulder, while his shirt filled and bagged with the soft wind that blew up from the southwest. The smell of violets was in the breeze, but the boy didn't mind that—he had a nibble. He was bare-footed—one foot. A crutch lay beside him, and the lower part of the left leg of the tow-linen trousers was empty. "Chawed off by the kyars," he said, sententiously, discouraging further questioning on the subject, spitting on a wriggling angleworm as he baited his hook. "Makes 'em bite better"—not the worms, evidently, but the fish. "Got any ter-backer?" he inquired a minute later. "Thank 'ee. Where do I live?" he continued, growing gracious under the softening influence of the weed. "Over

193

there in that white house. Not the one you're lookin' at—furder to the right—I live there.

"I wonder" (musingly) "how the jamboree is a-comin' on by this time? The old-un—I mean daddy, the old man—has been cuttin' up rough and mother has had to reel him in. She's a da-i-sy," he ran on, his voice changing into song in which he took cognizance of the fact that she was also "a darling" and "a dumpling." "Don't you ever go for to think that she knows I'm a-fishin'—for she don't. My mother's not that sort, not by a jay-you-gee, jugful. My mother is a lady and a Methodist, an' a mighty nice mess she made of it when she married the old man. Not that he's always been tuffy like he is now, fur he ain't no slouch when he keeps the budge—liquor, you know—out of himself. This last break of his'n was all along er gittin' into politics. A feller come along an' as't him to go to the primary. He went. Think from the time he got in that night that somebody set 'em up pretty lively.

"That's two weeks ago an' he's been a-keepin' it up ever since. My mother told Dutchy, the s'loon-keeper, not to sell the old man any more budge—in course she didn't say budge, she said 'toxicatin' drinks—an' he lafft at her. That's where he got left. My mother's folks is gritty; her brother, my Uncle Dave, was shot carryin' the colors over Mission Ridge. Yesterday the old man—Is he a railroad man? No, he's a cooper, an' you'd orter see what a head he's got on to his kag to-day. Well, daddy went round to Dutchy's again an' got full-er'n a goose. When he gets full he gits wealthy an' 'll squander his last nick. I went to Dutchy's to try to run the old man into the roundhouse—I mean take him home—where he could have his brass rubbed off and give his boiler a chance to cool, for the old machine did look awful hard. He was goin' about sixty mile an hour an' I looked to see a cylinder head fly out. That's what I told Jake, over to the I. B. & W. yards. Jake an' me's pards. I told daddy he must go home; that he wasn't doin' the fair thing by mother, when all of a suddent he give me one right here over my left ear. You can feel —it's about as big as a' Easter egg. Ale bottle, I guess it was. I sort o' took a tumble to myself then, and didn't know for a minute or two whether I was still on the main track or off on a siding.

"When I come to, things was lively, I tell you. My mother is a little woman—don't weigh over ninety pounds—but if you'd 'a' seen her yesterday, you'd 'a' thought she weighed a ton. Ever been into Dutchy's? Know what a nice spread of glassware he has behind his bar? Know that mirror that he smears with soap pictures, birds an' things? All gone. They tried to hold mother, half a dozen of 'em did, but they couldn't do it. The old man had sneaked off somewhere—first time she'd ever fol-lered him—an' he felt ornery. She told Dutchy that she'd begged him time 'n' again not to sell liquor to father, an' then she went for the glassware. Talk about Captain Bogardus bu'stin' glass balls!

Mother didn't leave nothin'. She had my baseball bat, and she did some of the heaviest battin' ever you see. I don't think she left a piece of that mirror big enough to scrape an ax-handle. Ought to seen Dutchy! It was better'n a cir-cu-ous! 'Somebody hold 'er,' sez he—ha, ha! Hold her? Nobody dared lay a finger on her. Orter see the scars on that baseball club. It's the boss club, you betcher boots.

"When it was all over mother just dropped as limp as a rag, and some of the neighbor women come and took her home. She was flighty an' out of her head like, and 'stericky for three or four hours. That sort o' sobered the old man, for she was awful bad, and he was afraid he was goin' to lose her. 'How could he ever raise Ez?' said the neighbors. Ez, that's me, Ezra. Mother got the name out of the Bible. Just as if I needed any raisin', for I'm a rooster as can take care of myself. But it would 'a' bu'sted me to lose mother. An' what would become of daddy? How could I ever raise him? Great Jemima! did you see that bite? I don't think Dutchy'll sell him any more budge very soon, do you? Mother an' the old man, they're a-makin' it up to-day. I think this time he'll swear off for keeps, an' I don't want to stand 'round with this goose-egg on my head to make mother mad every time she looks at me an' thinks about it. I want to give the old man a chance."

# THE CHAMPION CHECKER-PLAYER OF AMERIKY

OF course as fur as Checker-playin' 's concerned,
you can't jest adzactly claim 'at lots makes for-
tunes and lots gits bu'sted at it—but still, it's on'y
simple jestice to acknowledge 'at there're absolute
p'ints in the game 'at takes scientific principles to
figger out, and a mighty level-headed feller to *dim*-
onstrate, don't you understand!

Checkers is a' *old* enough game, ef age is any
rickommendation; and it's a' evident fact, too, 'at
"the tooth of time," as the feller says, which fer
the last six thousand years has gained some reputa-
tion fer a-eatin' up things in giner'l, don't 'pear to
'a' gnawed much of a hole in Checkers—jedgin'
from the checker-board of to-day and the ones 'at
they're uccasionally shovelin' out at *Pomp'y-i,* er
whatever its name is. Turned up a checker-board
there not long ago, I wuz readin' 'bout, 'at still had
the spots on—as plain and fresh as the modern
white-pine board o' our'n, squared off with pencil-
marks and pokeberry-juice. These is facts 'at history herself has dug out, and of course it ain't fer
me ner you to turn our nose up at Checkers,

whuther we ever tamper with the fool-game er not.
Fur's that's concerned, I don't p'tend to be no
checker-player *myse'f,*—but I knowed a feller onc't
'at *could* play, and sort o' made a business of it; and
*that* man, in my opinion, wuz a geenyus! Name
wuz Wesley Cotterl—John Wesley Cotterl—just
plain Wes, as us fellers round the shoe-shop ust
to call him; ust to allus make the shoe-shop his
headquarters-like; and, rain er shine, wet er dry,
you'd allus find *Wes* on hands, ready to banter
some feller fer a game, er jest a-settin' humped up
there over the checker-board all alone, a-cipherin'
out some new move er 'nuther, and whistlin' low
and solem' to hisse'f-like and a-payin' no attention
to nobody.

And *I'll* tell *you,* Wes Cotterl wuz no man's fool,
as sly as you keep it! He wuz a deep thinker, Wes
wuz; and ef he'd 'a' jest turned that mind o' his
loose on *preachin',* fer instunce, and the 'terperta-
tion o' the Bible, don't you know, Wes 'ud 'a'
worked p'ints out o' there 'at no livin' expounderers
ever got in gunshot of!

But Wes he didn't 'pear to be cut out fer nothin'
much but jest Checker-playin'. Oh, of course, he
*could* knock around his own wood-pile some, and
garden a little, more er less; and the neighbors ust
to find Wes purty handy 'bout trimmin' fruit-trees,
you understand, and workin' in among the worms
and cattapillers in the vines and shrubbery, and the
like. And handlin' bees!—They wuzn't no man
under the heavens 'at knowed more 'bout handlin'

bees 'n Wes Cotterl!—"Settlin' " the blame' things
when they wuz a-swarmin'; and a-robbin' hives, and
all sich fool-resks. W'y, I've saw Wes Cotterl, 'fore
now, when a swarm of bees 'ud settle in a' orchard,
—like they will sometimes, you know,—I've saw
Wes Cotterl jest roll up his shirt-sleeves and bend
down a' apple tree limb 'at wuz jest kivvered with
the pesky things, and scrape 'em back into the hive
with his naked hands, by the quart and gallon, and
never git a scratch! You couldn't *hire* a bee to sting
Wes Cotterl! But *lazy?*—I think that man had
railly ort to 'a' been a' Injun! He wuz the fust and
on'y man 'at ever I laid eyes on 'at wuz too lazy to
drap a checker-man to p'int out the right road fer
a feller 'at ast him onc't the way to Burke's Mill;
and Wes 'ithout ever a-liftin' eye er finger, jest
sort o' crooked out that mouth o' his'n in the direction the feller wanted, and says: *"H-yonder!"* and
went on with his whistlin'. But all this hain't
Checkers, and that's what I started out to tell ye.

Wes had a way o' jest natchurally a-cleanin' out
anybody and ever'body 'at 'ud he'p hold up a
checker-board! Wes wuzn't what you'd call a
*lively* player at all, ner a competiter 'at talked
much 'crost the board er made much furse over
a game whilse he *wuz* a-playin'. He had his
faults, o' course, and *would* take back moves
'casion'ly, er inch up on you ef you didn't watch
him, mebby. But, *as a rule,* Wes had the in-
sight to grasp the idy of whoever wuz a-playin'
ag'in' him, and *his* style o' game, you understand,

and wuz on the lookout continual'; and under sich circumstances *could* play as *honest* a game o' Checkers as the babe unborn.

One thing in *Wes's* favor allus wuz the feller's temper.—Nothin' 'peared to aggervate Wes, and nothin' on earth could break his slow and lazy way o' takin' his own time fer ever'thing.  You jest *couldn't crowd Wes* er git him rattled anyway.—Jest 'peared to have one fixed principle, and that wuz to take plenty o' time, and never make no move 'ithout a-cipherin' ahead on the prob'ble consequences, don't you understand!  "Be shore you're right," Wes 'ud say, a-lettin' up fer a second on that low and sorry-like little wind-through-the-keyhole whistle o' his, and a-nosin' out a place whur he could swap one man fer two.—"Be shore you're right"—and somep'n' after this style wuz Wes's way: "Be shore you're right"—(whistling a long, lonesome bar of "Barbara Allen")—"and then"—(another long, retarded bar)—"go ahead!"—and by the time the feller 'ud git through with his whistlin', and a-stoppin' and a-startin' in ag'in, he'd be about three men ahead to your one.  And then he'd jest go on with his whistlin' 'sef nothin' had happened, and mebby you a-jest a-rearin' and a-callin' him all the mean, outlandish, ornry names 'at you could lay tongue to.

But Wes's good nature, I reckon, wuz the thing 'at he'ped him out as much as any other p'ints the feller had.  And *Wes' 'ud allus win, in the long run!*—I don't keer *who* played ag'inst him!  It wuz on'y

a question o' time with Wes o' waxin' it to the best
of 'em.  Lots o' players has *tackled* Wes, and right
at the *start* 'ud mebby give him trouble,—but in the
*long run,* now mind ye—*in the long run,* no mortal
man, I reckon, had any business o' rubbin' knees
with Wes Cotterl under no airthly checker-board
in all this vale o' tears!

I mind onc't th' come along a high-toned feller
from in around In'i'nop'lus som'er's.—Wuz a *lawyer,* er some *p'fessional* kind o' man.  Had a big yal-
ler, luther-kivvered book under his arm, and a bunch
o' these-'ere big en*velo*p's and a lot o' suppeenies
stickin' out o' his breast-pocket.   Mighty slick-
lookin' feller he wuz ; wore a stove-pipe hat, sort o'
set 'way back on his head—so's to show off his
Giner'l Jackson forr'ed, don't you know !  Well-sir,
this feller struck the place, on some business er
other, and then missed the hack 'at *ort* to 'a' tuk him
out o' here sooner'n it *did* take him out !—And
whilse he wuz a-loafin' round, sort o' lonesome—like
a feller allus *is* in a strange place, you know—he
kind o' drapped in on our crowd at the shoe-shop,
ostenchably to git a boot-strop stitched on, but *I*
knowed, the minute he set foot in the door, 'at *that*
feller wanted *comp'ny* wuss'n *cobblin'.*

Well, as good luck would have it, there set Wes,
as usual, with the checker-board in his lap, a-playin'
all by hisse'f, and a-whistlin' so low and solem'-like
and sad it railly made the crowd seem like a *religious* getherun' o' some kind er other, we wuz all so
quiet and still-like, as the man come in.

Well, the stranger stated his business, set down, tuk off his boot, and set there nussin' his foot and talkin' weather fer ten minutes, I reckon, 'fore he ever 'peared to notice Wes at all. We wuz all back-'ard, anyhow, 'bout talkin' much; besides, we knowed, long afore he come in, all about how hot the weather wuz, and the pore chance there wuz o' rain, and all that; and so the subject had purty well died out, when jest then the feller's eyes struck Wes and the checker-board,—and I'll never fergit the warm, salvation smile 'at flashed over him at the promisin' discovery. *"What!"* says he, a-grinnin' like a' angel and a-edgin' his cheer to'rds Wes, "have we a checker-board and checkers here?"

"We hev," says I, knowin' 'at Wes wouldn't let go o' that whistle long enough to answer—more'n to mebby nod his head.

"And who is your best player?" says the feller, kind o' pitiful-like, with another inquirin' look at Wes.

"Him," says I, a-pokin' Wes with a peg-float. But Wes on'y spit kind o' absent-like, and went on with his whistlin'.

"Much of a player, is he?" says the feller, with a sort o' doubtful smile at Wes ag'in.

"Plays a purty good hick'ry," says I, a-pokin' Wes ag'in. "Wes," says I, "here's a gentleman 'at 'ud mebby like to take a hand with you there, and give you a few idies," says I.

"Yes," says the stranger, eager-like, a-settin' his plug-hat keerful up in the empty shelvin', and a-rub-

bin' his hands and smilin' as confident-like as old
Hoyle hisse'f,—"Yes, indeed, I'd be glad to give the
gentleman" (meanin' Wes) "a' idy er two about
Checkers—ef *he'd* jest as lief,—'cause I reckon ef
there're any one thing 'at I *do* know more about 'an
another, it's Checkers," says he; "and there're no
game 'at delights me more—*pervidin'*, o' course, I
find a competiter 'at kin make it anyways in-
te*rest*in'."

"Got much of a rickord on Checkers?" says I.

"Well," says the feller, "I don't like to brag, but
I've never *be'n* beat—in any *legitimut* contest," says
he, "and I've played more'n one o' *them,*" he says,
"here and there round the country. Of course, *your
friend* here," he went on, smilin' sociable at Wes,
*"he'll* take it all in good part ef I should happen to
lead him a little—jest as *I'd* do," he says, "ef it wuz
possible fer him to lead *me."*

*"Wes,"* says I, *"has* warmed the wax in the yeers
of some mighty good checker-players," says I, as
he squared the board around, still a-whistlin' to
hisse'f-like, as the stranger tuk his place, a-smilin'-
like and roachin' back his hair.

"Move," says Wes.

"No," says the feller, with a polite flourish of his
hand; "the first move shall be your'n." And, by
jucks! fer all he wouldn't take even the advantage
of a starter, he flaxed it to Wes the fust game in
less'n fifteen minutes.

"Right shore you've given me your best player?"
he says, smilin' round at the crowd, as Wes set

squarin' the board fer another game and whistlin' as
onconcerned-like as ef nothin' had happened more'n
ordinary.

"'S your move," says Wes, a-squintin' out into the
game 'bout forty foot from shore, and a-whistlin'
purt' nigh in a whisper.

Well-sir, it 'peared-like the feller railly didn't *try*
to play; and you could see, too, 'at Wes knowed he'd
about met his match, and played accordin'.   He
didn't make no move at all 'at he didn't give keerful
thought to; whilse the feller—! Well, as I wuz say-
in', it jest 'peared-like *Checkers* wuz *child's-play* fer
him!   Putt in most o' the time 'long through the
game a-sayin' things calkilated to kind o' bore a'
ordinary man.   But Wes helt hisse'f purty level,
and didn't show no signs, and kep' up his *whistlin'*,
mighty well—considerin'.

"Reckon you play the *fiddle,* too, as well as
*Checkers?"* says the feller, laughin', as Wes come
a-whistlin' out of the little end of the second game
and went on a-fixin' fer the next round.

"'S my move!" says Wes, 'thout seemin' to notice
the feller's tantalizin' words whatsomever.

"'Ll! *this time,"* thinks I, "Mr. Smarty from the
metrolopin deestricts, *you're* liable to git *waxed—
shore!"*   But the *feller* didn't 'pear to think so at
all, and played right ahead as glib-like and keerless
as ever—'casion'ly a-throwin' in them sircastic remarks o' his'n,—'bout bein' "slow and shore" 'bout
things in gineral—"Liked to *see* that," he said:—
"Liked to see fellers do things with plenty o' *delib-*

*eration,* and even ef a feller *wuzn't* much of a checker-player, liked to see him *die* slow *anyhow!*—and then 'tend his own funeral," he says,—"and march in the p'session—to his own *music,*" says he.
—And jest then his remarks wuz brung to a close by Wes a-jumpin' two men, and a-lightin' square in the king-row. . . . "Crown that," says Wes, a-droppin' back into his old tune. And fer the rest o' *that* game Wes helt the feller purty level, but had to finally knock under—but by jest the clos'test kind o' shave o' winnin'.

"They ain't much use," says the feller, "o' keepin' *this* thing up—'less I could manage *some* way er other, to git beat *onc't 'n a while!*"

"Move," says Wes, a-drappin' back into the same old whistle and a-*settlin'* there.

"'Music has charms,' as the Good Book tells us," says the feller, kind o' nervous-like, and a-roachin' his hair back as ef some sort o' p'tracted headache wuz a-settin' in.

"Never wuz 'skunked,' wuz ye?" says Wes, kind o' suddent-like, with a fur-off look in them big white eyes o' his—and then a-whistlin' right on, 'sef he hadn't said *nothin'.*

"*Not much!*" says the feller, sort o' s'prised-like, as ef such a' idy as that had never struck him afore.
—"Never was 'skunked' *myse'f;* but I've saw fellers in my time 'at *wuz!*" says he.

But from that time on I noticed the feller 'peared to play more keerful, and railly la'nched into the game with somepin' like inter'st. Wes, he seemed to

be jest a-limberin'-up-like; and-sir, blame me! ef he
didn't walk the feller's log fer him *that* time, 'thout
no 'pearent trouble at all!

"And *now*," says Wes, all quiet-like, a-squarin'
the board fer another 'n',—"we're kind o' gittin' at
things *right*.   Move."   And away went that little
unconcerned whistle o' his ag'in, and *Mr. Cityman*
jest gittin' white and sweaty too—he wuz so nervous.   Ner he didn't 'pear to find much to laugh at
in the *next* game—ner the next *two* games nuther!
Things wuz a-gettin' mighty inter*est*in' 'bout them
times, and I guess the feller wuz ser'ous-like a-wak-
in' up to the solem' fact 'at it tuk 'bout all *his* spare
time to keep up his end o' the row, and even that
state o' 'pore satisfaction wuz a-creepin' furder and
furder away from him ever' new turn he undertook.
Whilse *Wes* jest 'peared to git more deliber't' and
certain ever' game; and that unendin' se'f-satisfied
and comfortin' little whistle o' his never drapped a
stitch, but toed out ever' game alike,—to'rds the *last,*
and, fer the *most* part, disaster's to the feller 'at
had started in with sich confi*dence* and actchul
promise, don't you know.

Well-sir, the feller stuck the whole *forenoon* out,
and then the *afternoon;* and then knuckled down
to it 'way into the night—yes, and plum *midnight!*—
And he buckled into the thing bright and airly *next
morning!*   And-sir, fer *two long days* and nights,
a-hardly a-stoppin' long enough to *eat,* the feller
stuck it out,—and Wes a-jest a-warpin' it to him
hand-over-fist, and leavin' him furder behind, ever'

game!—till finally, to'rds the last, the feller got so
blame-don worked up and excited-like, he jest
'peared actchully purt' nigh plum crazy and histur-
ical as a woman!

It wuz a-gittin' late into the shank of the second
day, and the boys hed jest lit a candle fer 'em to
finish out one of the clos'test games the feller'd
played Wes fer some time. But Wes wuz jest as
cool and ca'm as ever, and still a-whistlin' consolin'
to hisse'f-like, whilse the feller jest 'peared wore
out and ready to drap right in his tracks any minute.

*"Durn you!"* he snarled out at Wes, "hain't you
never goern to move?" And there set Wes, a-bal-
ancin' a checker-man above the board, a-studyin'
whur to set it, and a-fillin' in the time with that-air
whistle.

*"Flames and flashes!"* says the feller ag'in, "will
you *ever* stop that death-seducin' tune o' your'n long
enough to move?"—And as Wes deliber't'ly set his
man down whur the feller see he'd haf to jump it
and lose two men and a king, Wes wuz a-singin',
low and sad-like, as ef all to hisse'f:

> *"O we'll move that man, and leave him there.—*
> *Fer the love of B-a-r-b—bry Al-len!"*

Well-sir! the feller jest jumped to his feet, upset
the board, and tore out o' the shop stark-starin'
crazy—blame ef he wuzn't!—'cause some of us putt
out after him and overtook him 'way beyent the
'pike-bridge, and hollered to him;—and he shuk his
fist at us and hollered back and says, says he:

"Ef you fellers over here," says he, " 'll agree to *muzzle* that durn checker-player o' your'n, I'll bet fifteen hundred dollars to fifteen cents 'at I kin beat him 'leven games out of ever' dozen!—But there're *no money*," he says, "'at kin hire me to play him ag'in, on this aboundin' airth, on'y on them conditions—'cause that durn, eternal, infernal, dad-blasted whistle o' his 'ud beat the oldest man in Ameriky!"

# THE JUDKINS PAPERS

## FATHER AND SON

MR. JUDKINS' boy came home yesterday with a bottle of bugs in his pocket, and as the quiet little fellow sat on the back porch in his favorite position, his legs elbowed and flattened out beneath him like a letter "W," his genial and eccentric father came suddenly upon him.

"And what's the blame' boy up to now?" said Mr. Judkins, in an assumed tone of querulous displeasure, as he bent over the boy from behind and gently tweaked his ear.

"Oh, here, mister!" said the boy, without looking up; "you thist let up on that, will you!"

"What you got there, I tell you!" continued the smiling Mr. Judkins, in a still gruffer tone, relinquishing the boy's ear and gazing down upon the fluffy towhead with more than ordinary admiration. "What you got there?"

"Bugs," said the boy—"you know!"

"Dead, are they?" said Mr. Judkins.

"Some of 'em's dead," said the boy, carefully running a needle through the back of a large bumblebee. "All these uns is, you can bet! You don't think a feller 'ud try to string a live bumblebee, I reckon?"

"Well, no, 'Squire," said Mr. Judkins, airily, addressing the boy by one of the dozen nicknames he had given him; "not a live bumblebee—a real stem-winder, of course not. But what in the name o' limpin' Lazarus are you stringin' 'em fer?"

"Got a live snake-feeder," said the boy, ignoring the parental inquiry. "See him down there in the bottom, 'ith all th'other uns on top of him. Thist watch him now, an' you kin see him pant. I kin. Yes, an' I got a beetle 'at's purt' nigh alive, too—on'y he can't pull in his other wings. See 'em?" continued the boy, with growing enthusiasm, twirling the big-mouthed bottle like a kaleidoscope. "Hate beetles! 'cause they allus act so big, an' make s'much fuss about theirselves, an' don't know nothin' neither! Bet ef I had as many wings as a beetle I wouldn't let no boy my size knock the stuffin' out o' me with no bunch o' weeds, like I done him!"

"Howd'ye know you wouldn't?" said Mr. Judkins, austerely, biting his nails and winking archly to himself.

"W'y, I know I wouldn't," said the boy, " 'cause I'd keep up in the air where I could fly, and wouldn't come low down at all—bumpin' around 'mongst them bushes, an' buzzin' against things, and buttin' my brains out a-tryin' to git thrue fence cracks."

" 'Spect you'd ruther be a snake-feeder, wouldn't you, Bud?" said Mr. Judkins suggestively. "Snakefeeders has got about enough wings to suit you, ef you want more'n one pair, and every day's a picnic with a snake-feeder, you know. Nothin' to do but jes' loaf up and down the crick, and roost on reeds and cat-tails, er fool around a feller's fish-line and light on the cork and bob up and down with it till she goes clean under, don't you know?"

"Don't want to be no snake-feeder, neither," said the boy, " 'cause they gits gobbled up, first thing they know, by these 'ere big green bullfrogs ut they can't ever tell from the skum till they've lit right in their mouth—and then they're goners! No, sir;" continued the boy, drawing an extra quinine bottle from another pocket, and holding it up admiringly before his father's eyes: "There's the feller in there 'at I'd ruther be than have a pony!"

"W'y, it's a nasty p'izen spider!" exclaimed Mr. Judkins, pushing back the bottle with affected abhorrence, "and he's alive, too!"

"You bet he's alive!" said the boy, "and you kin bet he'll never come to no harm while I own him!" and as the little fellow spoke his face glowed with positive affection, and the twinkle of his eyes, as he continued, seemed wonderfully like his father's own. "Tell you, I like spiders! Spiders is awful fat—all but their head—and that's level, you kin bet! Flies hain't got no business with a spider. Ef a spider ever reaches fer a fly, he's his meat! The spider, he likes to loaf an' lay around in the shade an' wait fer flies an' bugs an' things to come a-foolin' round his place. He lays back in the hole in the corner of his web, an' waits till somepin' lights on it an' nen when he hears 'em buzzin', he thist crawls out an' fixes 'em so's they can't buzz, an' he's got the truck to do it with! I bet ef you'd unwind all the web-stuff out of thist one little spider not big-ger'n a pill, it 'ud be long enough fer a kite-string! Onc't they was one in our wood-house, an' a tater-bug got stuck in his web, and the spider worked purt' nigh two days 'fore he got him so's he couldn't move. Nen he couldn't eat him neither—'cause they's shells on 'em, you know, an' the spider didn't know how to hull him. Ever' time I'd go there the spider, he'd be a-wrappin' more stuff around th' ole bug, an' stoopin' down like he was a-whisperin' to him. An' one day I went in again, an' he was a-hangin', alas, and cold in death! An' I poked him with a splinter and his web broked off—'spect he'd used it all up on the wicked bug—and it killed him; an' I buried him in a' ink bottle, an' mashed the old bug 'ith a chip!"

"Yes," said Judkins, in a horrified tone, turning away to conceal the real zest and enjoyment his face must have betrayed; "yes, and some day you'll come home p'izened, er somepin'! And I want to say right here, my young man, ef ever you do, and it don't kill you, I'll lint you within an inch of your life!" And as the eccentric Mr. Judkins whirled around the corner of the porch he heard the boy murmur in his low, absent-minded way, "Yes, you will!"

## MR. JUDKINS' REMARKS

Judkins stopped us in front of the post-office yesterday to say that that boy of his was "the blamedest boy outside o' the annals o' history!" "Talk about this boy-naturalist out here at Indianapolis," says Judkins,—"why, he ain't nowhere to my boy! The little cuss don't do nothin' either only set around and look sleepy, and dern him, he gits off more dry things than you could print in your paper. Of late he's been a-displayin' a sort o' weakness for Nature, don't you know; and he's allus got a bottle o' bugs in his pocket. He come home yesterday evenin' with a blame' mud-turtle as big as an unabridged dictionary, and turned him over in the back yard and commenced biffin' away at him with a hammer and a cold-chisel. 'W'y, you're a-killin' the turtle,' says I. 'Kill nothin'!' says he, 'I'm thist a-takin' the lid off so's I can see his clock works.' Hoomh!" says Judkins: "He's a good one!—only," he added, "I wouldn't have the *boy* think so for the world!"

## JUDKINS' BOY ON THE MUD-TURTLE

The mud-turtle is not a beast of pray, but he dearly loves catfish bait. If a mud-turtle gits your big toe in his mouth he will hang on till it thunders. Then he will spit it out like he was disgusted. The mud-turtle can swim and keep his chin out of water ef he wants to, but he don't care ef he does sink.

The turtle can stay under water until his next birthday, and never crack a smile. He can breathe like a grown person, but he don't haf to, only when he is on dry land, and then I guess he jist does it to be soshibul. Always when you see bubbles a-comin' up in the swimmin' hole, you can bet your galluses they's a mud-turtle a-layin' down there, studyin' up some cheap way to get his dinner. Mud-turtles never dies, only when they make soup out of 'em. They is seven kinds of meat in the turtle, but I'd ruther eat jist plain burnt liver.

## ON FROGS

Frogs is the people's friend, but they can't fly. Onc't they was tadpoles about as big as lickerish drops, and after a while legs growed on 'em. Oh, let us love the frog—he looks so sorry. Frogs can swim better'n boys, and they don't haf to hold their nose when they dive, neither. Onc't I had a pet frog; and the cars run over him. It jist squashed him. Bet he never knowed what hurt him. Onc't they was a rich lady swallered one—when he was little, you know; and he growed up in her, and it didn't kill him at all. And you could hear him holler in her bosom. It was a tree-toad; and so every time he'd go p-r-r-r- w'y, then the grand lady she'd know it was going to rain, and make her little boy run out and put the tub under the spout. Wasn't that a b'utiful frog?

### ON PIRUTS

Piruts is reckless to a fault. They ain't afeard of nobody ner nothin'. Ef ever you insult a pirut onc't, he'll follow you to the grave but what he will revenge his wrongs. Piruts all look like pictures of "Buffalo Bill"—only they don't shave off the whiskers that sticks out over the collar of their low-necked shirt. Every day is a picknick for the piruts of the high seas. They eat gunpowder and drink blood to make 'em savage, and then they kill people all day, and set up all night and tell ghost stories and sing songs such as mortal ear would quail to listen to. Piruts never comes on shore only when they run out of tobacker; and then it's a cold day if they don't land at midnight, and disguize theirselves and slip up in town like a sleuth houn', so's the Grand Jury can't get on to 'em. They don't care fer the police any more than us people who dwells right in their midst. Piruts makes big wages and spends it like a king. "Come easy, go easy," is the fatal watchword of them whose deeds is Deth. Onc't they was a pirut turned out of the house and home by his cruel parents when he was but a kid, and so he always went by that name. He was thrust adrift without a nickel, and sailed fer distant shores to hide his shame fer those he loved. In the dead of night he stol'd a new suit of the captain's clothes. And when he growed up big enough to fit 'em, he gaily dressed hisself and went up and paced the quarter-deck in deep thought. He had not forgot how the captain onc't had lashed him to the jibboom-poop and whipped. That stung his proud spirit even then; and so the first thing he done was to slip up behind the cruel officer and push him overboard. Then the ship was his fer better er fer worse. And so he took command, and hung high upon the beetling mast the pirut flag. Then he took the bible his old mother give him, and tied a darnic round it and sunk it in the sand with a mocking laugh. Then it was that he was ready fer the pirut's wild seafaring life. He worked the business fer all they was in it fer many years, but was run in at last. And, standing on the gallus-tree, he sung a song which was all wrote off by hisself. And then they knocked the trap on him. And thus the brave man died and never made a kick. In life he was always careful with his means, and saved up vast welth, which he dug holes and buried, and died with the secret locked in his bosom to this day.

## ON HACKMENS

Hackmens has the softest thing in the bizness. They hain't got nothing to do but look humpshouldered and chaw tobacker and wait. Hackmens all look like detectives, and keeps still, and never even spits when you walk past 'em. And they're allus cold. A hackman that stands high in the p'fession can wear a' overcoat in dog-days and then look chilly and like his folks was all dead but the old man, and he wuz a drunkard. Ef a hackman would only be a blind fiddler he'd take in more

money than a fair-ground. Hackmens never gives
nothin' away. You can trust a hackman when you
can't trust your own mother. Some people thinks
when they hire a hack to take 'em some place that
the hackman has got some grudge ag'in' 'em—but
he hain't—he's allus that way. He loves you but he
knows his place, and smothers his real feelings. In
life's giddy scenes hackmens all wears a mask; but
down deep in their heart you can bet they are yourn
till deth. Some hackmens look like they was stuck
up, but they ain't—it's only 'cause they got on so
much clothes. Onc't a hackman wuz stabbed by a
friend of his in the same bizness, and when the
doctors was seein' how bad he wuz karved up, they
found he had on five shurts. They said that wuz all
that saved his life. They said ef he'd only had on
four shurts, he'd 'a' been a ded man. And the hackman hisse'f, when he got well, used to brag it wuz
the closest call he ever had, and laid for the other
hackman, and hit him with a car couplin' and killed
him, and come mighty nigh goin' to the penitenchary
fer it. Influenshal friends wuz all that saved him
that time. No five shurts would 'a' done it. The
mayor said that when he let him off, and brought
down the house, and made hisse'f a strong man fer
another term. Some mayors is purty slick, but a
humble hackman may sometimes turn out to be jist
as smooth. The only thing why a hackman don't
show up no better is 'cause he loses so much sleep.
That's why he allus looks like he had the headache,
and didn't care if he did. Onc't a hackman wuz

waitin' in front of a hotel one morning and wuz sort
o' dozin' like, and fell off his seat. And they run
and picked him up, and he wuz unconshus, and they
worked with him till 'way long in the afternoon
'fore they found out he wuz just asleep; and he
cussed fearful cause they waked him up, and wondered why people couldn't never tend to their own
bizness like he did.

ON DUDES

Everybody is allus a-givin' it to Dudes. Newspapers makes fun of 'em, and artists makes pictures
of 'em; and the only ones in the wide world that's
stuck on Dudes is me and the Dudes theirse'f, and
we love and cherish 'em with all a parent's fond
regards. And nobody knows much about Dudes
neither, 'cause they hain't been broke out long
enough yet to tell jist what the disease is. Some say
it's softinning of the brains, and others claim it
can't be that, on the groun's thay hain't got material
for the softinning to work on, &c., &c., till even
"Sientests is puzzled," as the good book says. And
if I wuz a-going to say what ails Dudes I'd have to
give it up, er pernounce it a' aggervated case of
Tyfoid blues, which is my 'onnest convictions.
That's what makes me kind o' stand in with 'em—
same as if they wuz the under-dog. I am willing to
aknolege that Dudes has their weakness, but so has
ever'thing. Even Oscar Wild, if put to the test;—
and I allus feel sorry for George Washington 'cause
he died 'fore he got to see Oscar Wild. And then

another reason why you oughten't to jump on to
Dudes is, they don't know what's the matter with
'em any more than us folks in whom they come in
daily contack. Dudes all walks and looks in the
face like they wuz on their way to fill an engagement
with a revolvin' lady wax-figger in some milliner-
winder, and had fergot the number of her place of
bizness. Some folks is mean enough to bitterly
a'sert that Dudes is strained in their manner and
fools from choice; but they ain't. It's a gift—Dudes
is Geenuses—that's what Dudes is!

### ON RED HAIR

Onc't a pore boy wuz red-hedded, and got mad at
the other boys when they'd throw it up to him.
And when they'd laugh at his red hed, and ast him
fer a light, er wuzn't he afeard he'd singe his cap,
and orto' wear a tin hat; er pertend to warm their
hands by him,—w'y, sometimes the red-hedded boy'd
git purty hot indeed, and once he told another boy
that wuz a-bafflin' him about his red hair that if he
wuz him he'd git a fine comb and go to canvassin'
his own hed, and then he'd be liabul to sceer up a
more livelier subjeck to talk about than red hair.
And then the other boy says, "You're a liar" and
that got the red-hedded boy into more trouble; for
the old man whipped him shameful' fer breakin' up
soil with the other boy. And this here red-hedded
boy had freckles, too. And warts. And nobody
ortn't to 'a' jumpt on to him fer that. Ef anybody

was a red-hedded boy they'd have also warts and freckles—and jist red hair's bad enough. Onc't another boy told him ef he wuz him he bet he could make a big day look sick some night. And when the red-hedded boy says "How?" w'y, the other boy he says "Easy enough. I'd jist march around bare-hedded in the torch-light p'cession."—"Yes, you would," says the red-hedded boy, and pasted him one with a shinny club, and got dispelled from school 'cause he wuz so high-tempered and impulsive. Ef I wuz the red-hedded boy I'd be a pirut; but he always said he was going to be a baker.

### THE CROSS-EYED GIRL

"You don't want to never tamper with a crosseyed girl," said Mr. Judkins, "and I'll tell you why: They've naturally got a better focus on things than a man would ever guess—studyin' their eyes, you understand. A man may think he's a-foolin' a cross-eyed girl simply because she's apparently got her eyes tangled on other topics as he's a-talkin' to her, but at the same time that girl may be a-lookin' down the windin' stairway of the cellar of his soul with one eye, and a-winkin' in a whisper to her own soul with the other, and her unconscious victim just a-takin' it for granted that nothin' is the matter with the girl, only just cross-eyes! You see I've studied 'em," continued Judkins, "and I'm on to one fact dead sure—and that is, their natures is as deceivin' as their eyes is! Knowed one once't that had her eyes mixed up thataway—sensitive little thing she was, and always referrin' to her 'misfortune,' as she called it, and eternally threatenin' to have some surgeon straighten 'em out like other folks'—and, sir, that girl so worked on my feelin's, and took such underholts on my sympathies that, blame me, before I knowed it I confessed to her that if it hadn't a been for her defective eyes (I made it 'defective') I never would have thought of lovin' her, and, furthermore if ever she did have 'em changed back normal, don't you understand, she might consider our engagement at an end—I did, honest. And that girl was so absolute crosseyed it warped her ears, and she used to amuse herself by watchin' 'em curl up as I'd be a-talkin' to her, and that maddened me, 'cause I'm naturally of a jealous disposition, you know, and so, at last, I just casually hinted that if she was really a-goin' to get them eyes carpentered up, why she'd better get at it, and that ended it.

And then the blame' girl turned right around and married a fellow that had a better pair of eyes than mine this minute! Then I struck another cross-eyed girl—not really a legitimate case, 'cause, in reality, she only had one off eye—the right eye, if I don't disremember—the other one was as square as a gage. And that girl was, if any difference, a more confusin' case than the other, and besides all that, she had some money in her own right, and wan't a-throwin' off no big discount on one game eye. But I finally got her interested, and I reckon something serious might 'a' come of it—but, you see, her father was dead and her stepmother sort o' shut down on my comin' to the house; besides that, she had three grown uncles, and you know how uncles is. I didn't want to marry no family, of course, and so I slid out of the scheme, and tackled a poor girl that clerked in a post-office. Her eyes was bad! I never did get the hang of them eyes of hern. She had purty hair, and a complexion, I used to tell her, which outrivaled the rose. But them eyes, you know! I didn't really appreciate how bad they was crossed, at first. You see, it took time. Got her to give me her picture, and I used to cipher on that, but finally worked her off on a young friend of mine who wanted to marry intellect—give her a good send-off to him—and she was smart—only them eyes, you know! Why, that girl could read a postal card, both sides at once, and smile at a personal friend through the office window at the same time!"

### HOMESICKNESS

There was a more than ordinary earnestness in the tone of Mr. Judkins as he said: "Referrin' to this thing of bein' homesick, I want to say right here that of all diseases, afflictions er complaints, this thing of bein' homesick takes the cookies! A man may think when he's got a' aggrivated case of janders, er white-swellin', say, er bone-erysipelas, that he's to be looked up to as bein' purty well fixed in this vale of trouble and unrest, but I want to tell you, when I want my sorrow blood-raw, don't you understand, you may give me homesickness—

straight goods, you know—and I'll get more clean,
legitimate agony out of that than you can out of
either of the other attractions—yes, er even if you'd
ring in the full combination on me! You see,
there's no way of treatin' homesickness only one—
and that is to get back home—but as that's a remedy
you can't get at no drug store, at so much per box—
and if you could, for instance, and only had enough
ready money anyhow to cover half the cost of a
full box—and nothin' but a full box ever reached
the case—why, it follers that your condition still
remains critical. And homesickness don't show no
favors. It's just as liable to strike you as me. High
er low, er rich er poor, all comes under her jurish-
diction, and whenever she once reaches fer a citizen, you can just bet she gits there Eli, ever' time!

"She don't confine herself to youth, nor make no
specialty of little children either, but she stalks
abroad like a census-taker, and is as conscientious.
She visits the city girl clean up to Maxinkuckee, and
makes her wonder how things really is back home
without her. And then she haunts her dreams, and
wakes her up at all hours of the night, and sings
old songs over for her, and talks to her in low
thrillin' tones of a young man whose salary ain't
near big enough fer two; and then she leaves her
photograph with her and comes away, and makes it
lively for the boys on the train, the conductor, the
brakeman and the engineer. She even nests out the
travelin' man, and yanks him out of his reclinin'
chair, and walks him up and down the car, and runs

him clean out of cigars and fine-cut, and smiles to
hear him swear. Then she gets off at little country stations and touches up the night operator, who
grumbles at his boy companion, and wishes to derna-
tion 'six' was in, so's he could 'pound his ear.'

"And I'll never forget," continued Mr. Judkins,
"the last case of homesickness I had, and the cure I
took for it. 'Tain't been more'n a week ago neither.
You see my old home is a'most too many laps from
this base to make it very often, and in consequence I
hadn't been there for five years and better, till this
last trip, when I just succumbed to the pressure,
and th'owed up my hands and went. Seemed like
I'd 'a' died if I hadn't. And it was glorious to rack
around the old town again—things lookin' just the
same, mighty nigh it, as they was when I was a
boy, don't you know. Run acrost an old school-
mate, too, and took supper at his happy little home,
and then we got us a good nickel cigar, and walked
and walked, and talked and talked! Tuck me all
around, you understand, in the meller twilight—till,
the first thing you know, there stood the old schoolhouse where me and him first learnt to chew tobacco, and all that! Well, sir! you hain't got no
idea of the feelin's that was mine! Why, I felt like
I could th'ow my arms around the dear old buildin'
and squeeze it till the cupolo would just pop out of
the top of the roof like the core out of a bile! And
I think if there ever was a' epoch in my life when
I could 'a' tackled poetry without no compunctions,
as the feller says, why, then was the time—shore!"

## ECCENTRIC MR. CLARK

ALL who knew Mr. Clark intimately, casually,
or by sight alone, smiled always, meeting
him, and thought, "What an odd man he is!" Not
that there was anything extremely or ridiculously
obtrusive in Mr. Clark's peculiarities either of feature, dress, or deportment, by which a graded estimate of his really quaint character might aptly be
given; but rather, perhaps, it was the curious
combination of all these things that had gained
for Mr. Clark the transient celebrity of being a
very eccentric man.

And Mr. Clark, of all the odd inhabitants of the
busy metropolis in which he lived, seemed least conscious of the fact of his local prominence. True
it was that when familiarly addressed as "Clark,
old boy," by sportive individuals he never recollected
having seen before, he would oftentimes stare
blankly in return, and with evident embarrassment;
but as these actions may have been attributable to
weak eyes, or to the confusion consequent upon
being publicly recognized by the quondam associates of bacchanalian hours, the suggestive facts only
served to throw his eccentricities in new relief.

And in the minds of many, that Mr. Clark was

somewhat given to dissipation, there was but little
doubt; for, although in no way, and at no time,
derelict in the rigid duties imposed upon him as
an accountant in a wholesale liquor house on South
John Street, a grand majority of friends had long
ago conceded that a certain puffiness of flesh and
a soiled-like pallor of complexion were in nowise
the legitimate result of over-application simply in
the counting-room of the establishment in which he
found employment; but as to the complicity of Mr.
Clark's direct associates in this belief, it is only
justice to the gentleman to state that by them
he was held above all such suspicion, from the
gray-haired senior of the firm, down to the pink-
nosed porter of the warerooms, who, upon every
available occasion, would point out the eccentric
Mr. Clark as "the on'y man in the biznez 'at never
sunk a 'thief' er drunk a drop o' 'goods' o' any
kind, under no consideration!"

And Mr. Clark himself, when playfully approached on the subject, would quietly assert that
never, under any circumstances, had the taste of
intoxicating liquors passed his lips, though at such
asseverations it was a noticeable fact that Mr.
Clark's complexion invariably grew more sultry
than its wont, and that his eyes, forever moist, grew
dewier, and that his lips and tongue would seem
covertly entering upon some lush conspiracy, which
in its incipiency he would be forced to smother with
his hastily drawn handkerchief. Then the eccentric
Mr. Clark would laugh nervously, and pouncing

on some subject so vividly unlike the one just preceding it as to daze the listener, he would ripple
ahead with a tide of eloquence that positively overflowed and washed away all remembrance of the
opening topic.

In point of age Mr. Clark might have been thirty,
thirty-five, or even forty years, were one to venture
an opinion solely by outward appearance and under
certain circumstances and surroundings. As, for
example, when a dozen years ago the writer of this
sketch rode twenty miles in a freight-caboose with
Mr. Clark as the only other passenger, he seemed
in age at first not less than thirty-five; but on
opening a conversation with him, in which he joined
with wonderful vivacity, a nearer view, and a prolonged and studious one as well, revealed the rather
curious fact that, at the very limit of all allowable
supposition, his age could not possibly have ex-
ceeded twenty-five.

What it was in the man that struck me as eccentric at that time I have never been wholly
able to define, but I recall accurately the most
trivial occurrences of our meeting and the very
subject-matter of our conversation. I even remember the very words in which he declined a drink
from my traveling-flask—for "It's a raw day," I
said, by way of gratuitous excuse for offering it.
"Yes," he said, smilingly motioning the temptation
aside; "it is a raw day; but you're rather young in
years to be doctoring the weather—at least you'd
better change the treatment—they'll all be raw days

for you after a while!" I confess that I even felt an inward pity for the man as I laughingly drained his health and returned the flask to my valise. But when I asked him, ten minutes later, the nature of the business in which he was engaged, and he handed me, in response and without comment, the card of a wholesale liquor house, with his own name in crimson letters struck diagonally across the surface, I winked naively to myself and thought "Ah-ha!" And as if reading my very musings, he said: "Why, certainly, I carry a full line of samples; but, my dear young friend, don't imagine for a minute that I refuse your brand on that account. You can rest assured that I have nothing better in my cases. Whisky is whisky wherever it is found, and there is no 'best' whisky—not in all the world!"

Truly, I thought, this is an odd source for the emanation of temperance sentiments—then said aloud: "And yet you engage in a business you dislike! Traffic in an article that you yourself condemn! Do I understand you?"

"Might there not be such a thing," he said quietly, "as inheriting a business—the same as inheriting an appetite? However, one advances by gradations: I shall *sell* no more. This is my last trip on the road in that capacity: I am coming in now to take charge of the firm's books. Would be glad to have you call on me any time you're in the city. Good-by." And, as he swung off the slowly moving train, now entering the city, and I stood watching him from the open door of the caboose as he rapidly walked down a suburban street, I was positive his gait was anything but steady—that the step—the figure—the whole air of the man was that of one then laboring under the effects of partial intoxication.

I have always liked peculiar people; no matter where I met them, no matter who they were; if once impressed with an eccentricity of character which I have reason to believe purely unaffected, I never quite forget the person, name or place of our first meeting, or where the interesting party may be found again. And so it was in the customary order of things that, during hasty visits to the city, I often called on the eccentric Mr. Clark, and, as he had promised on our first acquaintance, he seemed always glad to see and welcome me in his new office. The more I knew of him the more I liked him, but I think I never fully understood him. No one seemed to know him quite so well as that.

Once I had a little private talk regarding him with the senior partner of the firm for which he worked. Mr. Clark, just prior to my call, had gone to lunch—would be back in half an hour. Would I wait there in the office until his return? Certainly. And the chatty senior entertained me :—Queer fellow—Mr. Clark!—as his father was before him. Used to be a member of the firm—his father; in fact, founded the business—made a fortune at it—failed, for an unfortunate reason, and went "up the flume." Paid every dollar that he owed, however. sacrificing the

very home that sheltered his wife and children—
but never rallied. He had quite a family, then?
Oh, yes; had a family—not a large one, but a
bright one—only they all seemed more or less unfortunate. The father was unfortunate—very; and
died so, leaving his wife and two boys—the older
son much like the father—splendid business ca-
pacities, but lacked will—couldn't resist some things
—even weaker than the father in that regard, and
died at half his age.

But the younger brother—our Mr. Clark—remained, and he was sterling—"straight goods" in
all respects. Lived with his mother—was her
sole support. A proud woman, Mrs. Clark—
a proud woman, with a broken spirit—withdrawn entirely from the world, and had been
so for years and years. The Clarks, as had been
mentioned, were all peculiar—even the younger Mr.
Clark, our friend, I had doubtless noticed was an
odd genius, but he had stamina—something solid
about him, for all his eccentricities—could be relied
on. Had been with the house there since a boy
of twelve—took him for the father's sake; had never
missed a day's time in any line of work that ever
had been given in his charge—was weakly-looking,
too. Had worked his way from the cellar up—from
the least pay to the highest—had saved enough to
buy and pay for a comfortable house for his mother
and himself, and, still a lad, maintained the expense of companion, attendant and maid servant for
the mother. Yet, with all this burden on his shoul-

Riley Day at Anderson, June 3rd, 1913

ders, the boy had worried through some way, with a jolly smile and a good word for every one. "A boy, sir," the enthusiastic senior concluded—"a boy, sir, that never was a boy, and never had a taste of genuine boyhood in his life—no more than he ever took a taste of whisky, and you couldn't get that in him with a funnel!"

At this juncture Mr. Clark himself appeared, and in a particularly happy frame of mind. For an hour the delighted senior and myself sat laughing at the fellow's quaint conceits and witty sayings, the conversation at last breaking up with an abrupt proposition from Mr. Clark that I remain in the city overnight and accompany him to the theater, an invitation I rather eagerly accepted. Mr. Clark, thanking me, and pivoting himself around on his high stool, with a mechanical "Good afternoon!" was at once submerged in his books, while the senior, following me out and stepping into a carriage that stood waiting for him at the curb, waved me adieu, and was driven away. I turned my steps up the street, but remembering that my friend had fixed no place to meet me in the evening, I stepped back into the storeroom and again pushed open the glass door of the office.

Mr. Clark still sat on the high stool at his desk, his back toward the door, and his ledger spread out before him.

"Mr. Clark!" I called.

He made no answer.

"Mr. Clark!" I called again, in an elevated key.

He did not stir.

I paused a moment, then went over to him, letting my hand drop lightly on his arm.

Still no response. I only felt the shoulder heave, as with a long-drawn quavering sigh, then heard the regular though labored breathing of a weary man that slept.

I had not the heart to waken him; but lifting the still moistened pen from his unconscious fingers, I wrote where I might be found at eight that evening, folded and addressed the note, and laying it on the open page before him, turned quietly away.

"Poor man!" I mused compassionately, with a touch of youthful sentiment affecting me.—"Poor man! Working himself into his very grave, and with never a sign or murmur of complaint—worn and weighed down with the burden of his work, and yet with a nobleness of spirit and resolve that still conceals behind glad smiles and laughing words the cares that lie so heavily upon him!"

The long afternoon went by at last, and evening came; and, as promptly as my note requested, the jovial Mr. Clark appeared, laughing heartily, as we walked off down the street, at my explanation of the reason I had written my desires instead of verbally addressing him; and laughing still louder when I told him of my fears that he was overworking himself.

"Oh, no, my friend," he answered gaily; "there's no occasion for anxiety on that account.— But the fact is, old man," he went on, half apologetically, "the fact is, I haven't been so overworked, of late, as over-wakeful. There's something in the night I think, that does it. Do you know that the night is a great mystery to me—a great mystery! And it seems to be growing on me all the time. There's the trouble. The night to me is like some vast incomprehensible being. When I write the name 'night' I instinctively write it with a capital. And I like my night deep, and dark, and swarthy, don't you know. Now some like clear and starry nights, but they're too pale for me—too weak and fragile altogether! They're popular with the masses, of course, these blue-eyed, golden-haired, 'moonlight-on-the-lake' nights; but, somehow, I don't 'stand in' with them. My favorite night is the pronounced brunette—the darker the better. To-night is one of my kind, and she's growing more and more like it all the time. If it were not for depriving you of the theater, I'd rather just drift off now in the deepening gloom till swallowed up in it—lost utterly. Come with me, anyhow!"

"Gladly," I answered, catching something of his own enthusiasm; "I myself prefer it to the play."

"I heartily congratulate you on your taste," he said, diving violently for my hand and wringing it. "Oh, it's going to be grimly glorious!—a depth of darkness one can wade out into, and knead in his hands like dough!" And he laughed, himself, at this grotesque conceit.

And so we walked—for hours. Our talk—or, rather, my friend's talk—lulled and soothed at last

into a calmer flow, almost solemn in its tone, and
yet fretted with an occasional wildness of utterance
and expression.

Half consciously I had been led by my companion,
who for an hour had been drawing closer to me
as we walked. His arm, thrust through my own,
clung almost affectionately. We were now in some
strange suburb of the city, evidently, too, in a low
quarter, for from the windows of such business
rooms and shops as bore any evidence of respecta-
bility the lights had been turned out and the doors
locked for the night. Only a gruesome green light
was blazing in a little drug-store just opposite,
while at our left, as we turned the corner, a tumble-
down saloon sent out on the night a mingled
sound of clicking billiard-balls, discordant voices,
the harsher rasping of a violin, together with the
sullen plunkings of a banjo.

"I must leave you here for a minute," said my
friend, abruptly breaking a long silence, and loosen-
ing my arm. "The druggist over there is a patron
of our house, and I am reminded of a little business
I have with him. He is about closing, too, and
I'll see him now, as I may not be down this way
again soon. No; you wait here for me—right here,"
and he playfully but firmly pushed me back, ran
across the street, and entered the store. Through
the open door I saw him shake hands with the man
who stood behind the counter, and stand talking
in the same position for some minutes—both still
clasping hands, as it seemed; but as I mechanically

bent with closer scrutiny, the druggist seemed to be examining the hand of Mr. Clark and working at it, as though picking at a splinter in the palm—I I could not quite determine what was being done, for a glass show-case blurred an otherwise clear view of the arms of both from the elbows down. Then they came forward, Mr. Clark arranging his cuffs, and the druggist wrapping up some minute article he took from an upper show-case, and handing it to my friend, who placed it in the pocket of his vest and turned away. At this moment my attention was withdrawn by an extra tumult of jeers and harsh laughter in the saloon, from the door of which, even as my friend turned from the door opposite, a drunken woman reeled, and staggering round the corner as my friend came up, fell violently forward on the pavement, not ten steps in our advance. Instinctively, we both sprang to her aid, and bending over the senseless figure, peered curiously at the bruised and bleeding features. My friend was trembling with excitement. He clutched wildly at the limp form, trying, but vainly, to lift the woman to her feet. "Why don't you take hold of her?" he whispered hoarsely. "Help me with her— quick! quick! Lift her up!" I obeyed without a word, though with a shudder of aversion as a drop of hot red blood stung me on the hand.

"Now draw her arm about your shoulder—this way—and hold it so! And now your other arm around her waist—quick, man, quick, as you your-

self will want God's arm about you when you fail!
Now, come!" And with no other word we hurried
with our burden up the empty darkness of the
street.

I was utterly bewildered with it all, but something
kept me silent. And so we hurried on, and on, and
on, our course directed by my now wholly reticent
companion. Where he was going, what his purpose
was, I could not but vaguely surmise. I only recognized that his intentions were humane, which fact
was emphasized by the extreme caution he took to
avoid the two or three late pedestrians that passed
us on our way as we stood crowded in concealment
—once behind a low shed, once in an entry-way;
and once, at the distant rattle of a police whistle,
we hurried through the blackness of a narrow alley
into the silent street beyond. And on up this we
passed, until at last we paused at the gateway of a
cottage on our left. On to the door of that we went,
my friend first violently jerking the bell, then opening the door with a night-key, and with me lifting
the still senseless woman through the hall into a
dimly lighted room upon the right, and laying her
upon a clean white bed that glimmered in the corner.
He reached and turned the gas on in a flaring jet,
and as he did so, "This is my home," he whispered,
"and this woman is—my mother!" He flung himself upon his knees beside her as he spoke. He laid
his quivering lips against the white hair and the
ruddy wound upon the brow; then dappled with his

kisses the pale face, and stroked and petted and caressed the faded hands. "O God!" he moaned, "if I might only weep!"

The steps of some one coming down the stairs aroused him. He stepped quickly to the door, and threw it open. It was a woman servant. He simply pointed to the form upon the bed.

"Oh, sir!" exclaimed the frightened woman, "what has happened? What has happened to my poor dear mistress?"

"Why did you let her leave the house?"

"She sent me away, sir. I never dreamed that she was going out again. She told me she was very sleepy and wanted to retire, and I helped her to undress before I went. But she ain't bad hurt, is she?" she continued, stooping over the still figure and tenderly smoothing back the disheveled hair. —"It's only the cheek bruised and the forehead cut a little—it's the blood that makes it look like a bad hurt. See, when I bathe it, it is not a bad hurt, sir. She's just been—she's just worn out, poor thing— and she's asleep—that's all."

He made no answer to the woman's speech, but turned toward me. "Five doors from here," he said, "and to your left as you go out, you will find the residence of Dr. Worrel. Go to him for me, and tell him he is wanted here at once. Tell him my mother is much worse. He will understand. I would go myself, but must see about arranging for your comfort upon your return, for you will not leave me till broad daylight—you must not!" I bowed in silent acceptance of his wishes, and turned upon my errand.

Fortunately, the doctor was at home, and returned at once with me to my friend, where, after a careful examination of his patient, he assured the anxious son that the wounds were only slight, and that her unconscious condition was simply "the result of over-stimulation, perhaps," as he delicately put it. She would doubtless waken in her usual rational state—an occurrence really more to be feared than desired, since her peculiar sensitiveness might feel too keenly the unfortunate happening. "Anyway," he continued, "I will call early in the morning, and, in the event of her awakening before that time, I will leave a sedative with Mary, with directions she will attend to. She will remain here at her side. And as to yourself, Mr. Clark," the doctor went on in an anxious tone, as he marked the haggard face and hollow eyes, "I insist that you retire. You must rest, sir—worrying for the past week as you have been doing is telling on you painfully. You need rest—and you must take it."

"And I will," said Mr. Clark submissively. Stooping again, he clasped the sleeping face between his hands and kissed it tenderly. "Good night!" I heard him whisper—"good night—good night!" He turned, and motioning for me to follow, opened the door—"Doctor, good night! Good night, Mary!"

He led the way to his own room up-stairs. "And now, my friend," he said, as he waved me to an easy chair, "I have but two other favors to ask of you:

The first is, that you talk to me, or read to me, or tell me fairy tales, or riddles—anything, so that you keep it up incessantly, and never leave off till you find me fast asleep. Then in the next room you will find a comfortable bed. Leave me sleeping here, and you sleep there. And the second favor," he continued, with a slow smile and an affected air of great deliberation—"oh, well, I'll not ask the second favor of you now. I'll keep it for you till to-morrow." And as he turned laughingly away and paced three or four times across the room, in his step, his gait, the general carriage of the figure, I was curiously reminded of the time, years before, that I had watched him from the door of the caboose, as he walked up the suburban street till the movement of the train had hidden him from view.

"Well, what will you do?" he asked, as he wheeled a cozy-cushioned lounge close beside my chair, and removing his coat, flung himself languidly down.— "Will you talk or read to me?"

"I will read," I said, as I picked up a book to begin my vigil.

"Hold just a minute, then," he said, drawing a card and pencil from his vest.—"I may want to jot down a note or two.—Now, go ahead."

I had been reading in a low voice steadily for perhaps an hour, my companion never stirring from his first position, but although my eyes were never lifted from the book, I knew by the occasional sound of his pencil that he had not yet dropped asleep.

And so, without a pause, I read monotonously on.
At last he turned heavily. I paused. With his eyes
closed he groped his hand across my knees and
grasped my own. "Go on with the reading," he
said drowsily—"Guess I'm going to sleep now—but
you go right on with the story.—Good night!" His
hand fumbled lingeringly a moment, then was withdrawn and folded with the other on his breast.

I read on in a lower tone an hour longer, then
paused again to look at my companion. He was
sleeping heavily, and although the features in their
repose appeared unusually pale, a wholesome perspi-
ration, as it seemed, pervaded all the face, while the
breathing, though labored, was regular. I bent
above him to lower the pillow for his head, and the
movement half aroused him, as I thought at first,
for he muttered something as though impatiently;
but listening to catch his mutterings, I knew that
he was dreaming. "It's what killed father," I heard
him say. "And it's what killed Tom," he went on,
in a smothered voice; "killed both—killed both! It
shan't kill me; I swear it. I could bottle it—case
after case—and never touch a drop. If you never
take the first drink, you'll never want it. Mother
taught me that. What made her ever take the first?
Mother! mother! When I get to be a man, I'll
buy her all the fine things she used to have when
father was alive. Maybe I can buy back the old
home, with the roses up the walk and the sunshine
slanting in the hall."

And so the sleeper murmured on.  Sometimes
the voice was thick and discordant, sometimes low
and clear and tuneful as a child's.  "Never touch
whisky!" he went on, almost harshly.    "Never—
never!  Drop in the street first.  I did.  The doctor
will come then, and he knows what you want.  Not
whisky.—Medicine; the kind that makes you warm
again—makes you want to live; but don't ever dare
touch whisky.  Let other people drink it if they
want it.  Sell it to them; they'll get it anyhow; but
don't you touch it!  It killed your father, it killed
Tom, and—oh!—mother! mother! mother!"  Tears
actually teemed from underneath the sleeper's lids,
and glittered down the pallid and distorted features.
"There's a medicine that's good for you when you
want whisky," he went on.—"When you are weak,
and everybody else is strong—and always when the
flagstones give way beneath your feet, and the long
street undulates and wavers as you walk; why,
that's a sign for you to take that medicine—and
take it quick!  Oh, it will warm you till the little
pale blue streaks in your white hands will bulge out
again with tingling blood, and it will start up from
its stagnant pools and leap from vein to vein till it
reaches your being's furthest height and droops and
falls and folds down over icy brow and face like a
soft veil moistened with pure warmth.  Ah! it is
so deliriously sweet and restful!"

I heard a moaning in the room below, and then
steps on the stairs, and a tapping at the door.  It

was Mary. Mrs. Clark had awakened and was crying for her son. "But we must not waken him," I said. "Give Mrs. Clark the medicine the doctor left for her—that will quiet her."

"But she won't take it, sir. She won't do anything at all for me—and if Mr. Clark could only come to her, for just a minute, she would—"

The woman's speech was broken by a shrill cry in the hall, and then the thud of naked feet on the stairway. "I want my boy—my boy!" wailed the hysterical woman from without.

"Go to your mistress—quick," I said sternly, pushing the maid from the room.—"Take her back; I will come down to your assistance in a moment." Then I turned hastily to see if the sleeper had been disturbed by the woman's cries; but all was peaceful with him yet; and so, throwing a coverlet over him, I drew the door to silently and went below.

I found the wretched mother in an almost frenzied state, and her increasing violence alarmed me so that I thought it best to summon the physician again; and bidding the servant not to leave her for an instant, I hurried for the help so badly needed. This time the doctor was long delayed, although he joined me with all possible haste, and with all speed accompanied me back to the unhappy home. Entering the door, our ears were greeted with a shriek that came piercing down the hall till the very echoes shuddered as with fear. It was the patient's voice shrilling from the sleeper's room up-stairs:—"O God! My boy! my boy! I want my boy, and he will not waken for me!" An instant later we were both upon the scene.

The woman in her frenzy had broken from the servant to find her son. And she had found him.

She had wound her arms about him, and had dragged his still sleeping form upon the floor. He would not waken, even though she gripped him to her heart and shrieked her very soul out in his ears. He would not waken. The face, though whiter than her own, betokened only utter rest and peace. We drew her, limp and voiceless, from his side. "We are too late," the doctor whispered, lifting with his finger one of the closed lids, and letting it drop to again.—"See here!" He had been feeling at the wrist; and, as he spoke, he slipped the sleeve up, bared the sleeper's arm. From the wrist to elbow it was livid purple, and pitted and scarred with minute wounds—some scarcely sealed as yet with clotted blood.

"In heaven's name, what does it all mean?" I asked.

"Morphine," said the doctor, "and the hypodermic. And here," he exclaimed, lifting the other hand—"here is a folded card with your name at the top."

I snatched it from him, and I read, written in faint but rounded characters:

"I like to hear your voice. It sounds kind. It is like a far-off tune. To drop asleep, though, as I am doing now, is sweeter music—but read on,—I have taken something to make me sleep, and by mistake I have taken too much; but you will read right on. Now, mind you, this is not suicide, as God listens to the whisper of this pencil as I write! I did it by mistake. For years and years I have taken the same thing. This time I took too much—much more than I meant to—but I am glad. This is the second favor I would ask: Go to my employers to-morrow, show them this handwriting, and say I know for my sake they will take charge of my affairs and administer all my estate in the best way suited to my mother's needs. Good-by, my friend—I can only say 'good night' to you when I shall take your hand an instant later and turn away forever."

Through tears I read it all, and ending with his name in full, I turned and looked down on the face of this man that I had learned to love, and the full measure of his needed rest was with him; and the rainy day that glowered and drabbled at the eastern window of the room was as drearily stared back at by a hopeless woman's dull demented eyes.

# A NEST-EGG

BUT a few miles from the city here, and on the sloping banks of the stream noted more for its plenitude of "chubs" and "shiners" than the gamier two- and four-pound bass for which, in season, so many credulous anglers flock and lie in wait, stands a country residence, so convenient to the stream, and so inviting in its pleasant exterior and comfortable surroundings—barn, dairy, and spring-house—that the weary, sunburned, and disheartened fisherman, out from the dusty town for a day of recreation, is often wont to seek its hospitality.

The house in style of architecture is something of a departure from the typical farmhouse, being designed and fashioned with no regard to symmetry or proportion, but rather, as is suggested, built to conform to the matter-of-fact and most sensible ideas of its owner, who, if it pleased him, would have small windows where large ones ought to be, and vice versa, whether they balanced properly to the eye or not. And chimneys—he would have as many as he wanted, and no two alike, in either height or size. And if he wanted the front of the house turned from all possible view, as though abashed at any chance of public scrutiny, why, that was his affair and not the public's; and, with like perversity, if he chose to thrust his kitchen under

245

the public's very nose, what should the generally fagged-out, half-famished representative of that dignified public do but reel in his dead minnow, shoulder his fishing-rod, clamber over the back fence of the old farmhouse and inquire within, or jog back to the city, inwardly anathematizing that particular locality or the whole rural district in general. That is just the way that farmhouse looked to the writer of this sketch one week ago— so individual it seemed—so liberal, and yet so independent. It wasn't even weather-boarded, but, instead, was covered smoothly with cement, as though the plasterers had come while the folks were visiting, and so, unable to get at the interior, had just plastered the outside.

I am more than glad that I was hungry enough, and weary enough, and wise enough to take the house at its first suggestion; for, putting away my fishing-tackle for the morning, at least, I went up the sloping bank, crossed the dusty road, and confidently clambered over the fence.

Not even a growling dog to intimate that I was trespassing. All was open—gracious-looking—pastoral. The sward beneath my feet was velvet-like in elasticity, and the scarce visible path I followed through it led promptly to the open kitchen door. From within I heard a woman singing some old ballad in an undertone, while at the threshold a trim, white-spurred rooster stood poised on one foot, curving his glossy neck and cocking his wattled head as though to catch the meaning of the words.

I paused. It was a scene I felt restrained from breaking in upon, nor would I have, but for the sound of a strong male voice coming around the corner of the house:

"Sir. Howdy!"

Turning, I saw a rough-looking but kindly featured man of sixty-five, evidently the owner of the place.

I returned his salutation with some confusion and much deference. "I must really beg your pardon for this intrusion," I began, "but I have been tiring myself out fishing, and your home here looked so pleasant—and I felt so thirsty—and—"

"Want a drink, I reckon," said the old man, turning abruptly toward the kitchen door, then pausing as suddenly, with a backward motion of his thumb —"jest follow the path here down to the little brick—that's the spring—and you'll find 'at you've come to the right place fer drinkin'-worter! Hold on a minute tel I get you a tumbler—there's nothin' down there but a tin."

"Then don't trouble yourself any further," I said, heartily, "for I'd rather drink from a tin cup than a goblet of pure gold."

"And so'd I," said the old man, reflectively, turning mechanically, and following me down the path. " 'Druther drink out of a tin—er jest a fruit-can with the top knocked off—er—er—er a gourd," he added in a zestful, reminiscent tone of voice, that so heightened my impatient thirst that I reached the spring-house fairly in a run.

"Well-sir!" exclaimed my host, in evident delight, as I stood dipping my nose in the second cup-
ful of the cool, revivifying liquid, and peering in a
congratulatory kind of way at the blurred and rubi-
cund reflection of my features in the bottom of the
cup, "well-sir, blame-don! ef it don't do a feller
good to see you enjoyin' of it thataway! But don't
you drink too much o' the worter!—'cause there's
some sweet milk over there in one o' them crocks,
maybe; and ef you'll jest, kind o' keerful-like, lift
off the led of that third one, say, over there to
yer left, and dip you out a tinful er two o' that,
w'y, it'll do you good to drink it, and it'll do me
good to see you at it— But hold up!—hold up!"
he called, abruptly, as, nowise loath, I bent above
the vessel designated. "Hold yer hosses fer a second! Here's Marthy; let her git it fer ye."

If I was at first surprised and confused, meeting
the master of the house, I was wholly startled and
chagrined in my present position before its mistress.
But as I arose, and stammered, in my confusion,
some incoherent apology, I was again reassured and
put at greater ease by the comprehensive and forgiving smile the woman gave me, as I yielded her
my place, and, with lifted hat, awaited her further
kindness.

"I came just in time, sir," she said, half laughingly, as with strong, bare arms she reached across
the gurgling trough and replaced the lid that I had
partially removed.—"I came just in time, I see, to
prevent father from having you dip into the morn-

ing's-milk, which, of course, has scarcely a veil of cream over the face of it as yet. But men, as you are doubtless willing to admit," she went on jocularly, "don't know about these things. You must pardon father, as much for his well-meaning ignorance of such matters, as for this cup of cream, which I am sure you will better relish."

She arose, still smiling, with her eyes turned frankly on my own. And I must be excused when I confess that as I bowed my thanks, taking the proffered cup and lifting it to my lips, I stared with an uncommon interest and pleasure at the donor's face.

She was a woman of certainly not less than forty years of age. But the figure, and the rounded grace and fulness of it, together with the features and the eyes, completed as fine a specimen of physical and mental health as ever it has been my fortune to meet; there was something so full of purpose and resolve—something so wholesome, too, about the character—something so womanly—I might almost say manly, and would, but for the petty prejudice maybe occasioned by the trivial fact of a locket having dropped from her bosom as she knelt; and that trinket still dangles in my memory even as it then dangled and dropped back to its concealment in her breast as she arose. But her face, by no means handsome in the common sense of the word, was marked with a breadth and strength of outline and expression that approached the heroic—a face that once seen is forever fixed in memory—a per-

sonage once met one must know more of.  And so it
was, that an hour later, as I strolled with the old
man about his farm, looking, to all intents, with the
profoundest interest at his Devonshires, Shorthorns,
Jerseys, and the like, I lured from him something
of an outline of his daughter's history.

"There're no better girl 'n Marthy!" he said,
mechanically answering some ingenious allusion to
her worth.  "And yit," he went on reflectively,
stooping from his seat in the barn door and with
his open jack-knife picking up a little chip with the
point of the blade—"and yit—you wouldn't believe
it—but Marthy was the oldest o' three daughters,
and hed—I may say—hed more advantages o' mar-
ryin'—and yit, as I was jest goin' to say, she's the
very one 'at didn't marry.  Hed every advantage—
Marthy did.  W'y, we even hed her educated—her
mother was a-livin' then—and we was well enough
fixed to afford the educatin' of her, mother allus
contended—and we was—besides, it was Marthy's
notion, too, and you know how women is thataway
when they git their head set.  So we sent Marthy
down to Indianop'lus, and got her books and put
her in school there, and paid fer her keepin' and
ever'thing; and she jest—well, you may say, lived
there stiddy fer better'n four year.  O' course
she'd git back ever' once-an-a-while, but her visits
was allus, some-way-another, onsatisfactory-like,
'cause, you see, Marthy was allus my favorite, and
I'd allus laughed and told her 'at the other girls
could git marrid ef they wanted, but *she* was goin'

to be the 'nest-egg' of our family, and 'slong as I lived I wanted her at home with me. And she'd laugh and contend 'at she'd as li'f be an old maid as not, and never expected to marry, ner didn't want to.

"But she had me sceart onc't, though! Come out from the city one time, durin' the army, with a peart-lookin' young feller in blue clothes and gilt straps on his shoulders. Young lieutenant he was —name o' Morris. Was layin' in camp there in the city som'er's. I disremember which camp it was now adzackly—but anyway, it 'peared like he had plenty o' time to go and come, fer from that time on he kep' on a-comin'—ever' time Marthy 'ud come home, he'd come, too; and I got to noticin' 'at Marthy come home a good 'eal more'n she used to afore Morris first brought her. And blame' ef the thing didn't git to worryin' me! And onc't I spoke to mother about it, and told her ef I thought the feller wanted to marry Marthy I'd jest stop his comin' right then and there. But mother she sort o' smiled and said somepin' 'bout men a-never seein' through nothin'; and when I ast her what she meant, w'y, she ups and tells me 'at Morris didn't keer nothin' fer Marthy, ner Marthy fer Morris, and then went on to tell me that Morris was kind o' aidgin' up to'rds Annie—she was next to Marthy, you know, in p'int of years and experience, but ever'body allus said 'at Annie was the purtiest one o' the whole three of 'em. And so when mother told me 'at the signs p'inted to'rds Annie, w'y, of course, I hedn't no particular objections to that, 'cause Morris was of good fambly enough it turned out, and, in fact, was as stirrin' a young feller as ever I' want fer a son-in-law, and so I hed nothin' more to say—ner they wasn't no occasion to say nothin', 'cause right along about then I begin to notice 'at Marthy quit comin' home so much, and Morris kep' a-comin' more.

"Tel finally, one time he was out here all by hisself, 'long about dusk, come out here where I was feedin', and ast me, all at onct, and in a straightfor'ard way, ef he couldn't marry Annie; and, some-way-another, blame' ef it didn't make me happy as him when I told him yes! You see that thing proved, pine-blank, 'at he wasn't a-fishin' round fer Marthy. Well-sir, as luck would hev it, Marthy got home about a half-hour later, and I'll give you my word I was never so glad to see the girl in my life! It was foolish in me, I reckon, but when I see her drivin' up the lane— it was purt' nigh dark then, but I could see her through the open winder from where I was sittin' at the supper-table, and so I jest quietly excused myself, p'lite-like, as a feller will, you know, when they's comp'ny round, and slipped off and met her jest as she was about to git out to open the barn gate. 'Hold up, Marthy,' says I; 'set right where you air; I'll open the gate fer you, and I'll do anything else fer you in the world 'at you want me to!'

" 'W'y, what's pleased *you* so?' she says, laughin', as she druv through slow-like and a-ticklin' my nose with the cracker of the buggy-whip.—'What's pleased *you?*'

" 'Guess,' says I, jerkin' the gate to, and turnin' to lift her out.

" 'The new peanner's come?' says she, eager-like.

" 'Yer new peanner's come,' says I, 'but that's not it.'

" 'Strawberries for supper?' says she.

" 'Strawberries fer supper,' says I; 'but that ain't it.'

"Jest then Morris's hoss whinnied in the barn, and she glanced up quick and smilin' and says, 'Somebody come to see somebody?'

" 'You're a-gittin' warm,' says I.

" 'Somebody come to see *me?*' she says, anxious-like.

" 'No,' says I, 'and I'm glad of it—fer this one 'at's come wants to git married, and o' course I wouldn't harber in my house no young feller 'at was a-layin' round fer a chance to steal away the "Nest-egg," ' says I, laughin'.

"Marthy had riz up in the buggy by this time, but as I helt up my hands to her, she sort o' drawed back a minute, and says, all serious-like and kind o' whisperin':

" 'Is it *Annie?*'

"I nodded. 'Yes,' says I, 'and what's more, I've give my consent, and mother's give hern—the thing's all settled. Come, jump out and run in and be happy with the rest of us!' and I helt out my hands ag'in, but she didn't 'pear to take no heed. She

was kind o' pale, too, I thought, and swallered a
time er two like as ef she couldn't speak plain.

" 'Who is the man?' she ast.

" 'Who—who's the man,' I says, a-gittin' kind o'
out o' patience with the girl.—'W'y, you know who
it is, o' course.—It's Morris,' says I. 'Come, jump
down! Don't you see I'm waitin' fer ye?'

" 'Then take me,' she says; and blame-don! ef
the girl didn't keel right over in my arms as limber
as a rag! Clean fainted away! Honest! Jest the
excitement, I reckon, o' breakin' it to her so suddent-
like—'cause she liked Annie, I've sometimes
thought, better'n even she did her own mother.
Didn't go half so hard with her when her other
sister married. Yes-sir!" said the old man, by way
of sweeping conclusion, as he rose to his feet—
"Marthy's the on'y one of 'em 'at never married—
both the others is gone—Morris went all through
the army and got back safe and sound—'s livin' in
Idyho, and doin' fust-rate. Sends me a letter ever'
now and then. Got three little chunks o' grandchildren out there, and I never laid eyes on one
of 'em. You see, I'm a-gittin' to be quite a middle-
aged man—in fact, a very middle-aged man, you
might say. Sence mother died, which has be'n—
lem-me-see—mother's be'n dead som'er's in the
neighberhood o' ten years.—Sence mother died I've
be'n a-gittin' more and more o' *Marthy's* notion—
that is,—you couldn't ever hire *me* to marry nobody!
and them has allus be'n and still is the 'Nest-egg's'
views! Listen! That's her a-callin' fer us now.

You must sort o' overlook the freedom, but I told
Marthy you'd promised to take dinner with us to-
day, and it 'ud never do to disappoint her now.
Come on." And ah! it would have made the soul
of you either rapturously glad or madly envious to
see how meekly I consented.

I am always thinking that I never tasted coffee
till that day; I am always thinking of the crisp and
steaming rolls, ored over with the molten gold
that hinted of the clover-fields, and the bees that
had not yet permitted the honey of the bloom and
the white blood of the stalk to be divorced; I am
thinking that the young and tender pullet we happy
three discussed was a near and dear relative of the
gay patrician rooster that I first caught peering so
inquisitively in at the kitchen door; and I am always—always thinking of "The Nest-egg."

# "THE BOY FROM ZEENY"

HIS advent in our little country town was at once abrupt and novel. Why he came, when he came, or how he came, we boys never knew. My first remembrance of him is of his sudden appearance in the midst of a game of "Ant'ny-over," in which a dozen boys besides myself were most enthusiastically engaged. The scene of the exciting contest was the center of the main street of the town, the elevation over which we tossed the ball being the skeleton remains of a grand triumphal arch, left as a sort of cadaverous reminder of some recent political demonstration. Although I recall the boy's external appearance upon that occasion with some vagueness, I vividly remember that his trousers were much too large and long, and that his heavy, flapping coat was buttonless, and very badly worn and damaged at the sleeves and elbows. I remember, too, with even more distinctness, the hat he wore; it was a high, silk, bell-crowned hat— a man's hat and a veritable "plug"—not a new and shiny "plug," by any means, but still of dignity and gloss enough to furnish a noticeable contrast to the other appurtenances of its wearer's wardrobe. In fact, it was through this latter article of dress that

the general attention of the crowd came at last to
be drawn particularly to its unfortunate possessor,
who, evidently directed by an old-time instinct, had
mechanically thrust the inverted "castor" under a
falling ball, and the ball, being made of yarn
wrapped tightly over a green walnut, and dropping
from an uncommon height, had gone through the
hat like a round shot.

Naturally enough much merriment was occasioned by the singular mishap, and the victim of
the odd occurrence seemed himself inclined to join
in the boisterous laughter and make the most of
his ridiculous misfortune. He pulled the hat back
over his tousled head, and with the flapping crown
of it still clinging by one frayed hinge, he capered
through a grotesquely executed jig that made the
clamorous crowd about him howl again.

"Wo! what a hat!" cried Billy Kinzey, derisively,
and with a palpably rancorous twinge of envy in
his heart; for Billy was the bad boy of our town,
and would doubtless have enjoyed the strange boy's
sudden notoriety in thus being able to convert disaster into positive fun. "Wo! what a hat!" reiterated Billy, making a feint to knock it from the
boy's head as the still capering figure pirouetted
past him.

The boy's eye caught the motion, and he whirled
suddenly in a backward course and danced past his
reviler again, this time much nearer than before.
"Better try it," he said, in a low, half-laughing
tone that no one heard but Billy and myself. He

was out of range in an instant, still laughing as he went.

"Durn him!" said Billy, with stifling anger, clutching his fist and leaving one knuckle protruding in a very wicked-looking manner.—"Durn him! He better not sass me! He's afeard to come past here ag'in and say that! I'll knock his durn ole stovepipe in the middle o' nex' week!"

"You will, hey?" queried a revolving voice, as the boy twirled past again—this time so near that Billy felt his taunting breath blown in his face.

"Yes, I 'will, hey'!" said Billy, viciously; and with a side-sweeping, flat-handed lick that sounded like striking a rusty sheet of tin, the crownless "plug" went spinning into the gutter, while, as suddenly, the assaulted little stranger, with a peculiarly pallid smile about his lips and an electric glitter in his eye, adroitly flung his left hand forward, smiting his insulter such a blow in the region of the brow that the unguarded Billy went tumbling backward, his plucky assailant prancing wildly around his prostrate form.

"Oh! come and see me!" snarled the strange boy, in a contemptuous tone, cocking his fists up in a scientific manner, and dropping into a stoop-shouldered swagger that would have driven envy into the heart of a bullying hack-driver. "Git the bloke on his pins!" he sneered, turning to the crowd.— "S'pose I'm goin' to hit a man w'en he's down?"

But his antagonist needed no such assistance. Stung with his unlooked-for downfall, bleeding

from the first blow ever given him by mortal boy,
and goaded to absolute frenzy by the taunts of his
swaggering enemy, Billy sprang to his feet, and a
moment later had succeeded in closing with the
boy in a rough-and-tumble fight, in which his ad-
versary was at a disadvantage, being considerably
smaller, hampered, too, with his loose, unbuttoned
coat and baggy trousers. But, for all that, he did
some very efficient work in the way of a deft and
telling blow or two upon the nose of his overpower-
ing foe, who sat astride his wriggling body, but
wholly unable to get in a lick.

"Durn you!" said Billy, with his hand gripping
the boy's throat, "holler 'nough!"

"Holler nothin'!" gurgled the boy, with his eyes
fairly starting from his head.

"Oh, let him up, Billy," called a compassionate
voice from the excited crowd.

"Holler 'nough and I will," said Billy, in a tragic
whisper in the boy's ear. "Durn ye! holler 'Calf-
rope!'"

The boy only shook his head, trembled convul-
sively, let fall his eyelids, and lay limp and, to all
appearances, unconscious.

The startled Billy loosed his hold, rose half-way
to his feet, then fiercely pounced again at his rival.

But it was too late.—The ruse had succeeded,
and the boy was once more on his feet.

"You fight like a dog!" said the strange boy, in
a tone of infinite contempt—"and you *air* a dog!
Put up yer props like a man and come at me, and

I'll meller yer head till yer mother won't know you! Come on! I dare you!"

This time, as Billy started forward at the challenge, I regret to say that in his passion he snatched up from the street a broken buggy-spoke, before which warlike weapon the strange boy was forced warily to retreat. Step by step he gave way, and step by step his threatening foe advanced. I think, perhaps, part of the strange boy's purpose in thus retreating was to arm himself with one of the "ax-handles" that protruded from a churn standing in front of a grocery, toward which he slowly backed across the sidewalk. However that may be, it is evident he took no note of an open cellar-way that lay behind him, over the brink of which he deliberately backed, throwing up his hands as he disappeared.

We heard a heavy fall, but heard no cry. Some loungers in the grocery, attracted by the clamor of the throng without, came to the door inquiringly; one man, learning what had happened, peered down the stairway of the cellar, and called to ask the boy if he was hurt, which query was answered an instant later by the appearance of the boy himself, his face far whiter than his shirt, and his lips trembling, but his teeth clenched.

"Guess I broke my arm ag'in," he said, briefly, as the man leaned over and helped him up the steps, the boy sweeping his keen eyes searchingly over the faces of the crowd. "It's the *right* arm, though," he continued, glancing at the injured member dang-

ling helplessly at his side—*"this-'un's* all right yet!"
and as he spoke he jerked from the man's assistance, wheeled round, and an instant later, as a
buggy-spoke went hurtling through the air, he
slapped the bewildered face of Billy with his open
hand. "Dam' coward!" he said.

Then the man caught him, and drew him back,
and the crowd closed in between the combatants,
following, as the boy with the broken arm was
hurried down street to the doctor's office, where the
door was immediately closed on the rabble and all
the mystery within—not an utter mystery, either,
for three or four enterprising and sagacious boys
slipped off from the crowd that thronged in front,
and climbing by a roundabout way and over a high
board fence into the back yard, secretly posted themselves at the blinded window in the rear of the little
one-roomed office and breathlessly awaited news
from within.

"They got him laid out on the settee," whispered
a venturous boy who had leaned a board against
the window-sill and climbed into a position commanding the enviable advantage of a broken win-
dow-pane. "I kin see him through a hole in the
curtain. Keep still!

"They got his coat off, and his sleeve rolled up,"
whispered the boy, in continuation—"and the doctor's a-givin' him some medicine in a tumbler. Now
he's a-pullin' his arm. Gee-mun-nee! I kin hear the
bones crunch!"

"Hain't he a-cryin'?" queried a milk-faced boy, with very large blue eyes and fine white hair, and a grieved expression as he spoke.—"Hain't he a-cryin'?"

"Well, he hain't!" said the boy in the window, with unconscious admiration. "Listen!

"I heerd him thist tell 'em 'at it wasn't the first time his arm was broke. Now keep still!" and the boy in the window again bent his ear to the broken pane.

"He says both his arm's be'n broke," continued the boy in the window—"says this-'un 'at's broke now's be'n broke two times 'fore this time."

"Dog-gone! hain't he a funny feller!" said the milk-faced boy, with his big eyes lifted wistfully to the boy in the window.

"He says onc't his pap broke his arm w'en he was whippin' him," whispered the boy in the window.

"Bet his pa's a wicked man!" said the milk-faced boy, in a dreamy, speculative way—"s'pect he's a drunkard, er somepin'!"

"Keep still," said the boy at the window; "they're tryin' to git him to tell his pap's name and his, and he won't do it, 'cause he says his pap comes and steals him ever' time he finds out where he is."

The milk-faced boy drew a long, quavering breath and gazed suspiciously round the high board fence of the enclosure.

"He says his pap used to keep a liberty-stable in Zeeny—in Ohio som'er's,—but he daresn't stay

round *there* no more, 'cause he broke up there, and
had to skedaddle er they'd clean him out! He says
he hain't got no mother, ner no brothers, ner no
sisters, ner no nothin'—on'y," the boy in the window
added, with a very dry and painful swallow, "he
says he hain't got nothin' on'y thist the clothes on
his back!"

"Yes, and I bet," broke in the milk-faced boy,
abruptly, with his thin lips compressed, and his
big eyes fixed on space—"yes, and I bet he kin lick
Billy Kinzey, ef his arm *is* broke!"

At this juncture, some one inside coming to raise
the window, the boy at the broken pane leaped to
the ground, and, flocking at his heels, his frightened
comrades bobbed one by one over the horizon of the
high fence and were gone in an instant.

So it was the hero of this sketch came to be
known as "The Boy from Zeeny."

The Boy from Zeeny, though evidently predis-
posed to novel and disastrous happenings, for once,
at least, had come upon a streak of better fortune;
for the doctor, it appeared, had someway taken a
fancy to him, and had offered him an asylum at
his own home and hearth—the compensation stipu-
lated, and suggested by the boy himself, being a
conscientious and efficient service in the doctor's
stable. Even with his broken arm splinted and
bandaged and supported in a sling, The Boy from
Zeeny could daily be seen loping the doctor's spirited
horse up the back alley from the stable to the of-

fice, with the utter confidence and careless grace
of a Bedouin. When, at last, the injured arm was
wholly well again, the daring feats of horsemanship
of which the boy was capable were listened to with
incredulity by the "good" boys of the village school,
who never played "hooky" on long summer after-
noons, and, in consequence, never had a chance of
witnessing The Boy from Zeeny loping up to the
"swimmin'-hole," a mile from town, barebacked,
with nothing but a halter, and his face turned
toward the horse's tail. In fact The Boy from
Zeeny displayed such a versatility of accomplishments, and those, too, of a character but faintly
represented in the average boy of the country town,
that, for all the admiration their possessor evoked,
an equal envy was aroused in many a youthful
breast.

"The boys in this town's down on you!" said
a cross-eyed, freckled-faced boy, one day, to The
Boy from Zeeny.

The Boy from Zeeny was sitting in the alley
window of the hayloft of the doctor's stable, and
the cross-eyed boy had paused below, and, with his
noward-looking eyes upturned, stood waiting the effect of this intelligence.

"What do I care for the boys in this town?" said
The Boy from Zeeny.

"The boys in this town," repeated the cross-eyed
boy, with a slow, prophetic flourish of his head—
"the boys in this town says 'cause you come from

Zeeny and blacked Billy Kinzey's eye, 'at you think
you're goin' to run things round here! And you'll
find out you ain't the bosst o' this town!" and the
cross-eyed boy shook his head again with dire fore-
boding.

"Looky here, Cocky!" said The Boy from Zeeny,
trying to focus a direct gaze on the boy's delusive
eyes, "w'y don't you talk straight out from the
shoulder? I reckon 'the boys in this town,' as you
call 'em, didn't send *you* round here to tell me what
*they* was goin' to do! But ef you want to take it
up fer 'em, and got any sand to back you, jest say it,
and I'll come down there and knock them durn
twisted eyes o' yourn straight ag'in!"

"Yes, you will!" muttered the cross-eyed boy,
with dubious articulation, glancing uneasily up the
alley.

"What?" growled The Boy from Zeeny, thrusting
one dangling leg farther out the window, supporting
his weight by the palms of his hands, and poised as
though about to spring—"what 'id you say?"

"Didn't say nothin'," said the cross-eyed boy,
feebly; and then, as a sudden and most bewildering smile lighted up his defective eyes, he exclaimed:
"Oh, I tell you what le's do! Le's me and you
git up a show in your stable, and don't let none o'
the other boys be in it! I kin turn a handspring
like you, and purt' nigh walk on my hands; and
you kin p'form on the slack-rope—and spraddle
out like the 'inja-rubber man'—and hold a pitch-

fork on yer chin—and stand up on a horse 'ithout
a-holdin'—and—and—Oh! ever'thing!" And as the
cross-eyed boy breathlessly concluded this list of
strong attractions, he had The Boy from Zeeny so
thoroughly inoculated with the enterprise that he
warmly closed with the proposition, and the prepa-
rations and the practise for the show were at once
inaugurated.

Three hours later, an extremely cross-eyed boy,
with the freckles of his face thrown into vivid relief
by an intense pallor, rushed pantingly into the
doctor's office with the fateful intelligence that The
Boy from Zeeny had "fell and broke his arm ag'in."
And this time, as it seemed, the hapless boy had
surpassed the seriousness of all former fractures,
this last being of a compound nature, and very
painful in the setting, and tedious in recovery; the
recovery, too, being anything but perfect, since it
left the movement of the elbow somewhat restricted,
and threw the little fellow's arm into an unnatural
position, with the palm of the hand turned forward
as he walked. But for all that, the use of it was,
to all appearances, little impaired.

Doubtless it was through such interludes from
rough service as these accidents afforded that The
Boy from Zeeny had acquired the meager education
he possessed. The doctor's wife, who had from the
first been kind to him, grew to like him very much.
Through her gentle and considerate interest he was
stimulated to study by the occasional present of a

simple volume. Oftentimes the good woman would devote an hour to his instruction in the mysteries of the book's orthography and rhetoric.

Nor was The Boy from Zeeny a dull pupil, nor was he an ungrateful one. He was quick to learn, and never prouder than when a mastered lesson gained for him the approbation of his patient instructor.

The history of The Boy from Zeeny, such as had been gathered by the doctor and his wife, was corroborative in outline with the brief hint of it communicated to the curious listeners at the rear window of the doctor's office on the memorable day of the boy's first appearance in the town. He was without family, save a harsh, unfeeling father, who, from every evidence, must have neglected and abused the child most shamefully, the circumstantial proof of this fact being evidenced in the boy's frank acknowledgment that he had repeatedly "run away" from him, and his still firm resolve to keep his name a secret, lest he might thereby be traced to his present security and fall once more into the hands of his unnatural parent.

Certain it was that the feelings of all who knew the lad's story showed hearty sympathy with him, and when one morning it was rumored that The Boy from Zeeny had mysteriously disappeared, and the rumor rapidly developed into an unquestionable fact, there was a universal sense of regret in the little town, which in turn resolved itself into positive indignation when it was learned from the doc-

tor that an explanation, printed in red keel on the
back of a fragment of circus-poster, had been
found folded and tucked away in the buckle-strap
of his horse's bridle.   The somewhat remarkable
communication, in sprawling capitals, ran thus:

"Paps got me agin.   I haf to go.   Dam him.   Doc tel
her to keep my boocks.   Good by.   I fed ole Charly.   I
fed him otes and ha an corn.   He wont need no more fer
a weak.   An brand to.   Doc tel her good by."

It was a curious bit of composition—uncouth, as-
suredly, and marred, maybe, with an unpardonable
profanity—but it served.   In the silence and gloom
of the old stable, the doctor's fingers trembled as
he read, and the good wife's eyes, peering anxiously
above his heaving shoulder, filled and overflowed
with tears.

I wish that it were in the veracious sequence of
this simple history to give this wayward boy back
to the hearts that loved him, and that still in memory
enshrine him with affectionate regard; but the hapless lad—the little ragged twelve-year-old that
wandered out of nowhere into town, and wandered
into nowhere out again—never returned.   Yet we
who knew him in those old days—we who were
children with him, and, in spite of boyish jealousy
and petty bickerings, admired the gallant spirit of
the lad—are continually meeting with reminders of
him; the last instance of which, in my own experience, I can not refrain from offering here:

For years I have been a wanderer from the dear

old town of my nativity, but through all my wan-
derings a gracious fate has always kept me somewhere in its pleasant neighborhood, and, in consequence, I often pay brief visits to the scenes of my
long-vanished boyhood. It was during such a visit,
but a few short years ago, that remembrances of
my lost youth were most forcibly recalled by the
progress of the county fair, which institution I
was permitted to attend through the kindness of an
old chum who drove me over in his buggy.

Although it was not the day for racing, we found
the track surrounded by a dense crowd of clamorous and applauding people.

"What does it mean?" I asked my friend, as he
guided his horse in and out among the trees toward
the edge of the enclosure.

"It's Professor Andrus, I suspect," he answered,
rising in the buggy as he spoke, and peering eagerly
above the heads of the surging multitude.

"And who's Professor Andrus?" I asked, striking
a match against the tire of the now stationary buggy-
wheel, and lighting the stump of my cigar.

"Why, haven't you heard of the famous Professor?" he answered, laughingly—immediately adding
in a serious tone: "Professor Andrus is the famous
'horse-tamer' who has been driving the country absolutely wild here for two or three days. Stand up
here where you can see!" he went on, excitedly.

"Yonder he comes! Isn't that splendid?"

And it was.

Across the sea of heads, and facing toward us

down the track, I caught sight of a glossy span of horses that in their perfect beauty of symmetry, high heads and tossing manes looked as though they were just prancing out of some Arabian dream. The animals seemed nude of rein or harness, save only a jeweled strap that crossed the breast of each, together with a slender trace at either side connecting with a jaunty little phaeton whose glittering wheels slivered the sunshine into splinters as they spun. Upon the narrow seat of the airy vehicle sat the driver. No lines were wound about his hands —no shout or lash to goad the horses to their telling speed. They were simply directed and controlled by the graceful motions of a long and slender whip which waved slowly to and fro above their heads. The great crowd cheered the master as he came. He arose deliberately, took off his hat, and bowed. The applause was deafening. Still standing, he whizzed past us and was gone. But something in the manner of the handsome fellow struck me with a strange sense of familiarity. Was it the utter disregard of fear that I saw on his face? Was it the keenness of the eye and the perfect self-possession of the man? Or was it—was it the peculiar way in which the right arm had dropped to his side after his salute to us while curving past us, and did I fancy, for that reason, that the palm of his hand turned forward as he stood?

"Clear the track, there!" came a far voice across the ring.—"Don't cross there, in God's name! Drive back!"

The warning evidently came too late. There was an instant's breathless silence, then a far-away, pent-sounding clash, then utter havoc in the crowd: The ropes about the ring were broken over, and a tumultuous tide of people poured across the ring, myself borne on the very foremost wave.

"Jest the buggy smashed, that's all!" cried a voice. "The hosses hain't hurt—ner the man."

The man referred to was the Professor. I caught a glimpse of him as he rose from the grassy bank where he had been flung. He was very pale, but calm. An uncouth man brought him his silk hat from where it had rolled in the dust.

"Wish you'd just take this handkerchief and brush it off," said the Professor; "I guess I've broke my arm."

It was The Boy from Zeeny.

# WHERE IS MARY ALICE SMITH?

"WHERE—is—Mary—Alice—Smith? Oh—
she—has—gone—home!" It was the thin
mysterious voice of little Mary Alice Smith herself
that so often queried and responded as above—
every word accented with a sweet and eery intonation, and a very gaiety of solemn earnestness that
baffled the cunning skill of all childish imitators. A
slender wisp of a girl she was, not more than ten
years in appearance, though her age had been
given to us as fourteen. The spindle ankles that
she so airily flourished from the sparse concealment
of a worn and shadowy calico skirt seemed scarce
a fraction more in girth than the slim blue-veined
wrists she tossed among the loose and ragged tresses
of her yellow hair, as she danced around the room.
She was, from the first, an object of curious and
most refreshing interest to our family—to us children in particular—an interest, though years and
years have interposed to shroud it in the dull dust
of forgetfulness, that still remains vivid and bright
and beautiful. Whether an orphan child only, or
with a father that could thus lightly send her adrift,
I do not know now, nor do I care to ask, but I do
recall distinctly that on a raw bleak day in early
winter she was brought to us, from a wild country

settlement, by a reputed uncle—a gaunt round-shouldered man, with deep eyes and sallow cheeks and weedy-looking beard, as we curiously watched him from the front window stolidly swinging this little, blue-lipped, red-nosed waif over the muddy wagon-wheel to father's arms, like so much country produce. And even as the man resumed his seat upon the thick board laid across the wagon, and sat chewing a straw, with spasmodic noddings of the head, as some brief further conference detained him, I remember mother quickly lifting my sister up from where we stood, folding and holding the little form in unconscious counterpart of father and the little girl without. And how we gathered round her when father brought her in, and mother fixed a cozy chair for her close to the blazing fire, and untied the little summer hat, with its hectic trimmings, together with the dismal green veil that had been bound beneath it round the little tingling ears. The hollow, pale blue eyes of the child followed every motion with an alertness that suggested a somewhat suspicious mind.

"Dave gimme that!" she said, her eyes proudly following the hat as mother laid it on the pillow of the bed. "Mustn't git it mussed up, sir! er you'll have Dave in yer wool!" she continued warningly, as our childish interest drew us to a nearer view of the gaudy article in question.

Half awed, we shrank back to our first wonderment, one of us, however, with the bravery to ask: "Who's Dave?"

"Who's Dave?" reiterated the little voice half scornfully.—"W'y, Dave's a great big boy! Dave works on Barnes's place. And he kin purt' nigh make a full hand, too. Dave's purt' nigh tall as your pap! He's purt' nigh growed up—Dave is! And—David—Mason—Jeffries," she continued, jauntily teetering her head from left to right, and for the first time introducing that peculiar deliberation of accent and undulating utterance that we afterward found to be her quaintest and most charming characteristic—"and—David—Mason—Jeffries—he—likes—Mary—Alice—Smith!" And then she broke abruptly into the merriest laughter, and clapped her little palms together till they fairly glowed.

"And who's Mary Alice Smith?" clamored a chorus of merry voices.

The elfish figure straightened haughtily in the chair. Folding the slender arms tightly across her breast, and tilting her wan face back with an imperious air, she exclaimed sententiously, "W'y, Mary Alice Smith is me—that's who Mary Alice Smith is!"

It was not long, however, before her usual bright and infectious humor was restored, and we were soon piloting the little stranger here and there about the house, and laughing at the thousand funny little things she said and did. The winding stairway in the hall quite dazed her with delight. Up and down she went a hundred times, it seemed. And she would talk and whisper to herself, and oftentimes

would stop and nestle down and rest her pleased
face close against the steps and pat one softly with
her slender hand, peering curiously down at us
with half-averted eyes. And she counted them and
named them, every one, as she went up and down.

"I'm mighty glad I'm come to live in this-here
house," she said.

We asked her why.

"Oh, 'cause," she said, starting up the stairs again
by an entirely novel and original method of her
own— " 'cause Uncle Tomps ner Aunt 'Lizabeth
don't live here; and when they ever come here to
git their dinners, like they will ef you don't watch
out, w'y, then I kin slip out here on these-here
stairs and play like I was climbin' up to the Good
World where my mother is—that's why!"

Then we hushed our laughter, and asked her
where her home was, and what it was like, and
why she didn't like her Uncle Tomps and Aunt
'Lizabeth, and if she wouldn't want to visit them
sometimes.

"Oh, yes," she artlessly answered in reply to the
concluding query; "I'll want to go back there lots
o' times; but not to see them! I'll—only—go—back
—there—to—see"—and here she was holding up
the little flared-out fingers of her left hand, and
with the index finger of the right touching their
pink tips in ordered notation with the accent of
every gleeful word—"I'll—only—go—back—there
—to—see—David— Mason—Jeffries —'cause—he's
—the—boy—fer—me!" And then she clapped her

hands again and laughed in that half-hysterical, half-
musical way of hers till we all joined in and made
the echoes of the old hall ring again. "And then,"
she went on, suddenly throwing out an imperative
gesture of silence—"and then, after I've been in this-
here house a long, long time, and you all gits so's
you like me awful—awful—awful well, then some
day you'll go in that room there—and that room
there—and in the kitchen—and out on the porch—
and down the cellar—and out in the smoke-house—
and the wood-house—and the loft—and all around
—oh, ever' place—and in here—and up the stairs—
and all them rooms up there—and you'll look behind
all the doors—and in all the cubboards—and under
all the beds—and then you'll look sorry-like, and
holler out, kind o' skeert, and you'll say: 'Where—
is—Mary—Alice—Smith?' And then you'll wait
and listen and hold yer breath; and then somepin' 'll
holler back, away fur off, and say: 'Oh—she—has—
gone—home!' And then ever'thing'll be all still
ag'in, and you'll be afraid to holler any more—and
you dursn't play—and you can't laugh, and yer
throat'll thist hurt and hurt, like you been a-eatin'
too much calamus-root er somepin'!" And as the
little gipsy concluded her weird prophecy, with a
final flourish of her big pale eyes, we glanced fur-
tively at one another's awestruck faces, with a
superstitious dread of a vague indefinite disaster
most certainly awaiting us around some shadowy
corner of the future. Through all this speech she
had been slowly and silently groping up the wind-

ing steps, her voice growing fainter and fainter, and the littly pixy form fading, and wholly vanishing at last around the spiral banister of the upper landing. Then down to us from that alien recess came the voice alone, touched with a tone as of wild entreaty and despair: "Where—is—Mary—Alice—Smith?" And then a long breathless pause, in which our wide-eyed group below huddled still closer, pale and mute. Then—far off and faint and quavering with a tenderness of pathos that dews the eyes of memory even now—came, like a belated echo, the voice all desolate: "Oh—she—has—gone—home!"

What a queer girl she was, and what a fascinating influence she unconsciously exerted over us! We never tired of her presence; but she, deprived of ours by the many household tasks that she herself assumed, so rigidly maintained and deftly executed, seemed always just as happy when alone as when in our boisterous, fun-loving company. Such resources had Mary Alice Smith—such a wonderful inventive fancy! She could talk to herself—a favorite amusement, I might almost say a popular amusement, of hers, since these monologues at times would involve numberless characters, chipping in from manifold quarters of a wholesale discussion, and querying and exaggerating, agreeing and controverting, till the dishes she was washing would clash and clang excitedly in the general badinage. Loaded with a pyramid of glistening cups and saucers, she would improvise a gallant line of march

from the kitchen table to the pantry, heading an
imaginary procession, and whistling a fife-tune that
would stir your blood. Then she would trippingly
return, rippling her rosy fingers up and down the
keys of an imaginary portable piano, or stammering
flat-soled across the floor, chuffing and tooting like
a locomotive. And she would gravely propound to
herself the most intricate riddles—ponder thoughtfully and in silence over them—hazard the most
ridiculous answers, and laugh derisively at her
own affected ignorance. She would guess again
and again, and assume the most gleeful surprise
upon at last giving the proper answer, and then
she would laugh jubilantly, and mockingly scout
herself with having given out "a fool-riddle" that
she could guess "with both eyes shut."

"Talk about riddles," she said abruptly to us,
one evening after supper, as we lingered watching
her clearing away the table—"talk about riddles,
it—takes— David—Mason—Jeffries—to—tell—riddles! Bet you don't know

> 'Riddle-cum, riddle-cum right!
> Where was I last Saturd'y night?
> The winds blow—the boughs did shake—
> I saw the hole a fox did make!' "

Again we felt that indefinable thrill never separate from the strange utterance, suggestive always
of some dark mystery, and fascinating and holding
the childish fancy in complete control.

"Bet you don't know this-'un neether:

'A holler-hearted father,
    And a hump-back mother—
Three black orphants
    All born together!' "

We were dumb.

"You can't guess nothin'!" she said half pityingly.
"W'y, them's easy as fallin' off a chunk! First-un's
a man named Fox, and he kilt his wife and chopped
her head off, and they was a man named Wright
lived in that neighberhood—and he was a-goin'
home—and it was Saturd'y night—and he was
a-comin' through the big woods—and they was a
storm—and Wright he clumb a tree to git out of
the rain, and while he was up there here come
along a man with a dead woman—and a pickax,
and a spade. And he drug the dead woman under
the same tree where Mr. Wright was—so ever'
time it 'ud lightnin', w'y, Wright he could look down
and see him a-diggin' a grave there to bury the
woman in. So Wright, he kep' still tel he got her
buried all right, you know, and went back home;
and then he clumb down and lit out fer town, and
waked up the constabul—and he got a supeeny and
went out to Fox's place, and had him jerked up
'fore the gran' jury. Then, when Fox was in
court and wanted to know where their proof was
that he kilt his wife, w'y, Wright he jumps up and
says that riddle to the judge and all the neighbers
that was there. And so when they got it all studied
out— w'y, they tuk old Fox out and hung him under
the same tree where he buried Mrs. Fox under. And

that's all o' that'n; and the other'n—I promised—
David—Mason—Jeffries—I    wouldn't—never—tell
—no—livin'—soul —'less—he—gimme—leef,—er—
they—guessed— it —out—their—own—se'f!'' And
as she gave this rather ambiguous explanation of
the first riddle, with the mysterious comment on the
latter in conclusion, she shook her elfin tresses back
over her shoulders with a cunning toss of her head
and a glimmering twinkle of her pale bright eyes
that somewhat reminded us of the fairy godmother
in *Cinderella.*

And Mary Alice Smith was right, too, in her early
prognostications regarding the visits of her Uncle
Tomps and Aunt 'Lizabeth.  Many times through
the winter they "jest dropped in," as Aunt 'Lizabeth
always expressed it, "to see how we was a-gittin' on
with Mary Alice."   And once, "in court week,"
during a prolonged trial in which Uncle Tomps and
Aunt 'Lizabeth rather prominently figured, they
"jest dropped in" on us and settled down and dwelt
with us for the longest five days and nights we
children had ever in our lives experienced.  Nor
was our long term of restraint from childish sports
relieved wholly by their absence, since Aunt 'Lizabeth had taken Mary Alice back with them, saying
that "a good long visit to her dear old home—pore
as it was—would do the child good."

And then it was that we went about the house in
moody silence, the question, "Where—is—Mary—
Alice—Smith?" forever yearning at our lips for utterance, and the still belated echo in the old hall

overhead forever answering, "Oh—she—has—gone
—home!"

It was early spring when she returned. And
we were looking for her coming, and knew a week
beforehand the very day she would arrive—for had
not Aunt 'Lizabeth sent special word by Uncle
Tomps, who "had come to town to do his millin', and
git the latest war news, not to fail to jest drop in
and tell us that they was layin' off to send Mary
Alice in next Saturd'y."

Our little town, like every other village and metropolis throughout the country at that time, was,
to the children at least, a scene of continuous holiday and carnival. The nation's heart was palpitating with the feverish pulse of war, and already
the still half-frozen clods of the common highway
were beaten into frosty dust by the  tread of mar-
shaled men; and the shrill shriek of the fife, and
the hoarse boom and jar and rattling patter of the
drums stirred every breast with something of that
rapturous insanity of which true patriots and heroes
can alone be made.

But on the day—when Mary Alice Smith was
to return—what was all the gallant tumult of the
town to us? I remember how we ran far up
the street to welcome her—for afar off we had
recognized her elfish face and eager eyes peering expectantly from behind the broad shoulders of a
handsome fellow mounted on a great high-stepping
horse that neighed and pranced excitedly as we ran
scurrying toward them.

"Whoo-ee!" she cried in perfect ecstasy, as we paused in breathless admiration. "Clear—the—track — there,—old—folks — young—folks!—fer—Mary—Alice—Smith—and—David — Mason—Jeffries—is—come—to—town!"

O what a day that was! And how vain indeed would be the attempt to detail here a tithe of its glory, or our happiness in having back with us our dear little girl, and her hysterical delight in seeing us so warmly welcome to the full love of our childish hearts the great, strong, round-faced, simple-natured "David—Mason—Jeffries"! Long and long ago we had learned to love him as we loved the peasant hero of some fairy tale of Christian Andersen's; but now that he was with us in most wholesome and robust verity, our very souls seemed scampering from our bodies to run to him and be caught up and tossed and swung and dandled in his gentle giant arms.

All that long delicious morning we were with him. In his tender charge we were permitted to go down among the tumult and the music of the streets, his round good-humored face and big blue eyes lit with a luster like our own. And happy little Mary Alice Smith—how proud she was of him! And how closely and how tenderly, through all that golden morning, did the strong brown hand clasp hers! A hundred times at least, as we promenaded thus, she swung her head back jauntily to whisper to us in that old mysterious way of hers that "David—Mason—Jeffries—and—Mary—Alice

—Smith — knew — something—that—we—couldn't
—guess!" But when he had returned us home, and
after dinner had started down the street alone, with
little Mary Alice clapping her hands after him
above the gate and laughing in a strange new voice,
and with the backs of her little fluttering hands
vainly striving to blot out the big tear-drops that
gathered in her eyes, we vaguely guessed the secret
she and David kept. That night at supper-time we
knew it fully. He had enlisted.

. . . . . . .

Among the list of "killed" at Rich Mountain, Virginia, occurred the name of "Jeffries, David M."
We kept it from her as long as we could. At last
she knew.

. . . . . .

"It don't seem like no year ago to me!" Over
and over she had said these words. The face was
very pale and thin, and the eyes so bright—so
bright! The kindly hand that smoothed away the
little sufferer's hair trembled and dropped tenderly
again upon the folded ones beneath the snowy
spread.

"Git me out the picture again!"

The trembling hand lifted once more and searched
beneath the pillow.

She drew the thin hands up, and, smiling, pressed
the pictured face against her lips. "David—Mason
—Jeffries," she said—"le's—me—and—you—go—
play—out—on—the—stairs!"

And ever in the empty home a voice goes moaning on and on, and "Where is Mary Alice?" it cries, and "Where— is — Mary — Alice — Smith?" And the still belated echo, through the high depths of the old hall overhead, answers quaveringly back, "Oh—she—has—gone—home!" But her voice— it is silent evermore!

"Oh, where is Mary Alice Smith?" She taught us how to call her thus—and now she will not answer us! Have we no voice to reach her with? How sweet and pure and glad they were in those old days, as we recall the accents ringing through the hall—the same we vainly cry to her. Her fancies were so quaint—her ways so full of prankish mysteries! We laughed then; now, upon our knees, we wring our lifted hands and gaze, through streaming tears, high up the stairs she used to climb in childish glee, to call and answer eerily. And now, no answer anywhere!

How deft the little finger-tips in every task! The hands, how smooth and delicate to lull and soothe! And the strange music of her lips! The very crudeness of their speech made chaster yet the childish thought her guileless utterance had caught from spirit-depths beyond our reach. And so her homely name grew fair and sweet and beautiful to hear, blent with the echoes pealing clear and vibrant up the winding stair: "Where—where is Mary Alice Smith?" She taught us how to call her thus —but oh, she will not answer us! We have no voice to reach her with.

# THE OLD MAN

*[Response made to the sentiment, "The Old Man,"
at a dinner of the Indianapolis
Literary Club.]*

"You are old, Father William," the young man said,
"And your hair has become very white;
And yet you incessantly stand on your head—
Do you think, at your age, it is right?"

THE OLD MAN never grows so old as to become either stale, juiceless, or unpalatable. The older he grows, the mellower and riper he becomes. His eyes may fail him, his step falter, and his bigmouthed shoes—"a world too wide for his shrunk shank"—may cluck and shuffle as he walks; his rheumatics may make great knuckles of his knees; the rusty hinges of his vertebræ may refuse cunningly to articulate, but all the same the "backbone" of the old man has been time-seasoned, tried, and tested, and no deerskin vest was ever buttoned round a tougher! Look at the eccentric kinks and curvings of it—its abrupt depression at the base, and its rounded bulging at the shoulders; but don't laugh with the smart young man who airily observes how full-chested the old man would be if his head were only turned around, and don't kill the young man, either, until you take him out some place and tell him that the old man got himself warped up in that shape along about the time when everybody had to hump himself. Try to bring before the young man's defective mental vision a dissolving view of a "good old-fashioned barn-raisin' "—and the old man doing all the "raisin' " himself, and "grubbin'," and "burnin' " logs and "underbrush," and "dreenin' " at the same time, and trying to coax something besides calamus to grow in the spongy little tract of swamp-land that he could stand in the middle of and "wobble" and shake the whole farm. Or, if you can't recall the many salient features of the minor disadvantages under which the old man used to labor, your pliant limbs may soon overtake him, and he will smilingly tell you of trials and privations of the early days, until your anxiety about the young man just naturally stagnates, and dries up, and evaporates, and blows away.

In this little side-show of existence the old man is always worth the full price of admission. He is not only the greatest living curiosity on exhibition, but the object of the most genial solicitude and interest to the serious observer. It is even good to look upon his vast fund of afflictions, finding prominent above them all that wholesome patience that surpasseth understanding; to dwell compassionately upon his prodigality of aches and ailments, and yet, by his pride in their wholesale possession, and his thorough resignation to the inevitable, continually to

be rebuked, and in part made envious of the old
man's right-of-title situation. Nature, after all, is
kinder than unkind to him, and always has a compensation and a soothing balm for every blow that
age may deal him. And in the fading embers of
the old man's eyes there are, at times, swift flashes
and rekindlings of the smiles of youth, and the old
artlessness about the wrinkled face that dwelt there
when his cheeks were like the pippins, and his

> "Red lips, redder still,
> Kissed by strawberries on the hill."

And thus it is the children are intuitively drawn
toward him, and young, pure-faced mothers are
forever hovering about him, with just such humor-
ings and kindly ministrations as they bestow on
the little emperor of the household realm, strapped
in his high chair at the dinner-table, crying "Amen"
in the midst of "grace," and ignoring the "substantials" of the groaning board, and at once insisting
upon a square deal of the more "temporal blessings"
of jelly, cake, and pie. And the old man has justly
earned every distinction he enjoys. Therefore let
him make your hearthstone all the brighter with the
ruddy coal he drags up from it with his pipe, as he
comfortably settles himself where, with reminiscent
eyes, he may watch the curling smoke of his tobacco as it indolently floats, and drifts and drifts,
and dips at last, and vanishes up the grateful flue.
At such times, when a five-year-old, what a haven

every boy has found between the old grandfather's knees! Look back in fancy at the faces blending there—the old man's and the boy's—and, with the nimbus of the smoke-wreaths round the brows, the gilding of the firelight on cheek and chin, and the rapt and far-off gazings of the eyes of both, why, but for the silver tinsel of the beard of one and the dusky elf-locks of the other, the faces seem almost like twins.

With such a view of age, one feels like whipping up the lazy years and getting old at once. In heart and soul the old man is not old—and never will be. He is paradoxically old, and that is all. So it is that he grows younger with increasing years, until old age at worst is always at a level par with youth. Who ever saw a man so old as not secretly and most heartily to wish the veteran years upon years of greater age? And at what great age did ever any old man pass away and leave behind no sudden shock, and no selfish hearts still to yearn after him and grieve on unconsoled? Why, even in the slow declining years of old Methuselah—the banner old man of the universe,—so old that history grew absolutely tired waiting for him to go off some place and die—even Methuselah's taking off must have seemed abrupt to his immediate friends, and a blow to the general public that doubtless plunged it into the profoundest gloom. For nine hundred and sixty-nine years this durable old man had "smelt the rose above the mold," and doubtless had a thousand times been told by congratulating friends that he didn't

look a day older than nine hundred and sixty-eight;
and necessarily the habit of living, with him, was
hard to overcome.

In his later years what an oracle he must
have been, and with what reverence his friends
must have looked upon the "little, glassy-headed,
hairless man," and hung upon his every utterance! And with what unerring gift of prophecy
could he foretell the long and husky droughts
of summer — the gracious rains, at last, — the
milk-sick breeding autumn and the blighting
winter, simply by the way his bones felt after a century's casual attack of inflammatory rheumatism!
And, having annually frosted his feet for some
odd centuries—boy and man—we can fancy with
what quiet delight he was wont to practise his prog-
nosticating facilities on "the boys," forecasting the
coming of the then fledgling cyclone and the gosling
blizzard, and doubtless even telling the day of the
month by the way his heels itched. And with what
wonderment and awe must old chronic maladies
have regarded him—tackling him singly or in solid
phalanx, only to drop back pantingly, at last, and
slink away dumfounded and abashed! And with
what brazen pride the final conquering disease must
have exulted over its shameless victory! But this is
pathos here, and not a place for ruthless speculation: a place for asterisks—not words. Peace!
peace! The man is dead! "The fever called living
is over at last." The patient slumbers. He takes

his rest. He sleeps. Come away! He is the oldest
dead man in the cemetery.

Whether the hardy, stall-fed old man of the country, or the opulent and well-groomed old man of
the metropolis, he is one in our esteem and the still
warmer affections of the children. The old man
from the country—you are always glad to see him
and hear him talk. There is a breeziness of the
woods and hills and a spice of the bottom-lands and
thickets in everything he says, and dashes of shadow
and sunshine over the waving wheat are in all the
varying expressions of his swarthy face. The grip
of his hand is a thing to bet on, and the undue
loudness of his voice in greeting you is even lulling
and melodious, since unconsciously it argues for the
frankness of a nature that has nothing to conceal.
Very probably you are forced to smile, meeting the
old man in town, where he never seems at ease,
and invariably apologizes in some way for his presence, saying, perhaps, by way of explanation: "Yes-
sir, here I am, in spite o' myself. Come in day
afore yisterd'y. Boys was thrashin' on the place,
and the beltin' kept a-troublin' and delayin' of 'em
—and I was potterin' round in the way anyhow,
tel finally they sent me off to town to git some
whang-luther and ribbets, and while I was in,
I thought—I thought I'd jest run over and see the
Jedge about that Henry County matter; and as I
was knockin' round the court-house, first thing I
knowed I'll be switched to death ef they didn't pop

me on the jury! And here I am, eatin' my head off up here at the tavern. Reckon, tho', the county'll stand good for my expenses. Ef hit cain't, I kin!" And, with the heartiest sort of a laugh, the old man jogs along, leaving you to smile till bedtime over the happiness he has unconsciously contributed.

Another instance of the old man's humor under trying circumstances was developed but a few days ago. This old man was a German citizen of an inundated town in the Ohio valley. There was much of the pathetic in his experience, but the bravery with which he bore his misfortunes was admirable. A year ago his little home was first invaded by the flood, and himself and wife, and his son's family, were driven from it to the hills for safety—but the old man's telling of the story can not be improved upon. It ran like this: "Last year, ven I svwim out fon dot leedle home off mine, mit my vife, unt my son, his vife unt leedle girls, I dink dot's der last time goot-by to dose proberty! But afder der vater is gone down, unt dry oop unt eberding, dere vas yet der house dere. Unt my friends dey sait, 'Dot's all you got yet.—Vell, feex oop der house—dot's someding! feex oop der house, unt you vood still hatt yet a home!' Vell, all summer I go to work, unt spent me eberding unt feex der proberty. Den I got yet a morgage on der house! Dees time here der vater come again—till I vish it vas last year vonce! Unt now all I safe is my vife, unt my son his vife, unt my leedle grandchilderns! Else everding is gone! All—everyding!—Der house gone—

unt—unt—der morgage gone, too!" And then the
old Teutonic face "melted all over in sunshiny
smiles," and, turning, he bent and lifted a sleepy
little girl from a pile of dirty bundles in the depot
waiting-room and went pacing up and down the
muddy floor, saying things in German to the child.
I thought the whole thing rather beautiful. That's
the kind of an old man who, saying good-by to
his son, would lean and kiss the young man's hand,
as in the Dutch regions of Pennsylvania, two or
three weeks ago, I saw an old man do.

Mark Lemon must have known intimately and
loved the genteel old man of the city when the once
famous domestic drama of "Grandfather White-
head" was conceived. In the play the old man—a
once prosperous merchant—finds a happy home in
the household of his son-in-law.   And here it is
that the gentle author has drawn at once the poem,
the picture, and the living proof of the old Words-
worthian axiom, "The child is father to the man."
The old man, in his simple way, and in his great
love for his wilful little grandchild, is being continually distracted from the grave sermons and
moral lessons he would read the boy.   As, for instance, aggrievedly attacking the little fellow's
neglect of his books and his inordinate tendency
toward idleness and play—the culprit, in the meantime, down on the floor clumsily winding his top—
the old man runs on something in this wise:

"Play! play! play! Always play and no work, no
study, no lessons. And here you are, the only child

of the most indulgent parents in the world—parents
that, proud as they are of you, would be ten times
prouder only to see you at your book, storing
your mind with useful knowledge, instead of, day
in, day out, frittering away your time over your
toys and your tops and marbles. And even when
your old grandfather tries to advise you and wants
to help you, and is always ready and eager to assist
you, and all—why, what's it all amount to? Coax
and beg and tease and plead with you, and yet—and
yet"— (Mechanically kneeling as he speaks)—
"Now that's not the way to wind your top! How
many more times will I have to show you!" And
an instant later the old man's admonitions are entirely forgotten, and his artless nature—dull now to
everything but the childish glee in which he shares—
is all the sweeter and more lovable for its simplicity.

And so it is, Old Man, that you are always touching the very tenderest places in our hearts—unconsciously appealing to our warmest sympathies,
and taking to yourself our purest love. We look
upon your drooping figure, and we mark your tot-
tering step and trembling hand, yet a reliant something in your face forbids compassion, and a something in your eye will not permit us to look sorrowfully on you. And, however we may smile at your
quaint ways and old-school oddities of manner and
of speech, our merriment is ever tempered with the
gentlest reverence.

# THE GILDED ROLL

NOSING around in an old box—packed away, and lost to memory for years—an hour ago I found a musty package of gilt paper, or rather, a roll it was, with the green-tarnished gold of the old sheet for the outer wrapper. I picked it up mechanically to toss it into some obscure corner, when, carelessly lifting it by one end, a child's tin whistle dropped therefrom and fell tinkling on the attic floor. It lies before me on my writing table now—and so, too, does the roll entire, though now a roll no longer,—for my eager fingers have un-rolled the gilded covering, and all its precious con-tents are spread out beneath my hungry eyes.

Here is a scroll of ink-written music. I don't read music, but I know the dash and swing of the pen that rained it on the page. Here is a letter, with the selfsame impulse and abandon in every syllable; and its melody—however sweet the other —is far more sweet to me. And here are other let-ters like it—three—five—and seven, at least. Bob wrote them from the front, and Billy kept them for me when I went to join him. Dear boy! Dear boy!

Here are some cards of bristol-board. Ah! when Bob came to these there were no blotches then.

What faces—what expressions! The droll, ridiculous, good-for-nothing genius, with his "sad mouth,"
as he called it, "upside down," laughing always—
at everything, at big rallies, and mass-meetings and
conventions, county fairs, and floral halls, booths,
watermelon-wagons, dancing-tents, the swing, the
Daguerrean-car, the "lung-barometer," and the air-
gun man. Oh! what a gifted, good-for-nothing boy
Bob was in those old days! And here's a picture
of a girlish face—a very faded photograph—even
fresh from "the gallery," five and twenty years ago,
it was a faded thing. But the living face—how
bright and clear that was!—for "Doc," Bob's awful
name for her, was a pretty girl, and brilliant, clever,
lovable every way. No wonder Bob fancied her!
And you could see some hint of her jaunty loveliness in every fairy face he drew, and you could
find her happy ways and dainty tastes unconsciously assumed in all he did—the books he read—the
poems he admired, and those he wrote; and, ringing clear and pure and jubilant, the vibrant beauty
of her voice could clearly be defined and traced
through all his music. Now, there's the happy pair
of them—Bob and Doc. Make of them just whatever your good fancy may dictate, but keep in mind
the stern, relentless ways of destiny.

You are not at the beginning of a novel, only at
the threshold of one of a hundred experiences that
lie buried in the past, and this particular one most
happily resurrected by these odds and ends found
in the gilded roll.

You see, dating away back, the contents of this package, mainly, were hastily gathered together after a week's visit out at the old Mills farm; the gilt paper, and the whistle, and the pictures, they were Billy's; the music pages, Bob's, or Doc's; the letters and some other manuscripts were mine.

The Mills girls were great friends of Doc's, and often came to visit her in town; and so Doc often visited the Mills's. This is the way that Bob first got out there, and won them all, and "shaped the thing" for me, as he would put it; and lastly, we had lugged in Billy,—such a handy boy, you know, to hold the horses on picnic excursions, and to watch the carriage and the luncheon, and all that.— "Yes, and," Bob would say, "such a serviceable boy in getting all the fishing tackle in proper order, and digging bait, and promenading in our wake up and down the creek all day, with the minnow-bucket hanging on his arm, don't you know!"

But jolly as the days were, I think jollier were the long evenings at the farm. After the supper in the grove, where, when the weather permitted, always stood the table ankle-deep in the cool green plush of the sward; and after the lounge upon the grass, and the cigars, and the new fish stories, and the general invoice of the old ones, it was delectable to get back to the girls again, and in the old "best room" hear once more the lilt of the old songs and the staccatoed laughter of the piano mingling with the alto and falsetto voices of the Mills girls, and the gallant soprano of the dear girl Doc.

This is the scene I want you to look in upon,
as, in fancy, I do now—and here are the materials
for it all, husked from the gilded roll:

Bob, the master, leans at the piano now, and Doc
is at the keys, her glad face often thrown up side-
wise toward his own. His face is boyish—for there
is yet but the ghost of a mustache upon his lip.
His eyes are dark and clear, of over-size when looking at you, but now their lids are drooped above
his violin, whose melody has, for the time, almost
smoothed away the upward kinkings of the corners of his mouth. And wonderfully quiet now
is every one, and the chords of the piano, too, are
low and faltering; and so, at last, the tune itself
swoons into the universal hush, and—Bob is rasping, in its stead, the ridiculous, but marvelously
perfect imitation of the "priming" of a pump, while
Billy's hands forget the "chiggers" on the bare
backs of his feet, as, with clapping palms, he dances
round the room in ungovernable spasms of delight.
And then we all laugh; and Billy, taking advantage
of the general tumult, pulls Bob's head down and
whispers, "Git 'em to stay up 'way late to-night!"
And Bob, perhaps remembering that we go back
home to-morrow, winks at the little fellow and whispers, "You let me manage 'em! Stay up till broad
daylight if we take a notion—eh?" And Billy
dances off again in newer glee, while the inspired
musician is plunking a banjo imitation on his en-
chanted instrument, which is unceremoniously

drowned out by a circus-tune from Doc that is absolutely inspiring to every one but the barefooted brother, who drops back listlessly to his old position on the floor and sullenly renews operations on his "chigger" claims.

"Thought you was goin' to have pop-corn to-night all so fast!" he says, doggedly, in the midst of a momentary lull that has fallen on a game of whist. And then the oldest Mills girl, who thinks cards stupid anyhow, says: "That's so, Billy; and we're going to have it, too; and right away, for this game's just ending, and I shan't submit to being bored with another. I say 'pop-corn' with Billy! And after that," she continues, rising and addressing the party in general, "we must have another literary and artistic tournament, and that's been in contemplation and preparation long enough; so you gentlemen can be pulling your wits together for the exercises, while us girls see to the refreshments."

"Have you done anything toward it!" queries Bob, when the girls are gone, with the alert Billy in their wake.

"Just an outline," I reply. "How with you?"

"Clean forgot it—that is, the preparation; but I've got a little old second-hand idea, if you'll all help me out with it, that'll amuse us some, and tickle Billy, I'm certain."

So that's agreed upon; and while Bob produces his portfolio, drawing paper, pencils and so on, I turn to my note-book in a dazed way and begin counting my fingers in a depth of profound abstraction, from which I am barely aroused by the reappearance of the girls and Billy.

"Goody, goody, goody! Bob's goin' to make pictures!" cries Billy, in additional transport to that the cake pop-corn had produced.

"Now, you girls," says Bob, gently detaching the affectionate Billy from one leg and moving a chair to the table, with a backward glance of intelligence toward the boy,—"you girls are to help us all you can, and we can all work; but, as I'll have all the illustrations to do, I want you to do as many of the verses as you can—that'll be easy, you know,— because the work entire is just to consist of a series of fool-epigrams, such as, for instance,—listen, Billy:

Here lies a young man
Who in childhood began
    To swear, and to smoke, and to drink,—
In his twentieth year
He quit swearing and beer,
    And yet is still smoking, I think."

And the rest of his instructions are delivered in lower tones, that the boy may not hear; and then, all matters seemingly arranged, he turns to the boy with —"And now, Billy, no lookin' over shoulders, you know, or swinging on my chair-back while I'm at work. When the pictures are all finished, then you can take a squint at 'em, and not before. Is that all hunky, now?"

"Oh! who's a-goin' to look over your shoulder— only *Doc*." And as the radiant Doc hastily quits that very post, and dives for the offending brother, he scrambles under the piano and laughs derisively.

And then a silence falls upon the group—a gracious quiet, only intruded upon by the very juicy and exuberant munching of an apple from a remote fastness of the room, and the occasional thumping of a bare heel against the floor.

At last I close my note-book with a half slam.

"That means," says Bob, laying down his pencil, and addressing the girls,—"that means he's concluded his poem, and that he's not pleased with it in any manner, and that he intends declining to read it, for that self-acknowledged reason, and that he expects us to believe every affected word of his entire speech—"

"Oh, don't!" I exclaim.

"Then give us the wretched production, in all its hideous deformity!"

And the girls all laugh so sympathetically, and Bob joins them so gently, and yet with a tone, I know, that can be changed so quickly to my further discomfiture, that I arise at once and read, without apology or excuse, this primitive and very callow poem recovered here to-day from the gilded roll:

### A BACKWARD LOOK

As I sat smoking, alone, yesterday,
  And lazily leaning back in my chair,
Enjoying myself in a general way—
Allowing my thoughts a holiday
  From weariness, toil and care,—

My fancies—doubtless, for ventilation—
  Left ajar the gates of my mind,—
And Memory, seeing the situation,
  Slipped out in the street of "Auld Lang Syne"—

Wandering ever with tireless feet
  Through scenes of silence, and jubilee
Of long-hushed voices; and faces sweet
Were thronging the shadowy side of the street
  As far as the eye could see;
Dreaming again, in anticipation,
  The same old dreams of our boyhood's days
That never come true, from the vague sensation
  Of walking asleep in the world's strange ways.

Away to the house where I was born!
  And there was the selfsame clock that ticked
From the close of dusk to the burst of morn,
When life-warm hands plucked the golden corn
  And helped when the apples were picked.
And the "chany dog" on the mantel-shelf,
  With the gilded collar and yellow eyes,
Looked just as at first, when I hugged myself
  Sound asleep with the dear surprise.

And down to the swing in the locust-tree,
  Where the grass was worn from the trampled ground,
And where "Eck" Skinner, "Old" Carr, and three
Or four such other boys used to be
  Doin' "sky-scrapers," or "whirlin' round":
And again Bob climbed for the bluebird's nest,
  And again "had shows" in the buggy-shed
Of Guymon's barn, where still, unguessed,
  The old ghosts romp through the best days dead!

And again I gazed from the old schoolroom
  With a wistful look, of a long June day,
When on my cheek was the hectic bloom

Caught of Mischief, as I presume—
  He had such a "partial" way,
It seemed, toward me.—And again I thought
  Of a probable likelihood to be
Kept in after school—for a girl was caught
  Catching a note from me.

And down through the woods to the swimming-hole—
  Where the big, white, hollow, old sycamore grows,—
And we never cared when the water was cold,
And always "ducked" the boy that told
  On the fellow that tied the clothes.—
When life went so like a dreamy rhyme,
  That it seems to me now that then
The world was having a jollier time
  Than it ever will have again.

The crude production is received, I am glad to note, with some expressions of favor from the company though Bob, of course, must heartlessly dissipate my weak delight by saying, "Well, it's certainly bad enough; though," he goes on with an air of deepest critical sagacity and fairness, "considered, as it should be, justly, as the production of a jour.-poet, why, it might be worse—that is, a little worse."

"Probably," I remember saying,—"probably I might redeem myself by reading you this little amateurish bit of verse, enclosed to me in a letter by mistake, not very long ago." I here fish an envelope from my pocket, the address of which all recognize as in Bob's almost printed writing. He smiles vacantly at it—then vividly colors.

"What date?" he stoically asks.

"The date," I suggestively answer, "of your last letter to our dear Doc, at boarding-school, two days exactly in advance of her coming home—this veritable visit now."

Both Bob and Doc rush at me—but too late. The letter and contents have wholly vanished. The youngest Miss Mills quiets us—urgently distracting us, in fact, by calling our attention to the immediate completion of our joint production; "For now," she says, "with our new reinforcement, we can, with becoming diligence, soon have it ready for both printer and engraver, and then we'll wake up the boy (who has been fortunately slumbering for the last quarter of an hour), and present to him, as designed and intended, this matchless creation of our united intellects." At the conclusion of this speech we all go good-humoredly to work, and at the close of half an hour the tedious, but most ridiculous, task is announced completed.

As I arrange and place in proper form here on the table the separate cards—twenty-seven in number— I sigh to think that I am unable to transcribe for you the best part of the nonsensical work—the illustrations. All I can give is the written copy of—

## BILLY'S ALPHABETICAL ANIMAL SHOW

A was an elegant Ape
Who tied up his ears with red tape,
   And wore a long veil
   Half revealing his tail
Which was trimmed with jet bugles and crape.

B was a boastful old Bear
Who used to say,—"Hoomh! I declare
  I can eat—if you'll get me
  The children, and let me—
Ten babies, teeth, toe-nails and hair!"


C was a Codfish who sighed
When snatched from the home of his pride,
  But could he, embrined,
  Guess this fragrance behind,
How glad he would be to have died!


D was a dandified Dog
Who said,—"Though it's raining like a frog
  I wear no umbrellah,
  Me boy, for a fellah
Might just as well travel incog!"


E was an elderly Eel
Who would say,—"Well, I really feel—
  As my grandchildren wriggle
  And shout 'I should giggle'—
A trifle run down at the heel!"


F was a Fowl who conceded
*Some* hens might hatch more eggs than *she* did,—
  But she'd children as plenty
  As eighteen or twenty,
And that was quite all that she needed.


G was a gluttonous Goat
Who, dining one day, *table d'hôte,*
  Ordered soup-bone, *au fait,*
  And fish, *papier-mâché,*
And a *filet* of Spring overcoat.

H was a high-cultured Hound
Who could clear forty feet at a bound,
And a coon once averred
That his howl could be heard
For five miles and three-quarters around.


I was an Ibex ambitious
To dive over chasms auspicious;
He would leap down a peak
And not light for a week,
And swear that the jump was delicious.


J was a Jackass who said
He had such a bad cold in his head,
If it wasn't for leaving
The rest of us grieving,
He'd really rather be dead.


K was a profligate Kite
Who would haunt the saloons every night;
And often he ust
To reel back to his roost
Too full to set up on it right.


L was a wary old Lynx
Who would say,—"Do you know wot I thinks?—
I thinks ef you happen
To ketch me a-nappin'
I'm ready to set up the drinks!"


M was a merry old Mole,
Who would snooze all the day in his hole,
Then—all night, a-rootin'
Around and galootin'—
He'd sing "Johnny, Fill up the Bowl!"

N was a caustical Nautilus
  Who sneered, "I suppose, when they've *caught* all us,
    Like oysters they'll serve us,
    And can us, preserve us,
And barrel, and pickle, and bottle us!"

O was an autocrat Owl—
  Such a wise—such a wonderful fowl!
    Why, for all the night through
    He would hoot and hoo-hoo,
And hoot and hoo-hooter and howl!

P was a Pelican pet,
  Who gobbled up all he could get;
    He could eat on until
    He was full to the bill,
And there he had lodgings to let!

Q was a querulous Quail,
  Who said: "It will little avail
    The efforts of those
    Of my foes who propose
To attempt to put salt on my tail!"

R was a ring-tailed Raccoon,
  With eyes of the tinge of the moon,
    And his nose a blue-black,
    And the fur on his back
A sad sort of sallow maroon.

S is a Sculpin—you'll wish
  Very much to have one on your dish,
    Since all his bones grow
    On the outside, and so
He's a very desirable fish.

T was a Turtle, of wealth,
  Who went round with particular stealth,
    "Why," said he, "I'm afraid
    Of being waylaid
When I even walk out for my health!"


U was a Unicorn curious,
  With one horn, of a growth so *luxurious,*
    He could level and stab it—
    If you didn't grab it—
Clean through you, he was so blamed furious!


V was a vagabond Vulture
  Who said: "I don't want to insult yer,
    But when you intrude
    Where in lone solitude
I'm a-preyin', you're no man o' culture!"


W was a wild *Wood*chuck,
  And you just bet that he *could* "chuck"—
    He'd eat raw potatoes,
    Green corn, and tomatoes,
And tree roots, and call it all *"good* chuck!"


X was a kind of X-cuse
  Of some-sort-o'-thing that got loose
    Before we could name it,
    And cage it, and tame it,
And bring it in general use.


Y is the Yellowbird,—bright
  As a petrified lump of starlight,
    Or a handful of lightning-
    Bugs, squeezed in the tight'ning
Pink fist of a boy, at night.

Z is the Zebra, of course!—
   A kind of a clown-of-a-horse,—
      Each other despising,
      Yet neither devising
   A way to obtain a divorce!

& here is the famous—what-is-it?
   Walk up, Master Billy, and quiz it:
      You've seen the *rest* of 'em—
      Ain't this the *best* of 'em,
   Right at the end of your visit?

At last Billy is sent off to bed. It is the prudent mandate of the old folks: But so loathfully the poor child goes, Bob's heart goes, too.—Yes, Bob himself, to keep the little fellow company for a while, and, up there under the old rafters, in the pleasant gloom, lull him to famous dreams with fairy tales. And it is during this brief absence that the youngest Mills girl gives us a surprise. She will read a poem, she says, written by a very dear friend of hers who, fortunately for us, is not present to prevent her. We guard door and window as she reads. Doc says she will not listen; but she does listen, and cries, too— out of pure vexation, she asserts. The rest of us, however, cry just because of the apparent honesty of the poem of—

### BEAUTIFUL HANDS

O your hands—they are strangely fair!
Fair—for the jewels that sparkle there,—
Fair—for the witchery of the spell
That ivory keys alone can tell;

But when their delicate touches rest
Here in my own do I love them best,
As I clasp with eager, acquisitive spans
My glorious treasure of beautiful hands!

Marvelous—wonderful—beautiful hands!
They can coax roses to bloom in the strands
Of your brown tresses; and ribbons will twine,
Under mysterious touches of thine,
Into such knots as entangle the soul
And fetter the heart under such a control
As only the strength of my love understands—
My passionate love for your beautiful hands.

As I remember the first fair touch
Of those beautiful hands that I love so much,
I seem to thrill as I then was thrilled,
Kissing the glove that I found unfilled—
When I met your gaze, and the queenly bow
As you said to me, laughingly, "Keep it now!" . . .
And dazed and alone in a dream I stand,
Kissing this ghost of your beautiful hand.

When first I loved, in the long ago,
And held your hand as I told you so—
Pressed and caressed it and gave it a kiss
And said "I could die for a hand like this!"
Little I dreamed love's fullness yet
Had to ripen when eyes were wet
And prayers were vain in their wild demands
For one warm touch of your beautiful hands.

Beautiful Hands!—O Beautiful Hands!
Could you reach out of the alien lands
Where you are lingering, and give me, to-night,
Only a touch—were it ever so light—

My heart were soothed, and my weary brain
Would lull itself into rest again;
For there is no solace the world commands
Like the caress of your beautiful hands.

.    .    .    .    .    .    .    .

Violently winking at the mist that blurs my sight,
I regretfully awaken to the here and now.  And is
it possible, I sorrowfully muse, that all this glory
can have fled away?—that more than twenty long,
long years are spread between me and that happy
night?  And is it possible that all the dear old faces
—Oh, quit it! quit it! Gather the old scraps up and
wad 'em back into oblivion, where they belong!

Yes, but be calm—be calm! Think of cheerful
things. You are not all alone. *Billy's* living yet.

I know—and six feet high—and sag-shouldered—
and owns a tin and stove-store, and can't hear thunder! *Billy!*

And the youngest Mills girl—she's alive, too.
S'pose I don't know that? I married her!
And Doc.—
*Bob* married her. Been in California for more
than fifteen years—on some blasted cattle-ranch, or
something,—and he's worth a half a million! And
am I less prosperous with this gilded roll?

JAMES WHITCOMB RILEY
September, 1913

# A WILD IRISHMAN

NOT very many years ago the writer was for some months stationed at South Bend, a thriving little city of northern Indiana. Its population is mainly on the one side of the St. Joseph River, but quite a respectable fraction thereof takes its industrial way to the opposite shore, and there gains an audience and a hearing in the rather imposing growth and hurly-burly of its big manufactories, and the consequent rapid appearance of multitudinous neat cottages, tenement houses and business blocks. A stranger entering South Bend proper on any ordinary day, will be at some loss to account for its prosperous appearance—its flagged and bouldered streets—its handsome mercantile blocks, banks, and business houses generally. Reasoning from cause to effect, and seeing but a meager sprinkling of people on the streets throughout the day, and these seeming, for the most part, merely idlers, and in nowise accessory to the evident thrift and opulence of their surroundings, the observant stranger will be puzzled at the situation. But when evening comes, and the outlying foundries, sewing-machine, wagon, plow, and other "works," together with the paper-mills

and all the nameless industries—when the operations of all these are suspended for the day, and the
workmen and workwomen loosed from labor—then,
as this vast army suddenly invades and overflows
bridge, roadway, street and lane, the startled stranger will fully comprehend the why and wherefore
of the city's high prosperity. And, once acquainted
with the people there, the fortunate sojourner will
find no ordinary culture and intelligence, and, as
certainly, he will meet with a social spirit and a
whole-souled heartiness that will make the place a
lasting memory. The town, too, is the home of
many world-known people, and a host of local
celebrities, the chief of which latter class I found,
during my stay there, in the person of Tommy Stafford, or "The Wild Irishman" as everybody called
him.

"Talk of odd fellows and eccentric characters,"
said Major Blowney, my employer, one afternoon,
"you must see our 'Wild Irishman' here before you
say you've yet found the queerest, brightest, clever-
est chap in all your travels. What d'ye say, Stockford?" And the Major paused in his work of
charging cartridges for his new breech-loading shotgun and turned to await his partner's response.

Stockford, thus addressed, paused above the
shield-sign he was lettering, slowly smiling as he
dipped and trailed his pencil through the ivory black
upon a bit of broken glass and said, in his deliberate,
half absent-minded way,—"Is it Tommy you're telling him about?" and then, with a gradual broaden-

ing of the smile, he went on, "Well, I should say so.
Tommy! What's come of the fellow, anyway? I
haven't seen him since his last bout with the mayor,
on his trial for shakin' up that fast-horse man."

"The fast-horse man got just exactly what he
needed, too," said the genial Major, laughing, and
mopping his perspiring brow. "The fellow was
barkin' up the wrong stump when he tackled
Tommy! Got beat in the trade, at his own game,
you know, and wound up by an insult that no Irishman would take; and Tommy just naturally wore
out the hall carpet of the old hotel with him!"

"And then collared and led him to the mayor's
office himself, they say!"

"Oh, he did!" said the Major, with a dash of
pride in the confirmation; "that's Tommy all over!"

"Funny trial, wasn't it?" continued the ruminat-
ing Stockford.

"Wasn't it though?" laughed the Major. "The
porter's testimony: You see, he was for Tommy,
of course, and on examination testified that the
horseman struck Tommy first. And here Tommy
broke in with: 'He's a-meanin' well, yer Honor, but
he's lyin' to ye—he's lyin' to ye. No livin' man iver
struck me first—nor last, nayther, for the matter o'
that!' And I thought—the—court—would—die!"
continued the Major, in a like imminent state of
merriment.

"Yes, and he said if he struck him first," supple-
mented Stockford, "he'd like to know why the
horseman was 'wearin' all the black eyes, and the

blood, and the boomps on that head of um!' And it's that talk that got him off with so light a fine!"

"As it always does," said the Major, coming to himself abruptly and looking at his watch. "Stock, you say you're not going along with our duck-shooting party this time? The old Kankakee is just lousy with 'em this season!"

"Can't go possibly," said Stockford, "not on account of the work at all, but the folks ain't just as well as I'd like to see them, and I'll stay here till they're better. Next time I'll try and be ready for you. Going to take Tommy, of course?"

"Of course! Got to have 'The Wild Irishman' with us! I'm going around to find him now." Then turning to me the Major continued, "Suppose you get on your coat and hat and come along? It's the best chance you'll ever have to meet Tommy. It's late anyhow, and Stockford'll get along without you. Come on."

"Certainly," said Stockford; "go ahead. And you can take him ducking, too, if he wants to go."

"But he doesn't want to go—and won't go," replied the Major with a commiserative glance at me. "Says he doesn't know a duck from a poll-parrot— nor how to load a shotgun—and couldn't hit a house if he were inside of it and the door shut. Admits that he nearly killed his uncle once, on the other side of a tree, with a squirrel runnin' down it. Don't want him along!"

When I reached the street with the genial Major, he gave me this advice: "Now, when you meet Tom-

my, you mustn't take all he says for dead earnest,
and you mustn't believe, because he talks loud, and
in italics every other word, that he wants to do all
the talking and won't be interfered with. That's the
way he's apt to strike folks at first—but it's their
mistake, not his. Talk back to him—controvert him
whenever he's aggressive in the utterance of his
opinions, and if you're only honest in the announcement of your own ideas and beliefs, he'll like you all
the better for standing by them. He's quick-tem-
pered, and perhaps a trifle sensitive, so share your
greater patience with him, and he'll pay you back by
fighting for you at the drop of the hat. In short, he's
as nearly typical of his gallant country's brave, impetuous, fun-loving race as one man can be."

"But is he quarrelsome?" I asked.

"Not at all. There's the trouble. If he'd only
quarrel there'd be no harm done. Quarreling's
cheap, and Tommy's extravagant. A big black-
smith here, the other day, kicked some boy out of his
shop, and Tommy, on his cart, happened to be passing at the time; and he just jumped off without a
word, and went in and worked on that fellow for
about three minutes, with such disastrous results that
they couldn't tell his shop from a slaughter-house;
paid an assault and battery fine, and gave the boy a
dollar besides, and the whole thing was a positive
luxury to him. But I guess we'd better drop the subject, for here's his cart, and here's Tommy. Hi!
there, you 'Fardown' Irish Mick!" called the Major,

in affected antipathy, "been out raiding the honest farmers' hen-roosts again, have you?"

We had halted at a corner grocery and produce store, as I took it, and the smooth-faced, shaven-headed man in woolen shirt, short vest, and suspenderless trousers so boisterously addressed by the Major, was just lifting from the back of his cart a coop of cackling chickens.

"Arrah! ye blasted Kerryonian!" replied the handsome fellow, depositing the coop on the curb and straightening his tall, slender figure; "I were jist thinkin' of yez and the ducks, and here ye come quackin' into the prisence of r'yalty, wid yer canvas-back suit upon ye and the schwim-skins bechuxt yer toes! How air yez, anyhow—and air we startin' for the Kankakee by the nixt post?"

"We're to start just as soon as we get the boys to-gether," said the Major, shaking hands. "The crowd's to be at Andrews' by four, and it's fully that now; so come on at once. We'll go 'round by Munson's and have Hi send a boy to look after your horse. Come; I want to introduce my friend here to you, and we'll all want to smoke and jabber a little in appropriate seclusion. Come on." And the impatient Major had linked arms with his hesitating ally and myself, and was turning the corner of the street.

"It's an hour's work I have yet wid the squawkers," mildly protested Tommy, still hanging back and stepping a trifle high; "but, as one Irishman

would say til another, 'Ye're wrong, but I'm wid
ye!'"

And five minutes later the three of us had joined
a very jolly party in a snug back room, with

> "The chamber walls depicted all around
> With portraitures of huntsman, hawk, and hound,
> And the hurt deer;"

and where, as well, drifted over the olfactory intelligence a certain subtle, warm-breathed aroma, that
genially combated the chill and darkness of the day
without, and, resurrecting long-dead Christmases,
brimmed the grateful memory with all comfortable
cheer.

A dozen hearty voices greeted the appearance of
Tommy and the Major, the latter adroitly pushing
the jovial Irishman to the front, with a mock-heroic
introduction to the general company, at the conclusion of which Tommy, with his hat tucked under
his left elbow, stood bowing with a grace of pose
and presence Lord Chesterfield might have applauded.

"Gintlemen," said Tommy, settling back upon his
heels and admiringly contemplating the group;
"gintlemen, I congratu-late yez wid a pride that
shoves the thumbs o' me into the arrum-holes of me
weshkit! At the inshtigation of the bowld *O'*Blowney—axin' the gintleman's pardon—I am here wid
no silver tongue of illoquence to para-lyze yez, but
I am prisent, as has been ripresinted, to jine wid yez

in a stupendous waste of gunpowder, and duck-
shot, and 'high-wines,' and ham sandwiches, upon
the silvonian banks of the ragin' Kankakee, where
the 'di-dipper' tips ye good-by wid his tail, and the
wild loon skoots like a sky-rocket for his exiled
home in the alien dunes of the wild morass—or, as
Tommy Moore so illegantly describes the blashted
birrud,—

> 'Away to the dizhmal shwamp he spheeds—
>   His path is rugged and sore,
> Through tangled juniper, beds of reeds,
> And many a fen where the serpent feeds,
>   *And birrud niver flew before—*
>   *And niver will fly any more'*

if iver he arrives back safe into civilization again—
and I've been in the poultry business long enough to
know the private opinion and personal integrity of
ivery fowl that flies the air or roosts on poles. But,
changin' the subject of my few small remarks here,
and thankin' yez wid an overflowin' heart but a dhry
tongue, I have the honor to propose, gintlemen, long
life and health to ivery mother's son o' yez, and success to the 'Duck-hunters of Kankakee.' "

"The duck-hunters of the Kankakee!" chorused
the elated party in such musical uproar that for a
full minute the voice of the enthusiastic Major—
who was trying to say something—could not be
heard. Then he said:

"I want to propose that theme—'The Duck-hunt-

ers of the Kankakee', for one of Tommy's impro-
visations. I move we have a song now from
Tommy on 'The Duck Hunters of the Kankakee.'"

"Hurrah! Hurrah! A song from Tommy," cried
the crowd. "Make us up a song, and put us all into
it! A song from Tommy! A song! A song!"

There was a queer light in the eye of the Irishman. I observed him narrowly—expectantly. Often
I had read of this phenomenal art of improvised
ballad-singing, but had always remained a little
skeptical in regard to the possibility of such a feat.
Even in the notable instances of this gift as displayed by the very clever Theodore Hook, I had
always half suspected some prior preparation—some
adroit forecasting of the sequence that seemed the
instant inspiration of his witty verses. Here was
evidently to be a test example, and I was all alert
to mark its minutest detail.

The clamor had subsided, and Tommy had drawn
a chair near to and directly fronting the Major's.
His right hand was extended, closely grasping the
right hand of his friend which he scarce perceptibly,
though measuredly, lifted and let fall throughout the
length of all the curious performance. The voice
was not unmusical, nor was the quaint old ballad-air
adopted by the singer unlovely in the least; simply
a monotony was evident that accorded with the
levity and chance-finish of the improvisation—and
that the song was improvised on the instant I am
certain—though in nowise remarkable, for other
reasons, in rhythmic worth or finish. And while his

smiling auditors all drew nearer, and leant, with
parted lips to catch every syllable, the words of the
strange melody trailed unhesitatingly into the lines
literally, as here subjoined:

> "One gloomy day in the airly Fall,
> Whin the sunshine had no chance at all—
> No chance at all for to gleam and shine
> And lighten up this heart of mine:
>
> "'Twas in South Bend, that famous town,
> Whilst I were a-strollin' round and round,
> I met some friends and they says to me:
> 'It's a hunt we'll take on the Kankakee!'"

"Hurrah for the Kankakee! Give it to us,
Tommy!" cried an enthusiastic voice between
verses. "Now give it to the Major!" And the song
went on:—

> "There's Major Blowney leads the van,
> As crack a shot as an Irishman,—
> For it's the duck is a tin decoy
> That his owld shotgun can't destroy:"

And a half-dozen jubilant palms patted the
Major's shoulders, and his ruddy, good-natured
face beamed with delight. "Now give it to the rest
of 'em, Tommy!" chuckled the Major. And the
song continued:—

> "And along wid 'Hank' is Mick Maharr,
> And Barney Pince, at 'The Shamrock' bar—
> There's Barney Pinch, wid his heart so true;
> And the Andrews Brothers they'll go too."

"Hold on, Tommy!" chipped in one of the Andrews; "you must give 'the Andrews Brothers' a better advertisement than that! Turn us on a full verse, can't you?"

"Make 'em pay for it if you do!" said the Major in an undertone. And Tommy promptly amended:—

> "O, the Andrews Brothers, they'll be there,
> Wid good se-gyars and wine to sphare,—
> They'll treat us here on fine champagne,
> And whin we're there they'll treat us again."

The applause here was vociferous, and only discontinued when a box of Havanas stood open on the table. During the momentary lull thus occasioned, I caught the Major's twinkling eyes glancing evasively toward me, as he leaned whispering some further instructions to Tommy, who again took up his desultory ballad, while I turned and fled for the street, catching, however, as I went, and high above the laughter of the crowd, the satire of this quatrain to its latest line:—

> "But R-R-Riley he'll not go, I guess,
> Lest he'd get lost in the wil-der-ness,
> And so in the city he will shtop
> For to curl his hair in the barber shop."

It was after six when I reached the hotel, but I had my hair trimmed before I went in to supper. The style of trimming adopted then I still rigidly

adhere to, and call it "the Tommy Stafford stubble-
crop."

Ten days passed before I again saw the Major.
Immediately upon his return—it was late afternoon when I heard of it—I determined tò take my
evening walk out the long street toward his pleasant
home and call on him there.   This I did, and
found him in a wholesome state of fatigue, slippers
and easy chair, enjoying his pipe on the piazza.   Of
course, he was overflowing with happy reminiscences of the hunt—the wood-and-water-craft—
boats—ambushes—decoys, and tramp, and camp,
and so on, without end;—but I wanted to hear him
talk of "The Wild Irishman"—Tommy; and I think,
too, now, that the sagacious Major secretly read my
desires all the time.   To be utterly frank with the
reader I will admit that I not only think the Major
divined my interest in Tommy, but I know he did;
for at last, as though reading my very thoughts, he
abruptly said, after a long pause, in which he
knocked the ashes from his pipe and refilled and
lighted it :—"Well, all I know of 'The Wild Irishman' I can tell you in a very few words—that is,
if you care at all to listen?"   And the crafty old
Major seemed to hesitate.

"Go on—go on !" I said eagerly.

"About forty years ago," resumed the Major
placidly, "in the little, old, unheard-of town Karn-
teel, County Tyrone, Province Ulster, Ireland,
Tommy Stafford was fortunate enough—despite
the contrary opinion on that point of his wretchedly

poor parents—to be born. And here, again, as I advised you the other day, you must be prepared for constant surprises in the study of Tommy's character."

"Go on," I said; "I'm prepared for anything."

The Major smiled profoundly and continued:—

"Fifteen years ago, when he came to America— and the Lord only knows how he got the passage-money—he brought his widowed mother with him here, and has supported, and is still supporting her. Besides," went on the still secretly smiling Major, "the fellow has actually found time, through all his adversities, to pick up quite a smattering of education, here and there—"

"Poor fellow!" I broke in sympathizingly, "what a pity it is that he couldn't have had such advantages earlier in life," and as I recalled the broad brogue of the fellow, together with his careless dress, recognizing beneath it all the native talent and brilliancy of a mind of most uncommon worth, I could not restrain a deep sigh of compassion and regret.

The Major was leaning forward in the gathering dusk, and evidently studying my own face, the expression of which, at that moment, was very grave and solemn, I am sure. He suddenly threw himself backward in his chair, in an uncontrollable burst of laughter. "Oh, I just can't keep it up any longer," he exclaimed.

"Keep what up?" I queried, in a perfect maze of bewilderment and surprise. "Keep what up?" I repeated.

"Why, all this twaddle, farce, travesty and by-play regarding Tommy! You know I warned you, over and over, and you mustn't blame me for the deception. I never thought you'd take it so in earnest!" and here the jovial Major again went into convulsions of laughter.

"But I don't understand a word of it all," I cried, half frenzied with the gnarl and tangle of the whole affair. "What 'twaddle, farce and by-play,' is it, anyhow?" And in my vexation, I found myself on my feet and striding nervously up and down the paved walk that joined the street with the piazza, pausing at last and confronting the Major almost petulantly. "Please explain," I said, controlling my vexation with an effort.

The Major arose. "Your striding up and down there reminds me that a little stroll on the street might do us both good," he said. "Will you wait until I get a coat and hat?"

He rejoined me a moment later, and we passed through the open gate; and saying, "Let's go down this way," he took my arm and turned into a street, where, cooling as the dusk was, the thick maples lining the walk seemed to throw a special shade of tranquillity upon us.

"What I meant was"—began the Major in a low serious voice,—"What I meant was—simply this: Our friend Tommy, though the truest Irishman in the world, is a man quite the opposite every way of the character he has appeared to you. All that rich brogue of his is assumed. Though he was poor, as I told you, when he came here, his native quickness, and his marvelous resources, tact, judgment, business qualities—all have helped him to the equivalent of a liberal education. His love of the humorous and the ridiculous is unbounded; but he has serious moments, as well, and at such times is as dignified and refined in speech and manner as any man you'd find in a thousand. He is a good speaker, can stir a political convention to highest excitement when he gets fired up; and can write an article for the press that goes spang to the spot. He gets into a great many personal encounters of a rather undignified character; but they are almost invariably bred of his innate interest in the 'under dog,' and the fire and tow of his impetuous nature."

My companion had paused here, and was looking through some printed slips in his pocketbook. "I wanted you to see some of the fellow's articles in print, but I have nothing of importance here—only some of his 'doggerel,' as he calls it, and you've had a sample of that. But here's a bit of the upper spirit of the man—and still another that you should hear him recite. You can keep them both if you care to. The boys all fell in love with that last one, particularly, hearing his rendition of it. So we had a lot printed, and I have two or three left. Put these two in your pocket and read them at your leisure."

But I read them there and then, as eagerly, too, as I append them here and now. The first is called—

## SAYS HE

"Whatever the weather may be," says he—
  "Whatever the weather may be,
It's plaze, if ye will, an' I'll say me say,—
Supposin' to-day was the winterest day,
Wud the weather be changing because ye cried,
Or the snow be grass were ye crucified?
The best is to make your own summer," says he,
"Whatever the weather may be," says he—
  "Whatever the weather may be!

"Whatever the weather may be," says he—
  "Whatever the weather may be,
It's the songs ye sing, an' the smiles ye wear,
That's a-makin' the sun shine everywhere;
An' the world of gloom is a world of glee,
Wid the bird in the bush, an' the bud in the tree,
An' the fruit on the stim of the bough," says he,
"Whatever the weather may be," says he—
  "Whatever the weather may be!

"Whatever the weather may be," says he—
  "Whatever the weather may be,
Ye can bring the Spring, wid its green an' gold,
An' the grass in the grove where the snow lies cold;
An' ye'll warm yer back, wid a smiling face,
As ye sit at yer heart, like an owld fireplace,
An' toast the toes o' yer sowl," says he,
"Whatever the weather may be," says he—
  "Whatever the weather may be!"

"Now," said the Major, peering eagerly above my
shoulder, "go on with the next. To my mind, it is
even better than the first. A type of character you'll

recognize.—The same 'broth of a boy,' only *Americanized,* don't you know."

And I read the scrap entitled—

### CHAIRLEY BURKE

It's Chairley Burke's in town, b'ys! He's down til
    "Jamesy's Place,"
Wid a bran'-new shave upon 'um, an' the fhwhuskers aff
    his face;
He's quit the Section-Gang last night, and yez can chalk
    it down
There's goin' to be the divil's toime, sence Chairley
    Burke's in town.

It's treatin' iv'ry b'y he is, an' poundin' on the bar
Till iv'ry man he's drinkin' wid must shmoke a foine cigar;
An' Missus Murphy's little Kate, that's coomin' there for
    beer,
Can't pay wan cint the bucketful, the whilst that Chairley's
    here!

He's joompin' oor the tops o' sthools, the both forninst an'
    back!
He'll lave yez pick the blessed flure, an' walk the straight-
    est crack!
He's liftin' barrels wid his teeth, and singin' "Garry
    Owen,"
Till all the house be strikin' hands, sence Chairley Burke's
    in town.

The Road-Yaird hands coomes dhroppin' in, an' niver goin'
    back;
An' there's two freights upon the switch—the wan on
    aither track—
An' Mr. Gearry, from The Shops, he's mad enough to
    swear,
An' durstn't spake a word but grin, the whilst that Chair-
    ley's there!

Och! Chairley! Chairley! Chairley Burke! ye divil, wid yer
  ways
O' dhrivin' all the throubles aff, these dhark an' ghloomy
  days!
Ohone! that it's meself, wid all the graifs I have to dhrown,
Must lave me pick to resht a bit, sence Chairley Burke's
  in town.

"Before we turn back, now," said the smiling
Major, as I stood lingering over the indefinable
humor of the last refrain, "before we turn back I
want to show you something eminently characteristic. Come this way a half-dozen steps."

As he spoke I looked up, first to observe that we
had paused before a handsome square brick residence, centering a beautiful smooth lawn, its emer-
ald only littered with the light gold of the earliest
autumn leaves. On either side of the trim walk
that led up from the gate to the carved stone bal-
lusters of the broad piazza, with its empty easy
chairs, were graceful vases, frothing over with
late blossoms, and wreathed with laurel-looking
vines; and, luxuriantly lacing the border of the
pave that turned the farther corner of the house,
blue, white and crimson, pink and violet, went fading away in perspective as my gaze followed the
gesture of the Major's.

"Here, come a little farther. Now do you see
that man there?"

Yes, I could make out a figure in the deepening
dusk—the figure of a man on the back stoop—a
tired-looking man, in his shirt-sleeves, who sat upon

a low chair—no, not a chair—an empty box. He
was leaning forward with his elbows on his knees,
and the hands dropped limp. He was smoking,
too, I could barely see his pipe, and but for the
odor of very strong tobacco, would not have known
he had a pipe. Why does the master of the house
permit his servants so to desecrate this beautiful
home? I thought.

"Well, shall we go now?" said the Major.

I turned silently and we retraced our steps. I
think neither of us spoke for the distance of a
square.

"Guess you didn't know the man there on the
back porch?" said the Major.

"No; why?" I asked dubiously.

"I hardly thought you would, and besides the
poor fellow's tired, and it was best not to disturb
him," said the Major.

"Why; who was it—some one I know?"

"It was Tommy."

"Oh," said I inquiringly, "he's employed there in
some capacity?"

"Yes, as master of the house."

"You don't mean it?"

"I certainly do. He owns it, and made every
cent of the money that paid for it!" said the Major
proudly. "That's why I wanted you particularly
to note that 'eminent characteristic' I spoke of.
Tommy could just as well be sitting, with a fine
cigar, on the front piazza in an easy chair, as, with
his dhudeen, on the back porch, on an empty box,

where every night you'll find him. It's the unconscious dropping back into the old ways of his father, and his father's father, and his father's father's father. In brief, he sits there the poor lorn symbol of the long oppression of his race."

# MRS. MILLER

JOHN B. McKINNEY, Attorney and Counselor at Law, as his sign read, was, for many reasons, a fortunate man. For many other reasons he was not. He was chiefly fortunate in being, as certain opponents often strove witheringly to designate him, "the son of his father," since that sound old gentleman was the wealthiest farmer in that section, with but one son and heir to supplant him, in time, in the rôle of "county god," and haply perpetuate the prouder title of "the biggest taxpayer on the assessment list." And this fact, too, fortunate as it would seem, was doubtless the indirect occasion of a liberal percentage of all John's misfortunes. From his earliest school-days in the little town, up to his tardy graduation from a distant college, the influence of his father's wealth invited his procrastination, humored its results, encouraged the laxity of his ambition, "and even now," as John used, in bitter irony, to put it, "it is aiding and abetting me in the ostensible practise of my chosen profession, a listless, aimless undetermined man of forty, and a confirmed bachelor at that!" At the utterance of his self-depreciating statement, John

generally jerked his legs down from the top of his
desk; and rising and kicking his chair back to the
wall he would stump around his littered office till
the manila carpet steamed with dust. Then he
would wildly break away, seeking refuge either in
the open street, or in his room at the old-time tavern, The Eagle House, "where," he would say, "I
have lodged and boarded, I do solemnly asseverate,
for a long, unbroken, middle-aged eternity of ten
years, and can yet assert, in the words of the more
fortunately-dying Webster, that 'I still live'!"

Extravagantly satirical as he was at times, John
had always an indefinable drollery about him that
made him agreeable company to his friends, at
least; and such an admiring friend he had con-
stantly at hand in the person of Bert Haines. Both
were Bohemians in natural tendency, and, though
John was far in Bert's advance in point of age, he
found the young man "just the kind of a fellow to
have around;" while Bert, in turn, held his senior
in profound esteem—looked up to him, in fact, and
even in his eccentricities strove to pattern himself
after him. And so it was, when summer days were
dull and tedious, these two could muse and doze the
hours away together; and when the nights were long,
and dark, and deep, and beautiful, they could drift
out in the noonlight of the stars, and with "the soft
complaining flute" and "warbling lute," "lay the
pipes," as John would say, for their enduring popu-
larity with the girls! And it was immediately subsequent to one of these romantic excursions, when

the belated pair, at two o'clock in the morning, had
skulked up a side stairway of the old hotel, and
gained John's room, with nothing more serious happening than Bert falling over a trunk and smashing
his guitar,—just after such a night of romance and
adventure it was that, in the seclusion of John's
room, Bert had something of especial import to
communicate.

"Mack," he said, as that worthy anathematized
a spiteful match, and then sucked his finger.

"Blast the all-fired old torch!" said John, wrestling
with the lamp-flue, and turning on a welcome flame
at last. "Well, you said 'Mack'! Why don't you
go on? And don't bawl at the top of your lungs,
either. You've already succeeded in waking every
boarder in the house with that guitar, and you want
to make amends now by letting them go to sleep
again!"

"But my dear fellow," said Bert with forced
calmness, "you're the fellow that's making all the
noise—and—"

"Why, you howling dervish!" interrupted John,
with a feigned air of pleased surprise and admiration. "But let's drop controversy. Throw the
fragments of your guitar in the wood-box there, and
proceed with the opening proposition."

"What I was going to say was this," said Bert,
with a half-desperate enunciation; "I'm getting
tired of this way of living—clean, dead-tired, and
fagged out, and sick of the whole artificial business!"

"Oh, yes!" exclaimed John, with a towering disdain, "you needn't go any further! I know just what malady is throttling you. It's reform—reform! You're going to 'turn over a new leaf,' and all that, and sign the pledge, and quit cigars, and go to work, and pay your debts, and gravitate back into Sunday-school, where you can make love to the preacher's daughter under the guise of religion, and desecrate the sanctity of the innermost pale of the church by confessions at Class of your 'thorough conversion'! Oh, you're going to—"

"No, but I'm going to do nothing of the sort," interrupted Bert resentfully. "What I mean—if you'll let me finish—is, I'm getting too old to be eternally undignifying myself with this 'singing of midnight strains under Bonnybell's window-panes,' and too old to be keeping myself in constant humiliation and expense by the borrowing and stringing up of old guitars, together with the breakage of the same, and the general wear-and-tear on a constitution that is slowly being sapped to its foundations by exposure in the night-air and the dew."

"And while you receive no further compensation in return," said John, "than, perhaps, the coy turning up of a lamp at an upper casement where the jasmine climbs; or an exasperating patter of invisible palms; or a huge dank wedge of fruit-cake shoved at you by the old man, through a crack in the door."

"Yes, and I'm going to have my just reward, is what I mean," said Bert, "and exchange the lover's

life for the benedict's. Going to hunt out a good
sensible girl and marry her." And as the young
man concluded this desperate avowal he jerked the
bow of his cravat into a hard knot, kicked his hat
under the bed, and threw himself on the sofa like
an old suit.

John stared at him with absolute compassion.
"Poor devil," he said half musingly, "I know just
how he feels—

> "Ring in the wind his wedding chimes,
>   Smile, villagers, at every door;
> Old churchyards stuffed with buried crimes,
>   Be clad in sunshine o'er and o'er.—"

"Oh, here!" exclaimed the wretched Bert, jumping to his feet; "let up on that dismal recitative. It
would make a dog howl to hear that!"

"Then you 'let up' on that suicidal talk of marrying," replied John, "and all that harangue of in-
coherency about your growing old. Why, my dear
fellow, you're at least a dozen years my junior,
and look at me!" and John glanced at himself in the
glass with a feeble pride, noting the gray sparse-
ness of his side-hair, and its plaintive dearth on
top. "Of course I've got to admit," he continued,
"that my hair is gradually evaporating; but for all
that, I'm 'still in the ring,' don't you know; as
young in society, for the matter of that, as yourself! And this is just the reason why I don't want
you to blight every prospect in your life by marrying at your age—especially a woman—I mean the

kind of woman you'd be sure to fancy at your age."

"Didn't I say 'a good sensible girl' was the kind I had selected?" Bert remonstrated.

"Oh!" exclaimed John, "you've selected her, then?—and without one word to me!" he ended, rebukingly.

"Well, hang it all!" said Bert impatiently; "I knew how *you* were, and just how you'd talk me out of it; and I made up my mind that for once, at least, I'd follow the dictations of a heart that—however capricious in youthful frivolities—should beat, in manhood, loyal to itself and loyal to its own affinity."

"Go it! Fire away! Farewell, vain world!" exclaimed the excited John.—"Trade your soul off for a pair of ear-bobs and a button-hook—a hank of jute hair and a box of lily-white! I've buried not less than ten old chums this way, and here's another nominated for the tomb."

"But you've got no *reason* about you," began Bert,—"I want to"—

"And so do *I* 'want to,'" broke in John finally, —"I want to get some sleep.—So 'register' and come to bed.—And lie up on edge, too, when you *do* come—'cause this old catafalque-of-a-bed is just about as narrow as your views of single blessedness! Peace! Not another word! Pile in! Pile in! I'm three-parts sick, anyhow, and I want rest!" And very truly he spoke.

It was a bright morning when the slothful John was aroused by a long vociferous pounding on the

door. He started up in bed to find himself alone—
the victim of his wrathful irony having evidently
risen and fled away while his pitiless tormentor
slept—"Doubtless to accomplish at once that ne-
farious intent as set forth by his unblushing con-
fession of last night," mused the miserable John.
And he ground his fingers in the corners of his
swollen eyes, and leered grimly in the glass at the
feverish orbs, blood-shot, blurred and aching.

The pounding on the door continued. John
looked at his watch; it was only eight o'clock.

"Hi, there!" he called viciously. "What do you
mean, anyhow?" he went on, elevating his voice
again; "shaking a man out of bed when he's just
dropping into his first sleep?"

"I mean that you're going to get up; that's what!"
replied a firm female voice. "It's eight o'clock, and I
want to put your room in order; and I'm not going
to wait all day about it, either! Get up and go
down to your breakfast, and let me have the room!"
And the clamor at the door was industriously renewed.

"Say!" called John querulously, hurrying on his
clothes, "Say, you!"

"There's no 'say' about it!" responded the determined voice: "I've heard about you and your
ways around this house, and I'm not going to put
up with it! You'll not lie in bed till high noon
when I've got to keep your room in proper order!"

"Oh, ho!" bawled John intelligently: "reckon
you're the new invasion here? Doubtless you're

that girl that's been hanging up the new window-
blinds that won't roll, and disguising the pillows
with clean slips, and hennin' round among my
books and papers on the table here, and aging me
generally till I don't know my own handwriting by
the time I find it! Oh, yes, you're going to revolutionize things here; you're going to introduce
promptness, and system, and order. See you've
even filled the wash-pitcher and tucked two starched
towels through the handle. Haven't got any tin
towels, have you? I rather like this new soap, too!
So solid and durable, you know; warranted not to
raise a lather. Might as well wash one's hands with
a door-knob!"

And as John's voice grumbled away into the
sullen silence again, the determined voice without
responded: "Oh, you can growl away to your
heart's content, Mr. McKinney, but I want you
to understand distinctly that I'm not going to humor you in any of your old bachelor, sluggardly,
slovenly ways, and whims and notions. And I
want you to understand, too, that I'm not hired
help in this house, nor a chambermaid, nor anything
of the kind. I'm the landlady here; and I'll give you
just ten minutes more to get down to your breakfast, or you'll not get any—that's all!" And as
the reversed cuff John was in the act of buttoning
slid from his wrist and rolled under the dresser, he
heard a stiff rustling of starched muslin flouncing
past the door, and the quick italicized patter of determined gaiters down the hall.

"Look here," said John to the bright-faced boy in the hotel office, a half hour later. "It seems the house here's been changing hands again."

"Yes, sir," said the boy, closing the cigar case, and handing him a lighted match. "Well, the new landlord, whoever he is," continued John, patronizingly, "is a good one. Leastwise, he knows what's good to eat, and how to serve it."

The boy laughed timidly,—"It ain't a 'landlord,' though—it's a landlady; it's my mother."

"Ah," said John, dallying with the change the boy had pushed toward him. "Your mother, eh? And where's your father?"

"He's dead," said the boy.

"And what's this for?" abruptly asked John, examining his change.

"That's your change," said the boy: "You got three for a quarter, and gave me a half."

"Well, *you* just keep it," said John, sliding back the change. "It's for good luck, you know, my boy. Same as drinking your long life and prosperity. And, oh yes, by the way, you may tell your mother I'll have a friend to dinner with me to-day."

"Yes, sir, and thank you, sir," said the beaming boy.

"Handsome boy!" mused John, as he walked down street. "Takes that from his father, though, I'll wager my existence!"

Upon his office desk John found a hastily written note. It was addressed in the well-known hand of his old chum. He eyed the missive apprehensively, and there was a positive pathos in his voice as he said aloud, "It's our divorce. I feel it!" The note, headed, "At the Office, Four in Morning," ran like this:

"Dear Mack—I left you slumbering so soundly that, by noon, when you waken, I hope, in your refreshed state, you will look more tolerantly on my intentions as partially confided to you this night. I will not see you here again to say good-by. I wanted to, but was afraid to 'rouse the sleeping lion.' I will not close my eyes to-night—fact is, I haven't time. Our serenade at Josie's was a pre-arranged signal by which she is to be ready and at the station for the five morning train. You may remember the lighting of three consecutive matches at her window before the igniting of her lamp. That meant, 'Thrice dearest one, I'll meet thee at the depot at four-thirty sharp.' So, my dear Mack, this is to inform you that, even as you read, Josie and I have eloped. It is all the old man's fault, yet I forgive him. Hope he'll return the favor. Josie predicts he will, inside of a week—or two weeks, anyhow. Good-by, Mack, old boy; and let a fellow down as easy as you can. Affectionately,

"BERT."

"Heavens!" exclaimed John, stifling the note in his hand and stalking tragically around the room. "Can it be possible that I have nursed a frozen viper? An ingrate? A wolf in sheep's clothing? An orang-outang in gent's furnishings?"

"Was you calling me, sir?" asked a voice at the door. It was the janitor.

"No!" thundered John; "Quit my sight! get out of my way! No, no, Thompson, I don't mean that," he called after him. "Here's a half-dollar for you, and I want you to lock up the office, and tell anybody that wants to see me that I've been set upon, and sacked and assassinated in cold blood; and I've fled to my father's in the country, and am lying there in the convulsions of dissolution, babbling of green fields and running brooks, and thirsting for the life of every woman that comes in gunshot!" And then, more like a confirmed invalid than a man in the strength and pride of his prime, he crept down into the street again, and thence back to his hotel.

Dejectedly and painfully climbing to his room, he encountered, on the landing above, a little woman in a jaunty dusting-cap and a trim habit of crisp muslin. He tried to evade her, but in vain. She looked him squarely in the face—occasioning him the dubious impression of either needing shaving very badly, or having egg-stains on his chin.

"You're the gentleman in Number 11, I believe?" Why, Mr. McKinney, are you ill?"

He nodded confusedly.

"Mr. McKinney is your name, I think," she queried, with a pretty elevation of the eyebrows.

"Yes, ma'am," said John rather abjectly. "You see, ma'am—But I beg pardon," he went on stammeringly, and with a very awkward bow—"I beg pardon, but I am addressing—ah—the—ah—the—"

"You are addressing the new landlady," she interpolated pleasantly. "Mrs. Miller is my name. I think we should be friends, Mr. McKinney, since I hear that you are one of the oldest patrons of the house."

"Thank you—thank you!" said John, completely embarrassed. "Yes, indeed!—ha, ha. Oh, yes—yes—really, we must be quite old friends, I assure you, Mrs.—Mrs.—"

"Mrs. Miller," smilingly prompted the little woman.

"Yes, ah, yes,—Mrs. Miller. Lovely morning, Mrs. Miller," said John, edging past her and backing toward his room.

But as Mrs. Miller was laughing outright, for some mysterious reason, and gave no affirmation in response to his proposition as to the quality of the weather, John, utterly abashed and nonplused, darted into his room and closed the door. "Deucedly extraordinary woman!" he thought; "wonder what's her idea!"

He remained locked in his room till the dinner-hour; and, when he promptly emerged for that occasion, there was a very noticeable improvement in his personal appearance, in point of dress, at least, though there still lingered about his smoothly-shaven features a certain haggard, care-worn, anxious look that would not out.

Next his own at the table he found a chair tilted forward, as though in reservation for some honored guest. What did it mean? Oh, he remembered

now. Told the boy to tell his mother he would have
a friend to dine with him. Bert—and, blast the fellow!—was, doubtless, dining then with a far prefer-
able companion—his wife—in a palace-car on the
P., C. & St. L., a hundred miles away. The thought
was maddening. Of course, now, the landlady
would have material for a new assault. And how
could he avert it? A despairing film blurred his
sight for the moment—then the eyes flashed dar-
ingly. "I will meet it like a man!" he said, mentally—"yea, like a State's Attorney,—I will invite
it! Let her do her worst!"

He called a servant, giving some message in an
undertone.

"Yes, sir," said the agreeable servant, "I'll go
right away, sir," and left the room.

Five minutes elapsed, and then a voice at his
shoulder startled him:

"Did you send for me, Mr. McKinney? What
is it I can do?"

"You are very kind, Mrs.—Mrs.—"

"Mrs. Miller," said the lady, with a smile that he
remembered.

"Now, please spare me even the mildest of re-
bukes. I deserve your censure, but I can't stand it
—I can't positively!" and there was a pleading
look in John's lifted eyes that changed the little
woman's smile to an expression of real solicitude.
"I have sent for you," continued John, "to ask of
you three great favors. Please be seated while I
enumerate them. First—I want you to forgive and

forget that ill-natured, uncalled-for grumbling of mine this morning when you awakened me."

"Why, certainly," said the landlady, again smiling, though quite seriously.

"I thank you," said John with dignity. "And, second," he continued—"I want your assurance that my extreme confusion and awkwardness on the occasion of our meeting later were rightly interpreted."

"Certainly—certainly," said the landlady with the kindliest sympathy.

"I am grateful—utterly," said John, with newer dignity. "And then," he went on,—"after informing you that it is impossible for the best friend I have in the world to be with me at this hour, as intended, I want you to do me the very great honor of dining with me. Will you?"

"Why, certainly," said the charming little landlady—"and a thousand thanks besides! But tell me something of your friend," she continued, as they were being served. "What is he like—and what is his name—and where is he?"

"Well," said John warily,—"he's like all young fellows of his age. He's quite young, you know—not over thirty, I should say—a mere boy, in fact, but clever—talented—versatile."

"—Unmarried, of course," said the chatty little woman.

"Oh, yes!" said John, in a matter-of-course tone —but he caught himself abruptly—then stared intently at his napkin—glanced evasively at the side-face of his questioner, and said,—"Oh, yes! Yes, indeed! He's unmarried.—Old bachelor like myself, you know. Ha! Ha!"

"So he's not like the young man here that distinguished himself last night?" said the little woman archly.

The fork in John's hand, half-lifted to his lips, faltered and fell back toward his plate.

"Why, what's that?" said John in a strange voice; "I hadn't heard anything about it—I mean I haven't heard anything about any young man. What was it?"

"Haven't heard anything about the elopement?" exclaimed the little woman in astonishment.— "Why it's been the talk of the town all morning. Elopement in high life—son of a grain-dealer, name of Hines, or Himes, or something, and a preacher's daughter—Josie somebody—didn't catch her last name. Wonder if you don't know the parties— Why, Mr. McKinney, are you ill?"

"Oh, no—not at all!" said John: "Don't mention it. Ha—ha! Just eating too rapidly, that's all. Go on with—you were saying that Bert and Josie had really eloped."

"What 'Bert'?" asked the little woman quickly.

"Why, did I say Bert?" said John, with a guilty look. "I meant Haines, of course, you know— Haines and Josie.—And did they really elope?"

"That's the report," answered the little woman, as though deliberating some important evidence; "and they say, too, that the plot of the runaway was quite ingenious. It seems the young lovers were assisted in their flight by some old fellow—friend of the young man's—Why, Mr. McKinney, you *are* ill, surely?"

John's face was as ashen.

"No—no!" he gasped painfully: "Go on—go on! Tell me more about the—the—the old fellow—the old reprobate! And is he still at large?"

"Yes," said the little woman, anxiously regarding the strange demeanor of her companion. "They say, though, that the law can do nothing with him, and that this fact only intensifies the agony of the broken-hearted parents—for it seems they have, till now, regarded him both as a gentleman and family friend in whom"—

"I really am ill," moaned John, waveringly rising to his feet; "but I beg you not to be alarmed. Tell your little boy to come to my room, where I will retire at once, if you'll excuse me, and send for my physician. It is simply a nervous attack. I am often troubled so; and only perfect quiet and seclusion restores me. You have done me a great honor, Mrs."—("Mrs. Miller," sighed the sympathetic little woman)—"Mrs. Miller,—and I thank you more than I have words to express." He bowed limply, turned through a side door opening on a stair, and tottered to his room.

During the three weeks' illness through which he passed, John had every attention—much more, indeed, than he had consciousness to appreciate. For the most part his mind wandered, and he talked of curious things, and laughed hysterically, and serenaded mermaids that dwelt in grassy seas of dew, and were bald-headed like himself. He played upon a fourteen-jointed flute of solid gold, with diamond holes, and keys carved out of thawless ice. His old father came at first to take him home; but he could not be moved, the doctor said.

Two weeks of John's illness had worn away, when a very serious-looking young man, in a traveling duster, and a high hat, came up the stairs to see him. A handsome young lady was clinging to his arm. It was Bert and Josie. She had guessed the very date of their forgiveness. John awoke even clearer in mind than usual that afternoon. He recognized his old chum at a glance, and Josie— now Bert's wife. Yes, he comprehended that. He was holding a hand of each when another figure entered. His thin white fingers loosened their clasp, and he held a hand toward the newcomer. "Here," he said, "is my best friend in the world—Bert, you and Josie will love her, I know; for this is Mrs.— Mrs."—"Mrs. Miller," said the radiant little woman. —"Yes,—Mrs. Miller," said John, very proudly.

# AT ZEKESBURY

THE little town, as I recall it, was of just enough dignity and dearth of the same to be an ordinary county seat in Indiana—"The Grand Old Hoosier State," as it was used to being howlingly referred to by the forensic stump orator from the old stand in the court-house yard—a political campaign being the wildest delight that Zekesbury might ever hope to call its own.

Through years the fitful happenings of the town and its vicinity went on the same—the same! Annually about one circus ventured in, and vanished, and was gone, even as a passing trumpet-blast; the usual rainy season swelled the "Crick," the driftage choking at "the covered bridge," and backing water till the old road looked amphibious; and crowds of curious townfolk struggled down to look upon the watery wonder, and lean awestruck above it, and spit in it, and turn mutely home again.

The usual formula of incidents peculiar to an uneventful town and its vicinity: The countryman from "Jessup's Crossing," with the corn-stalk coffin-measure, loped into town, his steaming little gray-and-red-flecked "roadster" gurgitating, as it were,

348

with that mysterious utterance that ever has commanded and ever must evoke the wonder and bewilderment of every boy; the small-pox rumor
became prevalent betimes, and the subtle aroma of
the asafetida-bag permeated the graded schools
"from turret to foundation-stone"; the still recur-
ring exposé of the poor-house management; the
farm-hand, with the scythe across his shoulder,
struck dead by lightning; the long-drawn quarrel
between the rival editors culminating in one of them
assaulting the other with a "sidestick," and the other
kicking the one down-stairs and thenceward *ad
libitum;* the tramp, suppositiously stealing a ride,
found dead on the railroad; the grand jury returning a sensational indictment against a bar-tender
*non est;* the Temperance outbreak; the "Revival;"
the Church Festival; and the "Free Lectures on
Phrenology, and Marvels of Mesmerism," at the
town hall. It was during the time of the last-men-
tioned sensation, and directly through this scientific investigation, that I came upon two of the
town's most remarkable characters. And however
meager my outline of them may prove, my material
for the sketch is most accurate in every detail, and
no deviation from the cold facts of the case shall
influence any line of my report.

For some years prior to this odd experience
I had been connected with a daily paper at the
state capital; and latterly a prolonged session of
the legislature, where I specially reported, having
told threateningly upon my health, I took both the

advantage of a brief vacation, and the invitation of a young bachelor senator, to get out of the city for a while, and bask my respiratory organs in the re-vivifying rural air of Zekesbury—the home of my new friend.

"It'll pay you to get out here," he said cordially, meeting me at the little station, "and I'm glad you've come, for you'll find no end of odd characters to amuse you." And under the very pleasant sponsorship of my senatorial friend, I was placed at once on genial terms with half the citizens of the little town—from the shirt-sleeved nabob of the county office to the droll wag of the favorite loafing-place—the rules and by-laws of which resort, by the way, being rudely charcoaled on the wall above the cutter's bench, and somewhat artistically culminating in an original dialect legend which ran thus:

> F'r instance, now, when *some* folks gits
> To relyin' on theyr wits,
> Ten to one they git too smart
> And *spile* it all, right at the start!
> Feller wants to jest go slow
> And do his *thinkin'* first, you know.
> *'F I can't think up somepin' good,*
> *I set still and chaw my cood!*

And it was at this inviting rendezvous, two or three evenings following my arrival, that the general crowd, acting upon the random proposition of one of the boys, rose as a man and wended its hilarious way to the town hall.

"Phrenology," said the little, old, bald-headed lecturer and mesmerist, thumbing the egg-shaped head of a young man I remembered to have met that afternoon in some law office; "phrenology," repeated the Professor—"or rather the *term* phrenology—is derived from two Greek words signifying *mind* and *discourse;* hence we find embodied in phrenology-proper, the science of intellectual measurement, together with the capacity of intelligent communication of the varying mental forces and their flexibilities, etc., etc. The study, then, of phrenology is, to simplify it wholly—is, I say, the general contemplation of the workings of the mind as made manifest through the certain corresponding depressions and protuberances of the human skull when, of course, in a healthy state of action and development, as we find the conditions exemplified in the subject before us."

Here the "subject" vaguely smiled.

"You recognize that mug, don't you?" whispered my friend. "It's that coruscating young ass, you know, Hedrick—in Cummings' office—trying to study law and literature at the same time, and tampering with 'The Monster that Annually,' don't you know?—where we found the two young students scuffling round the office, and smelling of peppermint?—Hedrick, you know, and Sweeney. Sweeney, the slim chap, with the pallid face, and frog-eyes, and clammy hands! You remember I told you 'there was a pair of 'em'? Well, they're up to something here to-night. Hedrick, there on the stage in front; and Sweeney—don't you see?—with the gang on the rear seats."

"Phrenology—again," continued the lecturer, "is, we may say, a species of mental geography, as it were; which—by a study of the skull—leads also to a study of the brain within, even as geology naturally follows the initial contemplation of the earth's surface. The brain, thurfur, or intellectual retort, as we may say, natively exerts a molding influence on the skull contour; thurfur is the expert in phrenology most readily enabled to accurately locate the multitudinous intellectual forces, and most exactingly estimate, as well, the sequent character of each subject submitted to his scrutiny. As, in the example before us—a young man, doubtless well known in your midst, though, I may say, an entire stranger to myself—I venture to disclose some characteristic trends and tendencies, as indicated by this phrenological depression and development of the skull proper, as later we will show, through the mesmeric condition, the accuracy of our mental diagnosis."

Throughout the latter part of this speech my friend nudged me spasmodically, whispering something which was jostled out of intelligent utterance by some inward spasm of laughter.

"In this head," said the Professor, straddling his malleable fingers across the young man's bumpy brow—"In this head we find Ideality large—abnormally large, in fact; thurby indicating—taken in conjunction with a like development of the perceptive qualities—language following, as well, in the prominent eye—thurby indicating, I say, our subject as especially endowed with a love for the beautiful—the sublime—the elevating—the refined and delicate—the lofty and superb—in nature, and in all the sublimated attributes of the human heart and beatific soul. In fact, we find this young man possessed of such natural gifts as would befit him for the exalted career of the sculptor, the actor, the artist, or the poet—any ideal calling; in fact, any calling but a practical, matter-of-fact vocation; though in poetry he would seem to best succeed."

"Well," said my friend seriously, "he's *feeling* for the boy!" Then laughingly: "Hedrick *has* written some rhymes for the county papers, and Sweeney once introduced him, at an Old Settlers' Meeting, as 'The Best Poet in Center Township,' and never cracked a smile! Always after each other that way, but the best friends in the world. *Sweeney's* strong suit is elocution. He has a native ability that way by no means ordinary, but even that gift he abuses and distorts simply to produce grotesque, and oftentimes, ridiculous effects. For instance, nothing more delights him than to 'loathfully' consent to answer a request, at The Mite Society, some evening, for 'an appropriate selection,' and then, with an elaborate introduction of the same, and an exalted tribute to the refined genius of the author, proceed with a most gruesome rendition of 'Alonzo The Brave and The Fair Imogene,' in a way to coagulate the blood and curl the hair of his fair

listeners with abject terror. Pale as a corpse, you
know, and with that cadaverous face, lit with those
malignant-looking eyes, his slender figure, and his
long thin legs and arms and hands, and his whole
diabolical talent and adroitness brought into play—
why, I want to say to you, it's enough to scare 'em
to death! Never a smile from him, though, till he
and Hedrick are safe out into the night again—
then, of course, they hug each other and howl
over it like Modocs! But pardon; I'm interrupting
the lecture. Listen."

"A lack of continuity, however," continued the
Professor, "and an undue love of approbation,
would, measurably, at least, tend to retard the
young man's progress toward the consummation of
any loftier ambition, I fear; yet as we have intimated, if the subject were appropriately educated
to the need's demand, he could doubtless produce
a high order of both prose and poetry—especially
the latter—though he could very illy bear being
laughed at for his pains."

"He's dead wrong there," said my friend; "Hedrick enjoys being laughed at; he's used to it—gets
fat on it!"

"Is fond of his friends," continued the Professor,
"and the heartier they are the better; might even
be convivially inclined—if so tempted—but prudent
—in a degree," loiteringly concluded the speaker,
as though unable to find the exact bump with which
to bolster up the last named attribute.

The subject blushed vividly—my friend's right

eyelid dropped, and there was a noticeable, though elusive sensation throughout the audience.

*"But!"* said the Professor explosively, "selecting a directly opposite subject, in conjunction with the study of the one before us [turning to the group at the rear of the stage and beckoning], we may find a newer interest in the practical comparison of these subjects side by side." And the Professor pushed a very pale young man into position.

"Sweeney!" whispered my friend delightedly; "now look out!"

"In *this* subject," said the Professor, "we find the practical business head. Square—though small —a trifle light at the base, in fact; but well balanced at the important points at least; thoughtful eye—wide-awake — crafty—quick—restless—a policy eye, though not denoting language—unless, perhaps, mere business forms and direct statements."

"Fooled again!" whispered my friend; "and I'm afraid the old man will fail to nest out the fact also that Sweeney is the cold-bloodedest guyer on the face of the earth, and with more diabolical resources than a prosecuting attorney; the Professor ought to know this, too, by this time—for these same two chaps have been visiting the old man in his room at the hotel;—that's what I was trying to tell you a while ago. The old chap thinks he's 'playing' the boys, is my idea; but it's the other way, or I lose my guess."

"Now, under the mesmeric influence—if the two subjects will consent to its administration," said the Professor, after some further tedious preamble, "we may at once determine the fact of my assertions, as will be proved by their action while in this peculiar state." Here some apparent remonstrance was met with from both subjects, though amicably overcome by the Professor first manipulating the stolid brow and pallid front of the imperturbable Sweeney—after which the same mysterious ordeal was loathfully submitted to by Hedrick— though a noticeably longer time was consumed in securing his final loss of self-control. At last, however, this curious phenomenon was presented, and there before us stood the two swaying figures, the heads dropped back, the lifted hands, with thumb and finger-tips pressed lightly together, the eyelids languid and half closed, and the features, in appearance, wan and humid.

"Now, sir!" said the Professor, leading the limp Sweeney forward, and addressing him in a quick sharp tone of voice.—"Now, sir, you are a great contractor—own large factories, and with untold business interests. Just look out there! [pointing out across the expectant audience] look there, and see the countless minions toiling servilely at your dread mandates. And yet—ha! ha! See! see!— They recognize the avaricious greed that would thus grind them in the very dust; they see, alas! they see themselves, half-clothed—half-fed, that you may glut your coffers. Half-starved, they listen to the wail of wife and babe, and with eyes upraised in prayer, they see *you* rolling by in gilded coach, and

swathed in silk attire. But—ha! again! Look—
look! they are rising in revolt against you! Speak
to them before too late! Appeal to them—quell
them with the promise of the just advance of wages
they demand!"

The limp figure of Sweeney took on something
of a stately and majestic air. With a graceful and
commanding gesture of the hand, he advanced a
step or two; then, after a pause of some seconds
duration, in which the lifted face grew pale, as it
seemed, and the eyes a denser black, he said:

> "But yesterday
> I looked away
> O'er happy lands, where sunshine lay
> In golden blots,
> Inlaid with spots
> Of shade and wild forget-me-nots."

The voice was low, but clear, and even musical.
The Professor started at the strange utterance,
looked extremely confused, and, as the boisterous
crowd cried "Hear, hear!" he motioned the subject to continue, with some gasping comment inter-
jected, which, if audible, would have run thus:
"My God! It's an inspirational poem!"

> "My head was fair
> With flaxen hair—"

resumed the subject.

"Yoop-ee!" yelled an irreverent auditor.

"Silence! silence!" commanded the excited Pro-

fessor in a hoarse whisper; then, turning enthusiastically to the subject—"Go on, young man! Go
on!—'*Thy head was fair with flaxen hair——*'"

> "My head was fair
> With flaxen hair,
> And fragrant breezes, faint and rare,
> And, warm with drouth
> From out the south,
> Blew all my curls across my mouth."

The speaker's voice, exquisitely modulated, yet
resonant as the twang of a harp, now seemed of itself to draw and hold each listener; while a certain
extravagance of gesticulation—a fantastic movement of both form and feature—seemed very near
akin to fascination.   And so flowed on the curious
utterance :—

> "And, cool and sweet,
> My naked feet
> Found dewy pathways through the wheat;
> And out again
> Where, down the lane,
> The dust was dimpled with the rain."

In the pause following there was a breathlessness
almost painful.   The poem went on:

> "But yesterday
> I heard the lay
> Of summer birds, when I, as they
> With breast and wing,
> All quivering
> With life and love, could only **sing**.

"My head was leant
Where, with it, blent
A maiden's, o'er her instrument;
While all the night,
From vale to height,
Was filled with echoes of delight.

"And all our dreams
Were lit with gleams
Of that lost land of reedy streams,
Along whose brim
Forever swim
Pan's lilies, laughing up at him."

And still the inspired singer held rapt sway.
"It is wonderful!" I whispered, under breath.
"Of course it is!" answered my friend. "But
listen; there is more:"

"But yesterday! . . . .
O blooms of May,
And summer roses—where away?
O stars above;
And lips of love,
And all the honeyed sweets thereof!—

"O lad and lass,
And orchard pass,
And briered lane, and daisied grass!
O gleam and gloom,
And woodland bloom,
And breezy breaths of all perfume!—

"No more for me
Or mine shall be
Thy raptures—save in memory,—
No more—no more—
Till through the Door
Of Glory gleam the days of yore."

This was the evident conclusion of the remarkable utterance, and the Professor was impetuously fluttering his hands about the subject's upward-staring eyes, stroking his temples, and snapping his fingers in his face.

"Well," said Sweeney, as he stood suddenly awakened, and grinning in an idiotic way, "how did the old thing work?" And it was in the consequent hilarity and loud and long applause, perhaps, that the Professor was relieved from the explanation of this rather astounding phenomenon of the idealistic workings of a purely practical brain—or, as my impious friend scoffed the incongruity later, in a particularly withering allusion, as the "blank-blanked fallacy, don't you know, of staying the hunger of a howling mob by feeding 'em on spring poetry!"

The tumult of the audience did not cease even with the retirement of Sweeney, and cries of "Hedrick! Hedrick!" only subsided with the Professor's high-keyed announcement that the subject was even then endeavoring to make himself heard, but could not until utter quiet was restored, adding the further appeal that the young man had already been a long time under the mesmeric spell, and ought not be so detained for an unnecessary period. "See," he concluded, with an assuring wave of the hand toward the subject, "see; he is about to address you. Now, quiet!—utter quiet, if you please!"

"Great heavens!" exclaimed my friend stiflingly; "just look at the boy! Get on to that position for a poet! Even Sweeney has fled from the sight of him!"

And truly, too, it was a grotesque pose the young man had assumed; not wholly ridiculous either, since the dwarfed position he had settled into seemed more a genuine physical condition than an affected one. The head, back-tilted, and sunk between the shoulders, looked abnormally large, while the features of the face appeared peculiarly child-like—especially the eyes—wakeful and wide apart, and very bright, yet very mild and very artless; and the drawn and cramped outline of the legs and feet, and of the arms and hands, even to the shrunken, slender-looking fingers, all combined to convey most strikingly to the pained senses the fragile frame and pixy figure of some pitiably afflicted child, unconscious altogether of the pathos of its own deformity.

"Now, mark the cuss, Horatio!" gasped my friend.

At first the speaker's voice came very low, and somewhat piping, too, and broken—an eery sort of voice it was, of brittle and erratic *timbre* and undulant inflection. Yet it was beautiful. It had the ring of childhood in it, though the ring was not pure golden, and at times fell echoless. The *spirit* of its utterance was always clear and pure and crisp and cheery as the twitter of a bird, and yet forever ran an undercadence through it like a low-pleading prayer. Half garrulously, and like a shallow brook might brawl across a shelvy bottom, the rhythmic little changeling thus began :—

"I'm thist a little crippled boy, an' never goin' to grow
An' git a great big man at all!—'cause Aunty told me so.
When I was thist a baby onc't I falled out of the bed
An' got 'The Curv'ture of the Spine'—'at's what the Doc-
    tor said.
I never had no Mother nen—fer my Pa runned away
An' dassn't come back here no more—'cause he was drunk
    one day
An' stobbed a man in thish-ere town, an' couldn't pay his
    fine!
An' nen my Ma she died—an' I got 'Curv'ture of the
    Spine'!"

A few titterings from the younger people in the audience marked the opening stanza, while a certain restlessness, and a changing to more attentive positions seemed the general tendency. The old Professor, in the meantime, had sunk into one of the empty chairs. The speaker went on with more gaiety :—

"I'm nine years old! An' you can't guess how much I
    weigh, I bet!—
Last birthday I weighed thirty-three!—An' I weigh thirty
    yet!
I'm awful little fer my size—I'm purt' nigh littler 'an
Some babies is!—an' neighbors all calls me 'The Little
    Man'!
An' Doc one time he laughed an' said: 'I 'spect, first think
    you know,
You'll have a little spike-tail coat an' travel with a show!'
An' nen I laughed—till I looked round an' Aunty was a-
    cryin'—
Sometimes she acts like that, 'cause I got 'Curv'ture of the
    Spine'!"

Just in front of me a great broad-shouldered countryman, with a rainy smell in his cumbrous overcoat, cleared his throat vehemently, looked startled at the sound, and again settled forward, his weedy chin resting on the knuckles of his hands as they tightly clutched the seat before him. And it was like being taken into a childish confidence as the quaint speech continued :—

"I set—while Aunty's washin'—on my little long-leg stool,
An' watch the little boys an' girls a-skippin' by to school;
An' I peck on the winder, an' holler out an' say:
'Who wants to fight The Little Man at dares you all to-
    day ?'
An' nen the boys climbs on the fence, an' little girls peeks
    through,
An' they all says: 'Cause you're so big, you think we're
    'feard o' you !'
An' nen they yell, an' shake their fist at me, like I shake
    mine—
They're thist in fun, you know, 'cause I got 'Curv'ture of
    the Spine' !''

"Well," whispered my friend, with rather odd irrelevance, I thought, "of course you see through the scheme of the fellows by this time, don't you?"

"I see nothing," said I, most earnestly, "but a poor little wisp of a child that makes me love him so I dare not think of his dying soon, as he surely must! There; listen!" And the plaintive gaiety of the homely poem ran on :—

"At evening, when the ironin' 's done, an' Aunty's fixed the
    fire,
An' filled an' lit the lamp, an' trimmed the wick an' turned
    it higher,
An' fetched the wood all in fer night, an' locked the kitchen
    door,
An' stuffed the ole crack where the wind blows in up
    through the floor—
She sets the kittle on the coals, an' biles an' makes the tea,
An' fries the liver an' the mush, an' cooks a egg fer me;
An' sometimes—when I cough so hard—her elderberry
    wine
Don't go so bad fer little boys with 'Curv'ture of the
    Spine'!"

"Look!" whispered my friend, touching me with
his elbow. "Look at the Professor!"

"Look at everybody!" said I. And the artless
little voice went on again half quaveringly:—

"But Aunty's all so childish-like on my account, you see,
I'm 'most afeard she'll be took down—an' 'at's what
    bothers *me!*—
'Cause ef my good ole Aunty ever would git sick an' die,
I don't know what she'd do in Heaven—till *I* come, by an'
    by:—
Fer she's so ust to all my ways, an' ever'thing, you know,
An' no one there like me, to nurse an' worry over so!—
'Cause all the little childerns there's so straight an' strong
    an' fine,
They's nary angel 'bout the place with 'Curv'ture of the
    Spine'!"

The old Professor's face was in his handkerchief;
so was my friend's in his; and so was mine in mine,

as even now my pen drops and I reach for it again.

I half regret joining the mad party that had gathered an hour later in the old law office where these two graceless characters held almost nightly revel, the instigators and conniving hosts of a reputed banquet whose *menu's* range confined itself to herrings, or "blind robins," dried beef, and cheese, with crackers, gingerbread, and sometimes pie ; the whole washed down with anything but

> "——Wines that heaven knows when
> Had sucked the fire of some forgotten sun,
> And kept it through a hundred years of gloom
> Still glowing in a heart of ruby."

But the affair was memorable.  The old Professor was himself lured into it and loudest in his praise of Hedrick's realistic art ; and I yet recall him at the orgie's height, excitedly repulsing the continued slurs and insinuations of the clammy-handed Sweeney, who, still contending against the old man's fulsome praise of his more fortunate rival, at last openly declared that Hedrick was *not* a poet, *not* a genius, and in no way worthy to be classed in the same breath with *himself*—"the gifted but unfortunate *Sweeney,* sir—the unacknowledged author, sir 'y gad, sir !—of the two poems that held you spellbound to-night !"

# A CALLER FROM BOONE

## BENJ. F. JOHNSON VISITS THE EDITOR

IT was a dim and chill and loveless afternoon in the late fall of eighty-three when I first saw the genial subject of this hasty sketch. From time to time the daily paper on which I worked had been receiving, among the general literary driftage of amateur essayists, poets and sketch-writers, some conceits in verse that struck the editorial head as decidedly novel; and, as they were evidently the production of an unlettered man, and an *old* man, and a farmer at that, they were usually spared the waste-basket, and preserved—not for publication, but to pass from hand to hand among the members of the staff as simply quaint and mirth-provoking specimens of the verdancy of both the venerable author and the Muse inspiring him. Letters as quaint as were the poems invariably accompanied them, and the oddity of these, in fact, had first called attention to the verses. I well remember the general merriment of the office when the first of the old man's letters was read aloud, and I recall, too, some of his comments on his own verse, verbatim. In one place he said: "I make no doubt you will find

366

some purty *sad* spots in my poetry, considerin'; but I hope you will bear in mind that I am a great sufferer with rheumatizum, and have been, off and on, sence the cold New Years. In the main, however," he continued, "I allus aim to write in a cheerful, comfortin' sperit, so's ef the stuff hangs fire, and don't do no good, it hain't a-goin' to do no harm,—and them's my honest views on poetry."

In another letter, evidently suspecting his poem had not appeared in print because of its dejected tone, he said: "The poetry I herewith send was wrote off on the finest Autumn day I ever laid eyes on! I never felt better in my life. The morning air was as invigoratin' as bitters with tanzy in it, and the folks at breakfast said they never saw such a' appetite on mortal man before. Then I lit out for the barn, and after feedin', I come back and tuck my pen and ink out on the porch, and jest cut loose. I writ and writ till my fingers was that cramped I couldn't hardly let go of the penholder. And the poem I send you is the upshot of it all. Ef you don't find it cheerful enough fer your columns, I'll have to knock under, that's all!" And that poem, as I recall it, certainly was cheerful enough for publication, only the "copy" was almost undecipherable, and the ink, too, so pale and vague, it was thought best to reserve the verses, for the time, at least, and later on revise, copy, punctuate, and then print it sometime, as much for the joke of it as anything. But it was still delayed, neglected, and in a week's time almost entirely forgotten. And so it was upon this chill and somber afternoon I speak of that an event occurred which most pleasantly reminded me of both the poem with the "sad spots" in it, and the "cheerful" one, "writ out on the porch" that glorious autumn day, that poured its glory through the old man's letter to us.

Outside and in the sanctum the gloom was too oppressive to permit an elevated tendency of either thought or spirit. I could do nothing but sit listless and inert. Paper and pencil were before me, but I could not write—I could not even think coherently, and was on the point of rising and rushing out into the streets for a wild walk, when there came a hesitating knock at the door.

"Come in!" I snarled, grabbing up my pencil and assuming a frightfully industrious air: "Come in!" I almost savagely repeated, "Come in! And shut the door behind you!" and I dropped my lids, bent my gaze fixedly upon the blank pages before me and began scrawling some disconnected nothings with no head or tail or anything.

"Sir; howdy," said a low and pleasant voice. And at once, in spite of my perverse resolve, I looked up. I someway felt rebuked.

The speaker was very slowly, noiselessly closing the door. I could hardly face him when he turned around. An old man, of sixty-five, at least, but with a face and an eye of the most cheery and wholesome expression I had ever seen in either youth or age. Over his broad bronzed forehead and white hair he wore a low-crowned, wide-brimmed black felt hat, somewhat rusted now, and with the band grease-crusted, and the binding frayed at intervals, and sagging from the threads that held it on. An old-styled frock coat of black, dull brown in streaks, and quite shiny about the collar and lapels. A waistcoat of no describable material or pattern, and a clean white shirt and collar of one piece, with a black string-tie and double bow, which would have been entirely concealed beneath the long white beard but for its having worked around to one side of the neck. The front outline of the face was cleanly shaven, and the beard, growing simply from the under chin and throat, lent the old pioneer the rather singular appearance of having hair all over him with this luxurious growth pulled out above his collar for mere sample.

I arose and asked the old man to sit down, handing him a chair decorously.

"No—no," he said—"I'm much obleeged. I hain't come in to bother you no more'n I can he'p. All I wanted was to know ef you got my poetry all right. You know I take yer paper," he went on, in an explanatory way, "and seein' you printed poetry in it once-in-a-while, I sent you some of mine—neighbors kindo' advised me to," he added apologetically, "and so I sent you some—two or three times I sent you some, but I hain't never seed hide-ner-hair of it in your paper, and as I wus in town to-day, anyhow, I jest thought I'd kindo' drap in and git it back, ef you ain't goin' to print it—'cause I allus save up most the things I write, aimin' sometime to git 'em

all struck off in pamphlet-form, to kindo' distribit
round 'mongst the neighbors, don't you know."

Already I had begun to suspect my visitor's iden-
tity, and was mechanically opening the drawer of
our poetical department.

"How was your poetry signed?" I asked.

"Signed by my own name," he answered proudly,
—"signed by my own name,—Johnson—Benjamin
F. Johnson, of Boone County—this state."

"And is this one of them, Mr. Johnson?" I asked,
unfolding a clumsily-folded manuscript, and closely
scrutinizing the verse.

"How does she read?" said the old man eagerly,
and searching in the meantime for his spectacles.
"How does she read?—Then I can tell you!"

"It reads," said I, studiously conning the old
man's bold but bad chirography, and tilting my chair
back indolently,—"it reads like this—the first verse
does,"—and I very gravely read :—

"Oh! the old swimmin'-hole!"—

"Stop! Stop!" said the old man excitedly—"Stop
right there! That's my poetry, but that's not the
way to read it by a long shot! Give it to me!" and
he almost snatched it from my hand. "Poetry like
this ain't no poetry at all, 'less you read it *natchurl*
and *in jest the same sperit 'at it's writ in,* don't you
understand. It's a' old man a-talkin', rickollect, and
a-feelin' kindo' sad, and yit kindo' sorto' good, too,
and I opine he wouldn't got that off with a face on
him like a' undertaker, and a voice as solemn as a

cow-bell after dark! He'd say it more like this."—
And the old man adjusted his spectacles and read :—

### "THE OLD SWIMMIN'-HOLE"

"Oh! the old swimmin'-hole! whare the crick so still and
    deep
Looked like a baby-river that was laying half asleep,
And the gurgle of the worter round the drift jest below
Sounded like the laugh of something we onc't ust to know
Before we could remember anything but the eyes
Of the angels lookin' out as we left Paradise;
But the merry days of youth is beyond our controle,
And it's hard to part ferever with the old swimmin'-hole."

I clapped my hands in genuine applause. "Read
on!" I said,—"Read on! Read all of it!"

The old man's face was radiant as he continued :—

"Oh! the old swimmin'-hole! In the happy days of yore,
When I ust to lean above it on the old sickamore,
Oh! it showed me a face in its warm sunny tide
That gazed back at me so gay and glorified,
It made me love myself, as I leaped to caress
My shadder smilin' up at me with sich tenderness.
But them days is past and gone, and old Time's tuck his
    toll
From the old man come back to the old swimmin'-hole.

"Oh! the old swimmin'-hole! In the long, lazy days
When the humdrum of school made so many "run-a-ways,"
How pleasant was the jurney down the old dusty lane,
Whare the tracks of our bare feet was all printed so plane
You could tell by the dent of the heel and the sole
They was lots o' fun on hands at the old swimmin'-hole.
But the lost joys is past! Let your tears in sorrow roll
Like the rain that ust to dapple up the old swimmin'-hole.

"Thare the bullrushes growed, and the cattails so tall,
And the sunshine and shadder fell over it all;
And it mottled the worter with amber and gold
Till the glad lilies rocked in the ripples that rolled;
And the snake-feeder's four gauzy wings fluttered by
Like the ghost of a daisy dropped out of the sky,
Or a wownded apple-blossom in the breeze's controle
As it cut acrost some orchurd to'rds the old swimmin'-hole.

"Oh! the old swimmin'-hole! When I last saw the place,
The scenes was all changed, like the change in my face;
The bridge of the railroad now crosses the spot
Whare the old divin'-log lays sunk and fergot.
And I stray down the banks whare the trees ust to be—
But never again will theyr shade shelter me!
And I wish in my sorrow I could strip to the soul,
And dive off in my grave like the old swimmin'-hole."

My applause was long and loud. The old man's interpretation of the poem was a positive revelation, though I was glad enough to conceal from him my moistened eyes by looking through the scraps for other specimens of his verse.

"Here," said I enthusiastically, "is another one, signed 'Benj. F. Johnson,' read me this," and I handed him the poem.

The old man smiled and took the manuscript. "This-here one's on *'The Hoss,'*" he said, simply clearing his throat. "They ain't so much fancy-work about this as the other'n, but they's jest as much *fact,* you can bet—'cause, they're no animal a-livin' 'at I love better 'an

## "THE HOSS"

"The hoss he is a splendud beast;
  He is man's friend, as heaven desined,
And, search the world from west to east,
  No honester you'll ever find!

"Some calls the hoss 'a pore dumb brute,'
  And yit, like Him who died fer you,
I say, as I theyr charge refute,
  'Fergive; they know not what they do!'

"No wiser animal makes tracks
  Upon these earthly shores, and hence
Arose the axium, true as facts,
  Extoled by all, as 'Good hoss-sense!'

"The hoss is strong, and knows his stren'th,—
  You hitch him up a time er two
And lash him, and he'll go his len'th
  And kick the dashboard out fer you!

"But, treat him allus good and kind,
  And never strike him with a stick,
Ner aggervate him, and you'll find
  He'll never do a hostile trick.

"A hoss whose master tends him right
  And worters him with daily care,
Will do your biddin' with delight,
  And act as docile as *you* air.

"He'll paw and prance to hear your praise,
  Because he's learnt to love you well;
And, though you can't tell what he says,
  He'll nicker all he wants to tell.

"He knows you when you slam the gate
   At early dawn, upon your way
Unto the barn, and snorts elate,
   To git his corn, er oats, er hay.

"He knows you, as the orphant knows
   The folks that loves her like theyr own,
And raises her and "finds" her clothes,
   And "schools" her tel a womern-grown!

"I claim no hoss will harm a man,
   Ner kick, ner run away, cavort,
Stump-suck, er balk, er 'catamaran,'
   Ef you'll jest treat him as you ort.

"But when I see the beast abused,
   And clubbed around as I've saw some,
I want to see his owner noosed,
   And jest yanked up like Absolum!

"Of course they's differunce in stock,—
   A hoss that has a little yeer,
And slender build, and shaller hock,
   Can beat his shadder, mighty near!

"Whilse one that's thick in neck and chist
   And big in leg and full in flank,
That tries to race, I still insist
   He'll have to take the second rank.

"And I have jest laid back and laughed,
   And rolled and wallered in the grass
At fairs, to see some heavy-draft
   Lead out at *first,* yit come in *last!*

"Each hoss has his appinted place,—
   The heavy hoss should plow the soil;—
The blooded racer, he must race,
   And win big wages fer his toil.

"I never bet—ner never wrought
  Upon my feller man to bet—
And yit, at times, I've often thought
  Of my convictions with regret.

"I bless the hoss from hoof to head—
  From head to hoof, and tale to mane!—
I bless the hoss, as I have said,
  From head to hoof, and back again!

"I love my God the first of all,
  Then Him that perished on the cross,
And next, my wife,—and then I fall
  Down on my knees and love the hoss."

Again I applauded, handing the old man still
another of his poems, and the last received. "Ah!"
said he, as his gentle eyes bent on the title; "this-
here's the cheerfullest one of 'em all. This is the
one writ, as I wrote you about—on that glorious
October morning two weeks ago—I thought your
paper would print this-un, shore!"

"Oh, it *will* print it," I said eagerly; "and it will
print the other two as well! It will print *anything*
that you may do us the honor to offer, and we'll
reward you beside just as you may see fit to designate.—But go on—go on! Read me the poem."

The old man's eyes were glistening as he responded with the poem entitled

### "WHEN THE FROST IS ON THE PUNKIN"

"When the frost is on the punkin and the fodder's in the
  shock,
And you hear the kyouck and gobble of the struttin' tur-
  key-cock,

And the clackin' of the guineys, and the cluckin' of the
    hens,
And the rooster's hallylooyer as he tiptoes on the fence;
O, it's then's the times a feller is a-feelin' at his best,
With the risin' sun to greet him from a night of peaceful
    rest,
As he leaves the house, bareheaded, and goes out to feed
    the stock,
When the frost is on the punkin and the fodder's in the
    shock.


"They's something kindo' harty-like about the atmusfere
When the heat of summer's over and the coolin' fall is
    here—
Of course we miss the flowers, and the blossums on the
    trees,
And the mumble of the hummin'-birds and buzzin' of the
    bees;
But the air's so appetizin'; and the landscape through the
    haze
Of a crisp and sunny morning of the airly autumn days
Is a pictur' that no painter has the colorin' to mock—
When the frost is on the punkin and the fodder's in the
    shock.


"The husky, rusty russel of the tossels of the corn,
And the raspin' of the tangled leaves, as golden as the
    morn;
The stubble in the furries—kindo' lonesome-like, but still
A-preachin' sermuns to us of the barns they growed to fill;
The strawstack in the medder, and the reaper in the shed;
The hosses in theyr stalls below—the clover overhead!—
O, it sets my hart a-clickin' like the tickin' of a clock,
When the frost is on the punkin and the fodder's in the
    shock!

Then your apples all is getherd, and the ones a feller
    keeps
Is poured around the celler-floor in red and yeller heaps;
And your cider-makin' 's over, and your wimmern-folks is
    through
With theyr mince and apple-butter, and theyr souse and
    saussage, too!  .  .  .
I don't know how to tell it—but ef sich a thing could be
As the Angels wantin' boardin', and they'd call around on
    *me*—
I'd want to 'commodate 'em—all the whole-indurin' flock—
When the frost is on the punkin and the fodder's in the
    shock!"


That was enough! "Surely," thought I, "here is a
diamond in the rough, and a 'gem,' too, 'of purest
ray serene'!" I caught the old man's hand and
wrung it with positive rapture; and it is needless to
go further in explanation of how the readers of our
daily came to an acquaintance through its columns
with the crude, unpolished, yet most gentle genius of
Benj. F. Johnson, of Boone.

# THE OLD SOLDIER'S STORY

AS TOLD BEFORE THE NEW ENGLAND SOCIETY IN NEW
YORK CITY

SINCE we have had no stories to-night I will venture, Mr. President, to tell a story that I have heretofore heard at nearly all the banquets I have ever attended. It is a story simply, and you must bear with it kindly. It is a story as told by a friend of us all, who is found in all parts of all countries, who is immoderately fond of a funny story, and who, unfortunately, attempts to tell a funny story himself—one that he has been particularly delighted with. Well, he is not a story-teller, and especially he is not a funny story-teller. His funny stories, indeed, are oftentimes touchingly pathetic. But to such a story as he tells, being a good-natured man and kindly disposed, we have to listen, because we do not want to wound his feelings by telling him that we have heard that story a great number of times, and that we have heard it ably told by a great number of people from the time we were children. But, as I say, we can not hurt his feelings. We can not stop him. We can not kill him; and so the story generally proceeds. He selects a very old story always, and generally tells it in about this fashion :—

I heerd an awful funny thing the other day—ha! ha! I don't know whether I kin git it off er not, but, anyhow, I'll tell it to you. Well!—le's see now how the fool-thing goes. Oh, yes!—W'y, there was a feller one time—it was during the army and this feller that I started in to tell you about was in the war and—ha! ha!—there was a big fight a-goin' on, and this feller was in the fight, and it was a big battle and bullets a-flyin' ever' which way, and bombshells a-bu'stin', and cannon-balls a-flyin' 'round promiskus; and this feller right in the midst of it, you know, and all excited and het up, and chargin' away; and the fust thing you know along come a cannon-ball and shot his head off—ha! ha! ha! Hold on here a minute!—no, sir; I'm a-gittin' ahead of my story; no, no; it didn't shoot his *head* off— I'm gittin' the cart before the horse there—shot his *leg* off; that was the way; shot his leg off; and down the poor feller drapped, and, of course, in that condition was perfectly he'pless, you know, but yit with presence o' mind enough to know that he was in a dangerous condition ef somepin' wasn't done fer him right away. So he seen a comrade a-chargin' by that he knowed, and he hollers to him and called him by name—I disremember now what the feller's name was. . . .

Well, that's got nothin' to do with the story, anyway; he hollers to him, he did, and says, "Hello, there," he says to him; "here, I want you to come

here and give me a lift; I got my leg shot off, and
I want you to pack me back to the rear of the battle"
—where the doctors always is, you know, during a
fight—and he says, "I want you to pack me back
there where I can get med-dy-cinal attention er I'm
a dead man, fer I got my leg shot off," he says,
"and I want you to pack me back there so's
the surgeons kin take keer of me." Well—
the feller, as luck would have it, ricko'nized him
and run to him and throwed down his own musket,
so's he could pick him up; and he stooped down and
picked him up and kindo' half-way shouldered·him
and half-way helt him betwixt his arms like, and
then he turned and started back with him—ha! ha!
ha! Now, mind, the fight was still a-goin' on—and
right at the hot of the fight, and the feller, all excited, you know, like he was, and the soldier that
had his leg shot off gittin' kindo' fainty like, and his
head kindo' stuck back over the feller's shoulder
that was carryin' him. And he hadn't got more'n a
couple o' rods with him when another cannon-ball
come along and tuk his head off, shore enough!—
and the curioust thing about it was—ha! ha!—that
the feller was a-packin' him didn't know that he
had been hit ag'in at all, and back he went—still
carryin' the deceased back—ha! ha! ha!—to where
the doctors could take keer of him—as he thought.
Well, his cap'n happened to see him, and he thought
it was a ruther cur'ous p'ceedin's—a soldier carryin'
a dead body out o' the fight—don't you see? And
so he hollers at him, and he says to the soldier, the

cap'n did, he says, "Hullo, there; where you goin'
with that thing?" the cap'n said to the soldier who
was a-carryin' away the feller that had his leg shot
off. Well, his head, too, by that time. So he says,
"Where you going with that thing?" the cap'n said
to the soldier who was a-carryin' away the feller that
had his leg shot off. Well, the soldier he stopped—
kinder halted, you know, like a private soldier will
when his presidin' officer speaks to him—and he says
to him, "W'y," he says, "Cap, it's a comrade o' mine
and the pore feller has got his leg shot off, and I'm
a-packin' him back to where the doctors is; and there
was nobody to he'p him, and the feller would 'a' died
in his tracks—er track ruther—if it hadn't a-been fer
me, and I'm a-packin' him back where the surgeons
can take keer of him; where he can get medical at-
tendance—er his wife's a widder!" he says, "'cause
he's got his leg shot off!" Then *Cap'n* says, "You
blame fool you, he's got his *head* shot off." So then
the feller slacked his grip on the body and let it
slide down to the ground, and looked at it a minute,
all puzzled, you know, and says, "W'y, he told me
it was his leg!" Ha! ha! ha!

# DIALECT IN LITERATURE

*And the common people heard him gladly*

OF what shall be said herein of dialect, let it be understood the term dialect referred to is of that general breadth of meaning given it to-day, namely, any speech or vernacular outside of the prescribed form of good English in its present state. The present state of the English is, of course, not any one of its prior states. So first let it be remarked that it is highly probable that what may have been the best of English once may now by some be counted as a weak, inconsequent *patois,* or dialect.

To be direct, it is the object of this article to show that dialect is not a thing to be despised in any event —that its origin is oftentimes of as royal caste as that of any speech. Listening back, from the standpoint of to-day, even to the divine singing of that old classic master to whom England's late laureate refers as

> ". . . the first warbler, whose sweet breath
> Preluded those melodious bursts that fill
> The spacious times of great Elizabeth
> With sounds that echo still";

382

or to whom Longfellow alludes, in his matchless
sonnet, as

> ". . . the poet of the dawn, who wrote
> The Canterbury Tales, and his old age
> Made beautiful with song"—

Chaucer's verse to us is *now* as veritably dialect as
to that old time it *was* the chastest English; and even
then his materials were essentially dialect when his
song was at best pitch. Again, our present dialect,
of most plebeian ancestry, may none the less prove
worthy. Mark the recognition of its own personal
merit in the great new dictionary, where what was,
in our own remembrance, the most outlandish dialect, is now good, sound, official English.

Since Literature must embrace all naturally exist-
ing materials—physical, mental and spiritual—we
have no occasion to urge its acceptance of so-called
dialect, for dialect *is* in Literature, and *has* been
there since the beginning of all written thought and
utterance. Strictly speaking, as well as paradoxically, all verbal expression is more or less dialectic,
however grammatical. While usage establishes
grammar, it no less establishes so-called dialect.
Therefore we may as rightfully refer to "so-called
grammar."

It is not really a question of Literature's position
toward dialect that we are called upon to consider,
but rather how much of Literature's valuable time
shall be taken up by this dialectic country cousin.
This question Literature her gracious self most

amiably answers by hugging to her breast voluminous tomes, from Chaucer on to Dickens, from
Dickens on to Joel Chandler Harris. And this affectionate spirit on the part of Literature, in the
main, we all most feelingly indorse.

Briefly summed, it would appear that dialect
means something more than mere rude form of
speech and action—that it must, in some righteous
and substantial way, convey to us a positive force
of soul, truth, dignity, beauty, grace, purity and
sweetness that may even touch us to the tenderness
of tears. Yes, dialect as certainly does all this as
that speech and act refined may do it, and for the
same reasons: it is simply, purely natural and
human.

Yes, the Lettered and the Unlettered powers are
at sword's points; and very old and bitter foemen,
too, they are. As fairly as we can, then, let us look
over the field of these contending forces and note
their diverse positions: First, *the Lettered*—they
who have the full advantages of refined education,
training, and association—are undoubtedly as
wholly out of order among the *Unlettered* as the
Unlettered are out of order in the exalted presence
of the Lettered. Each faction may in like aversion
ignore or snub the other; but a long-suffering Providence must bear with the society of both. There
may be one vague virtue demonstrated by this feud:
each division will be found unwaveringly loyal to
its kind, and mutually they desire no interchange of
sympathy whatever.—Neither element will accept

from the other any *patronizing* treatment; and, perhaps, the more especially does the *Unlettered* faction
reject anything in vaguest likeness of this spirit. Of
the two divisions, in graphic summary,—*one* knows
the very core and center of refined civilization, and
this only; the *other* knows the outlying wilds and
suburbs of civilization, and this only. Whose, therefore, is the greater knowledge, and whose the just
right of any whit of self-glorification?

A curious thing, indeed, is this factional pride, as
made equally manifest in both forces; in one, for
instance, of the Unlettered forces: The average
farmer, or countryman, knows, in reality, a far better and wider range of diction than he permits himself to use. He restricts and abridges the vocabulary of his speech, fundamentally, for the reason
that he fears offending his rural *neighbors,* to whom
a choicer speech might suggest, on his part, an as-
sumption—a spirit of conscious superiority, and
therewith an implied reflection on *their* lack of intelligence and general worthiness. If there is any
one text universally known and nurtured of the Unlettered masses of our common country, it is that
which reads, "All men are created equal." Therefore it is a becoming thing when true gentility pre-
fers to overlook some variations of the class who,
more from lack of cultivation than out of rude intent, sometimes almost compel a positive doubt of
the nice veracity of the declaration, or at least a
grief at the munificent liberality of the so-bequoted
statement. The somewhat bewildering position of

these conflicting forces leaves us nothing further to consider, but how to make the most and best of the situation so far as Literature may be hurt or helped thereby.

Equally with the perfect English, then, dialect should have full justice done it. Then always it is worthy, and in Literature is thus welcome. The writer of dialect should as reverently venture in its use as in his chastest English. His effort in the *scholarly* and *elegant* direction suffers no neglect— he is *schooled* in that, perhaps, he may explain. Then let him be *schooled* in *dialect* before he sets up as an expounder of it—a teacher, forsooth a master! The real master must not only know each varying light and shade of dialect expression, but he must as minutely know the inner character of the people whose native tongue it is, else his product is simply a pretense—a wilful forgery, a rank abomination. Dialect has been and is thus insulted, vilified, and degraded, now and continually; and through this outrage solely, thousands of generous-minded readers have been turned against dialect who otherwise would have loved and blessed it in its real form of crude purity and unstrained sweetness—

Honey dripping from the comb.

Let no impious faddist, then, assume its just interpretation. He may know everything else in the world, but not dialect, nor dialectic people, for both of which he has supreme contempt, which same, be sure, is heartily returned. Such a "superior" personage may even go among these simple country people and abide indefinitely in the midst of them, yet their more righteous contempt never for one instant permits them to be their real selves in his presence. In consequence, his most conscientious report of them, their ways, lives, and interests, is absolutely of no importance or value in the world. He never knew them, nor will he ever know them. They are not his kind of people, any more than he is their kind of man; and *their* disappointment grieves us more than his.

The master in Literature, as in any art, is that "divinely gifted man" who does just obeisance to all living creatures, "both man and beast and bird." It is this master only who, as he writes, can sweep himself aside and leave his humble characters to do the thinking and the talking. This man it is who celebrates his performance—not himself. His work he celebrates because it is not his only, but because he feels it to be the conscientious reproduction of life itself—as he has seen and known and felt it;—a representation it is of God's own script, translated and transcribed by the worshipful mind and heart and hand of genius. This virtue is impartially demanded in all art, and genius only can fully answer the demand in any art for which we claim perfection. The painter has his expression of it, with no slighting of the dialect element; so, too, the sculptor, the musician, and the list entire. In the line of Literature and literary material, an illustra-

tion of the nice meaning and distinction of the art
of dialect will be found in Charles Dudley Warner's
comment on George Cable's work, as far back as
1883, referring to the author's own rendition of it
from the platform. Mr. Warner says:

While the author was unfolding to his audience a life
and society unfamiliar to them and entrancing them with
pictures, the reality of which none doubted and the spell
of which none cared to escape, it occurred to me that here
was the solution of all the pother we have recently got into
about the realistic and the ideal schools in fiction. In
"Posson Jone," an awkward camp-meeting country preacher
is the victim of a vulgar confidence game; the scenes are
the street, a drinking-place, a gambling-saloon, a bull-ring,
and a calaboose; there is not a "respectable" character in
it. Where shall we look for a more faithful picture of low
life? Where shall we find another so vividly set forth in
all its sordid details? And yet see how art steps in, with
the wand of genius, to make literature! Over the whole the
author has cast an ideal light; over a picture that, in the
hands of a bungling realist, would have been repellent he
has thrown the idealizing grace that makes it one of the
most charming sketches in the world. Here is nature, as
nature only ought to be in literature, elevated but never departed from.

So we find dialect, as a branch of literature,
worthy of the high attention and employment of
the greatest master in letters—not the merest
mountebank. Turn to Dickens, in innumerable
passages of pathos: the death of poor Jo, or that
of the "Cheap John's" little daughter in her father's
arms, on the foot-board of his peddling cart before
the jeering of the vulgar mob; smile moistly, too,

at Mr. Sleary's odd philosophies; or at the trials of Sissy Jupe; or lift and tower with indignation, giving ear to Stephen Blackpool and the stainless nobility of his cloyed utterances.

The crudeness or the homeliness of the dialectic element does not argue its unfitness in any way. Some readers seem to think so; but they are wrong, and very gravely wrong. Our own brief history as a nation, and our finding and founding and maintaining of it, left our forefathers little time indeed for the delicate cultivation of the arts and graces of refined and scholarly attainments. And there is little wonder, and utter blamelessness on their part, if they lapsed in point of high mental accomplishments, seeing their attention was so absorbed by propositions looking toward the protection of their rude farm-homes, their meager harvests, and their half-stabled cattle from the dread invasion of the Indian. Then, too, they had their mothers and their wives and little ones to protect, to clothe, to feed, and to die for in this awful line of duty, as hundreds upon hundreds did. These sad facts are here accented and detailed not so much for the sake of being tedious as to indicate more clearly why it was that many of the truly heroic ancestors of "our best people" grew unquestionably dialect of caste —not alone in speech, but in every mental trait and personal address. It is a grievous fact for us to confront, but many of them wore apparel of the commonest, talked loudly, and doubtless said "thisaway" and "thataway," and "Watch y' doin' of?"

and "Whur y' goin' at?"—using dialect even in
their prayers to Him who, in His gentle mercy,
listened and was pleased; and who listens verily
unto this hour to all like prayers, yet pleased; yea,
haply listens to the refined rhetorical petitions of
those who are *not* pleased.

There is something more at fault than the language when we turn from or flinch at it; and, as
has been intimated, the wretched fault may be
skulkingly hidden away in the ambush of *ostensible*
dialect—that type of dialect so copiously produced
by its sole manufacturers, who, utterly stark and
bare of the vaguest idea of country life or country
people, at once assume that all their "gifted pens"
have to do is stupidly to misspell every word; vul-
garly mistreat and besloven every theme, however
sacred; maim, cripple, and disfigure language never
in the vocabulary of the countryman—then smuggle
these monstrosities of either rhyme or prose somehow into the public print that is innocently to smear
them broadcast all over the face of the country they
insult.

How different the mind and method of the true
intrepreter. As this phrase goes down the man
himself arises—the type perfect—Colonel Richard
Malcolm Johnston, who wrote "The Dukesborough
Tales"—an accomplished classical scholar and
teacher, yet no less an accomplished master and
lover of his native dialect of middle Georgia. He,
like Dickens, permits his rustic characters to think,
talk, act and live, just as nature designed them. He

does not make the pitiable error of either patronizing or making fun of them. He knows them and he loves them; and they know and love him in return. Recalling Colonel Johnston's dialectic sketches, with his own presentation of them from the platform, the writer notes a fact that seems singularly to obtain among all true dialect-writers, namely, that they are also endowed with native histrionic capabilities: *Hear,* as well as read, Twain, Cable, Johnston, Page, Smith, and all the list with barely an exception.

Did space permit, no better illustration of true dialect sketch and characterization might here be offered than Colonel Johnston's simple story of "Mr. Absalom Billingslea," or the short and simple annals of his like quaint contemporaries, "Mr. Bill Williams" and "Mr. Jonas Lively." The scene is the country and the very little country town, with landscape, atmosphere, simplicity, circumstance—all surroundings and conditions—*veritable*—everything rural and dialectic, no less than the simple, primitive, common, wholesome-hearted men and women who so naturally live and have their blessed being in his stories, just as in the life itself. This is the manifest work of the true dialect writer and expounder. In every detail, the most minute, such work reveals the master-hand and heart of the humanitarian as well as artist—the two are indissolubly fused—and the result of such just treatment of whatever lowly themes or characters we can but love and loyally approve with all our human hearts.

Such masters necessarily are rare, and such ripe
perfecting as is here attained may be in part the
mellowing result of age and long observation,
though it can be based upon the wisest, purest
spirit of the man as well as artist.

With no less approval should the work of Joel
Chandler Harris be regarded: His touch alike is
ever reverential. He has gathered up the bruised
and broken voices and the legends of the the slave,
and from his child-heart he has affectionately
yielded them to us in all their eery beauty and
wild loveliness. Through them we are made to
glorify the helpless and the weak and to revel in
their victories. But, better, we are taught that even
in barbaric breasts there dwells inherently the sense
of right above wrong—equity above law—and the
One Unerring Righteousness Eternal. With equal
truth and strength, too, Mr. Harris has treated the
dialectic elements of the interior Georgia country—
the wilds and fastnesses of the "moonshiners." His
tale of *Teague Poteet,* of some years ago, was
contemporaneous with the list of striking mountain
stories from that strong and highly gifted Tennes-
seean, Miss Murfree, or "Charles Egbert Crad-
dock." In the dialectic spirit her stories charm and
hold us. Always there is strangely mingled, but
most naturally, the gentle nature cropping out amid
the most desperate and stoical: the night scene in
the isolated mountain cabin, guarded ever without
and within from any chance down-swooping of the
minions of the red-eyed law; the great man-group

of gentle giants, with rifles never out of arm's-reach, in tender rivalry ranged admiringly around the crowing, wakeful little boy-baby; the return, at last, of the belated mistress of the house—the sister, to whom all do great, awkward reverence. Jealously snatching up the babe and kissing it, she querulously demands why he has not long ago been put to bed. "He 'lowed he wouldn't go," is the reply.

Thomas Nelson Page, of Virginia, who wrote *Meh Lady*—a positive classic in the negro dialect: his work is veritable—strong and pure and sweet; and as an oral reader of it the doubly gifted author, in voice and cadence, natural utterance, every possible effect of speech and tone, is doubtless without rival anywhere.

Many more, indeed, than may be mentioned now there are of these real benefactors and preservers of the wayside characters, times, and customs of our ever-shifting history. Needless is it to speak here of the earlier of our workers in the dialectic line—of James Russell Lowell's New England *Hosea Biglow,* Dr. Eggleston's *Hoosier School-Master,* or the very rare and quaint, bright prattle of *Helen's Babies.* In connection with this last let us very seriously inquire what this *real* child has done that Literature should so persistently refuse to give him an abiding welcome? Since for ages this question seems to have been left unasked, it may be timely now to propound it. Why not the real child in Literature? The real child is good enough (we all

know he is bad enough) to command our admiring
attention and most lively interest in real life, and
just as we find him "in the raw." Then why do we
deny him any righteous place of recognition in our
Literature? From the immemorial advent of our
dear old Mother Goose, Literature has been especially catering to the juvenile needs and desires, and
yet steadfastly overlooking, all the time, the very
principles upon which Nature herself founds and
presents this lawless little brood of hers—the children. It is not the children who are out of order;
it is Literature. And not only is Literature out of
order, but she is presumptuous; she is impudent.
She takes Nature's children and revises and corrects
them till "their own mother doesn't know them."
This is literal fact. So, very many of us are coming to inquire, as we've a right, why is the real child
excluded from a just hearing in the world of letters as he has in the world of fact? For instance,
what has the lovely little ragamuffin ever done of
sufficient guilt to consign him eternally to the monstrous penalty of speaking most accurate grammar
all the literary hours of the days of the years of his
otherwise natural life?—

> "Oh, mother, may I go to school
>   With brother Charles to-day?
> The air is very fine and cool;
>   Oh, mother, say I may!"

—Is this a real boy that would make such a request,
and is it the real language he would use? No, we

are glad to say that it is not. Simply it is a libel,
in every particular, on any boy, however fondly
and exactingly trained by parents however zealous
for his overdecorous future. Better, indeed, the
dubious sentiment of the most trivial nursery jingle,
since the latter at least maintains the lawless though
wholesome spirit of the child-genuine.—

> "Hink! Minx! The old witch winks—
>   The fat begins to fry;
> There's nobody home but Jumping Joan,
>   Father and mother and I."

Though even here the impious poet leaves the scar
of grammatical knowledge upon childhood's native
diction; and so the helpless little fellow is again
misrepresented, and his character, to all intents and
purposes, is assaulted and maligned outrageously
thereby.

Now, in all seriousness, this situation ought not
to be permitted to exist, though to change it seems
an almost insurmountable task. The general public,
very probably, is not aware of the real gravity of
the position of the case as even unto this day it
exists. Let the public try, then, to contribute the
real child to the so-called Child Literature of its
country, and have its real child returned as promptly
as it dare show its little tousled head in the presence
of that scholarly and dignified institution. Then
ask why your real child has been spanked back
home again, and the wise mentors there will virtually tell you that Child Literature wants no real

children in it, that the real child's example of defective grammar and lack of elegant deportment would furnish to its little patrician patrons suggestions very hurtful indeed to their higher morals, tendencies, and ambitions. Then, although the general public couldn't for the life of it see why or how, and might even be reminded that *it* was just such a rowdying child itself, and that its *father*— the Father of his Country—was just such a child; that Abraham Lincoln was just such a lovable, lawless child, and yet was blessed and chosen in the end for the highest service man may ever render unto man,—all—all this argument would avail not in the least, since the elegantly minded purveyors of Child Literature can not possibly tolerate the presence of any but the refined children—the very proper children—the studiously thoughtful, poetic children;— and these must be kept safe from the contaminating touch of our rough-and-tumble little fellows in "hodden gray," with frowzly heads, begrimed but laughing faces, and such awful, awful vulgarities of naturalness, and crimes of simplicity, and brazen faith and trust, and love of life and everybody in it. All other real people are getting into Literature; and without some real children along will they not soon be getting lonesome, too?

NOTES

# NOTES

p. 1

## TOD

Printed in *The Greenfield Commercial,* June 1, 1871; published in THE BOSS GIRL—1885, SKETCHES IN PROSE—1891. This early story is rich in the boy Riley's own experiences.

p. 6, ll. 19-20: *Casabianca,* by Felicia Dorothea Hemans; *The Speech of Logan* reported by John Gibson, and *Catiline's Defiance* by George Croly are selections appearing in *McGuffey's Readers* and *Sargent's Standard Speaker* used in the Greenfield schools in the poet's childhood.

p. 19

## A REMARKABLE MAN

Printed in *The Indianapolis Journal,* February 16, 1877; published in THE BOSS GIRL—1885, SKETCHES IN PROSE—1891. Of all his stories this is Mr. Riley's favorite. "The Remarkable Man" he met in Union City, Indiana, a noteworthy personage there at the time, not a writer, as in the story, but a phrenologist. This character made a deep impression on Mr. Riley and was often in his thoughts; yet it was two years after he met him before he wrote the story.

p. 39

## AN ADJUSTABLE LUNATIC

Dated April 20, 1878, printed in *The Indianapolis Journal,* April 23, 1878; published in THE BOSS GIRL—1885, SKETCHES IN PROSE—1891.

p. 58    TWIGGS AND TUDENS

Printed under *The Buzz Club Papers* in *The Indianapolis Saturday Herald,* September 28, 1878; published in ARMAZINDY—1894. The introductory part of the sketch did not appear in the early version.


p. 74    AN OLD SETTLER'S STORY


Printed in *The Indianapolis Journal,* October 27 and November 3, 1878; published in PIPES O' PAN AT ZEKESBURY (first edition only)—1888, NEGHBORLY POEMS (not in first edition)—1897. The early version of this sketch had the following introduction :—

At the conclusion of the afternoon session of a meeting of old settlers, held in Music Hall, October 3, 1878, it was my fortune—and my good fortune, I may truthfully add—to be thrown by the dispersing throng into a position from which I found it impossible to extricate myself, only as the laggard hand of time saw fit to lend assistance.

Being farthest from the entrance to the hall, and near enough to the speakers' stand to catch the full tide of antediluvian humanity that from that quarter surged upon me, I found myself hopelessly adrift upon a sea of heads—old heads, with scarce a one in sight with hair enough to foam in gray about the temples.

It was a curious gathering; yet, jostled, jarred and jolted almost beyond all tolerance, I could but find a dreamy speculation cropping from my troubled fancy, as in each rheumy eye I saw a latent light of pride, and nestled in the wrinkles of each withered face a look of cheerfulness and warm thanksgiving.

Directly in my front an old lady, with a parasol beneath her arm as big as an umbrella, and a back as broad as one, wabbled pantingly along, with abrupt pauses in which she invariably turned about with a good-natured and apologetic " 'Ll did you ever !" or "Don't it jest beat all !" while behind me, with two great horny hands set firmly on my shoulders, a hale old man of eighty years or more, most persistently and unpoetically tickled the back of my neck with

> "The lists of such a beard as youth gone out
> Had left in ashes;"

and following the suggestion which the additional burthen of his weight had thrown upon my rather irritated esthetic sensibilities, I was mentally christening him "My Old Man of the Sea," when in an evolution of the old lady's her eye caught his, and in the joyous recognition following, I learned his real name was "Uncle Tommy," for in response to that address, coupled with the old-time inquiry of "Don't it jest beat all?" he solemnly responded, "I have saw—I have saw many and many of a happy time; but I undertake to say that to-day's doin's has given more satisfaction, as fur an actual enjoyment's concerned, than we've had sence the good old-fashion' days went out o' style." And with this remark a certain unaccountable desire came over me to know this old man, and to make, if possible, my very uncomfortable proximity subserve this end, and be the means of placing in my possession such pure and unadulterated reminiscences of the past as had been vaguely hinted to my fancy in the quaint expression, "Sence the good old-fashion' days went out o' style."

How well my covert resolve succeeded; and how the curtain of the present slowly lifted, and how, with eager eye and ear, across a two-hours' desert of forgetfulness I journeyed at the will of Uncle Tommy, must find its own crude explanation in the following—

p. 120                          JAMESY

Dated Christmas, 1878, printed in *The Indianapolis Journal,* December 29, 1878, with the title, *The Boss Girl;* published in THE BOSS GIRL—1885, SKETCHES IN PROSE—1891.

p. 155                    TALE OF A SPIDER

Printed in *The Indianapolis Journal,* May 13, 1879; published in THE BOSS GIRL—1885,

SKETCHES IN PROSE—1891. This story is a fantasy of the writer's early days at Indianapolis, when he shared a room in the old Vinton Block with Dr. Franklin W. Hays who appears in this sketch.

p. 183 DREAMS

Printed in *The Kokomo Tribune,* May 24, 1879; hitherto unpublished in book form.

p. 188 THE OBJECT LESSON

First read by Mr. Riley at the Park Theater (Indianapolis), October 17, 1879; hitherto unpublished in book form. This was one of Mr. Riley's most popular recitations.

p. 193 EZ

Printed in *The Indianapolis Journal,* May 23, 1880; hitherto unpublished in book form.

p. 197
THE CHAMPION CHECKER-PLAYER OF AMERIKY

Printed in *The Indianapolis Journal,* September 5, 1880; published in PIPES O' PAN AT ZEKESBURY (not in first edition)—1898.

p. 209 THE JUDKINS PAPERS

This series was contributed to *The Anderson Democrat, The Indianapolis Journal* and *Life* from August, 1877, to June, 1883, entitled *Judkins' Boy* and *Trillpipe's Boy.* Of these sketches, those beginning with "Mud-Turtles" and ending with

"Dudes" appeared in *Life* from March 29 to May 31, 1883. In *Life* the name "Judkins" was used; in the newspapers, the name "Trillpipe."

p. 225    ECCENTRIC MR. CLARK

Printed in *The Indianapolis Journal,* May 6, 1882; published in THE BOSS GIRL—1885, SKETCHES IN PROSE—1891.

p. 245    A NEST-EGG

Printed in *The Indianapolis Journal,* June 3, 1882; published in THE BOSS GIRL—1885, SKETCHES IN PROSE—1891.

p. 256    "THE BOY FROM ZEENY"

Printed in *The Indianapolis Journal,* June 10, 1882, with the title, *The Boy from Xenia;* published in THE BOSS GIRL—1885, SKETCHES IN PROSE—1891.

p. 272    WHERE IS MARY ALICE SMITH?

Printed in *The Indianapolis Journal,* September 30, 1882; published in THE BOSS GIRL—1885, SKETCHES IN PROSE—1891. Mary Alice Smith is Little Orphant Annie. See the poem *Little Orphant Annie* and its note, Vol. III, p. 313.

T. P. O'Conner in an article in *The London Sunday Sun* of April 10, 1892, makes the following interesting comment on this story:—

It is a thorough American story, and yet I think it will say more to an English than an American reader; at least to an English reader that knows something of

the social condition of America. The scene is in the West
—perhaps I should say, the middle as distinguished from the
extreme West—which has grown up since the days in which
this story occurred. It is the story of what we should call a
maid-of-all-work told by one of the children in the house
in which she is employed. I have already commented on
the sweet sense Mr. Riley gives of the intimacy and tenderness of the relations between the children and the servants
of an American household; relations that, to me at least,
appear to make life so much tenderer, easier and more
human than the frigidity of relations in our own house-
holds, with their strict commercial basis. You can see
that the poor little girl, who is the heroine of this story,
instead of being looked down upon as a servant, is rather
looked up to by the children where she lives. The portrait
of the girl has that subtlety which is in nearly all Mr.
Riley's portraits of childhood. He seizes and reproduces
that indefinable wistfulness—that curiously-touching and
tender mysteriousness that is all about childhood—the mysteriousness that partly suggested to Wordsworth the music
and the eloquence of his greatest ode. . . . I find it hard
to understand how anybody could read the story without
dimmed eyes and quickened breath. I am grateful to the
author who by such a tale—it will take you at most half
an hour to read it—has brought home to my imagination,
more clearly than a thousand pages of historic dulness and
official record, the pathos, the pitifulness, the vast tragedy
of the American war.

p. 285           THE OLD MAN

Read as an introduction to the poem, *The Old
Man,* at a meeting of the Indianapolis Literary Club,
February 18, 1884; printed in *The Indianapolis
Journal,* February 20, 1884; published in THE BOSS
GIRL—1885, SKETCHES IN PROSE—1891.

p. 294           THE GILDED ROLL

Printed in *The Indianapolis Journal,* July 26,
1884; published in PIPES O' PAN AT ZEKESBURY—
1888.

p. 311 A WILD IRISHMAN

Printed in *The Indianapolis Journal,* August 2, 1884; published in PIPES O' PAN AT ZEKESBURY— 1888. The first version of this sketch did not include the poems, *Says He* and *Chairley Burke.*

p. 331 MRS. MILLER

Printed in *The Indianapolis Journal,* August 9, 1884; published in PIPES O' PAN AT ZEKESBURY— 1888.

p. 348 AT ZEKESBURY

Printed in *The Chicago Current,* April 24, 1886, with the title, *A Waste of Genius at Zekesbury;* published in PIPES O' PAN AT ZEKESBURY—1888.

p. 366 A CALLER FROM BOONE

The manuscript for this sketch, recently discovered among the papers preserved by Mr. Riley's sister, Elva Riley Eitel, bears no date, nor can a satisfactory one be determined. It was probably written in 1887 or soon afterward, when Mr. Riley was living at his sister's home in Indianapolis.

p. 378 THE OLD SOLDIER'S STORY

This sketch was written in the fall of 1888; not hitherto published in book form. Mr. Robert Burdette after a visit to Mr. Riley's, April 28, 1911, reported in *The Los Angeles Times* the following sketchy though true account of the origin of this story :—

It was while Mr. Riley and Edgar Wilson Nye were on a lecture tour. . . . One morning on their lyceum tour they landed in a city where they knew by past experience they would be assailed by self-appointed delegations of entertainers. They would be importuned to take long drives over rough and dusty roads to see things they had seen a thousand times and didn't want to see the first time. They would be dragged away to luncheon with people who made them tired and dragooned to dinner with folk who bored them. And Jim rebelled. They obtained privacy in their own rooms long enough to wash their faces and the poet said:

"Bill here's where I shake the committee on hospitality. I'm not going out of my room till we go to the hall to-night. I'll play ill, I'll do anything but wear myself out listening to a lot of old stories badly told all day and then go before the audience that pays its good money to hear us at our best so tired and worn out that I look and feel like a shadow on the scenery. Let's send away our genial friends and sleep till dinner time."

So Jim went dead, as he knows how to do, but Bill couldn't bear to disappoint the committee. He came back to dine at the hotel, however, pale and tired, but faintly smiling and trying to feel strong for the evening's work. Jim was mad. He determined to teach Bill a lesson.

"When we went down to dinner," he said, "I made up my mind I'd give him enough of his old stale, worm-eaten stories, such as I knew he'd been feeding on all afternoon. I began to tell him as earnestly as though it was newer than the hour, the oldest story I ever heard. I heard a circus clown tell it when I was a boy and the first eternity only knows how old it had to be before a clown would be allowed to use it. You've heard it long before you ever heard me tell it—the old man's story of the soldier carrying his wounded comrade off the battle-field—the comrade whose leg was first shot off and whose head was carried away by a second cannon-ball on their way to the field hospital. Well, I dragged the old thing out as long as I could, just to weary poor Bill. I told it in the forgetful fashion of an old man with confused memory; told the point two or three times before I came to it; went back again to pick up dropped stitches in the web of my story; wandered and maundered. Thinks I, I'll give this lad a taste of age-long stories that will sicken him of them forever. I made it as long and dreary as I knew how."

But to Riley's indignant amazement Nye received the narrative with convulsions of merriment. He choked over his meat and drink until he quit trying to eat and just listened, giggled, chuckled and roared. He declared it was the best thing Riley had ever done and insisted that he put it in his program.

At first Riley thought his joke-fellow had only detected the plot and was meeting it in his own way. But he convinced Jim that he was in earnest and, after about a month of this importunity, Riley told the story to an audience of two thousand people. The galleries fell, the house went wild, and he had to tell it again. Ever after it was one of his funniest numbers.

See *How to Tell a Story and Other Essays,* by Mark Twain; also Vol. I, p. 383.

p. 382    DIALECT IN LITERATURE

Read by Mr. Riley before the Indianapolis Literary Club, October 6, 1890, printed in *The Forum,* December, 1892; published in Neghborly Poems (not in first edition)—1897. In a letter to Benj. S. Parker, dated August 29, 1887, Mr. Riley said:—

I most conscientiously believe (outside of all its numberless deviations) there is a legitimate use for dialect, and as honorable a place for it as for the English, pure and unadulterated. The only trouble seems to be its *miss* use —its use by writers who fail wholly to interpret its *real spirit* and *character*—either through blind ignorance, or malicious perverseness, in what they are about. To range back to the very Genesis of all speech, we can only rightly conjecture a dialectic tongue—a deduction as natural as that a babe must first lisp—the child babble—and the youth and man gradually educate away all preceding blemishes. And I think it as absolutely necessary, in the general illustration of human life and character, to employ the dialect as the speech refined—its real value, of course, dependent on the downright wisdom and honesty of the writer who employs it. And my ambition in the use of dialect is simply as above outlined. That I have few endorsers among the scholarly I grievedly admit, yet am graciously assured and compensated by the homely approbation of my class and grade of fellow men. Once in a while, however (and there's, at last, a *discernible growth* of the tendency), some finished critic discriminates and estimates the dialectic purpose *exactly*. Let me quote from *Art Interchange* of August 13 :— It says of a dialect poem of mine in the August *Century* [*Nothin' to Say*] that it "is an illustration of the only possible excuse for this sort of work," in that "the tender and touching little poem does not depend on the dialect"—but that—"the feeling, the homely pathos of the verse makes it of value, and the dialect is simply its strongest and most fitting expression." Now I am very proud of this *detailed* estimate of the poem. That is the highest praise I seek or my ambition desires, and I think you will believe me and approve me there.

BIBLIOGRAPHY

# CONTENTS

## PART I—WORKS OF JAMES WHITCOMB RILEY

## PART II—RILEYANA

# PART I
## Works of James Whitcomb Riley

---

## INDIVIDUAL VOLUMES

1. "The | Old Swimmin'-Hole," | and | 'Leven More Poems, | by | Benj. F. Johnson, of Boone. | [James Whitcomb Riley.] | Indianapolis, Ind.: | George C. Hitt & Co. | 1883. | [copyright 1883]

Page dimensions, 4½ x 6¼ inches. Paper cover, with reproduction of title page; pp., (3) preliminary leaves (on third appears the half title "The Old Swimmin'-Hole," | and 'Leven More Poems. | ), 50 numbered pages, (1) blank leaf at end; uncut. Book issued in brown paper wrapper, with same wording on outside as appears on half title. The title page, cover and wrapper printed in red.

One thousand copies issued at the expense of Mr. Hitt and Mr. Riley. The latter formed the "Co." in the firm. The book was printed in Cincinnati by Robert Clarke & Co., and contains twelve poems originally published in *The Indianapolis Journal* over the pseudonym of "Benj. F. Johnson, of Boone." Preface is signed: "J. W. R. Indianapolis, Ind. July, 1883."

"The | Old Swimmin'-Hole," | and | 'Leven More Poems, | by | Benj. F. Johnson, of Boone. | [James Whitcomb Riley.] | Second Edition. | Indianapolis: | Merrill, Meigs & Co., Publishers and Booksellers. | 1883. |

4½ x 6¼. Paper cover with title as above on same. No title page; pp. 50, (6) blank leaves at end. On inside

**413**

of back cover appears the same caption as is used for half title in first edition. The volume was entirely reset and text was printed inside a red line border.

"The | Old Swimmin'-Hole," | and | 'Leven More Poems, | by | Benj. F. Johnson, of Boone. | [James Whitcomb Riley.] | Second Edition. | Indianapolis. | The Bowen-Merrill Co., Publishers and Booksellers. | 1886. |

4½ x 6¼. Paper cover with reproduction of title page; pp., (1) preliminary leaf, 50, (1) blank leaf at end. Title printed on page (3), verso "Publishers' Note." Preface pp. (7). Issued with paper wrapper same as first edition.

"The | Old Swimmin'-Hole," | and | 'Leven More Poems, | by | Benj. F. Johnson, of Boone. | [James Whitcomb Riley.] | Sixth Edition. | Indianapolis : | The Bowen-Merrill Co., Publishers and Booksellers. | 1888. |

4 x 6. Various parti-colored cloth bindings, with decorations, full title and author's name in gold on front cover; pp. (2) blank leaves, 50, (2) blank leaves at end; text printed inside a red line border; portrait as frontispiece. Also bound in limp leather in several colors with | The Old Swimmin' Hole. | Riley | stamped in gold at top of front cover and beneath a small gold harp; full gilt; first blank leaf front and back changed to decorated lining paper.

A Photographic Fac-simile of | The First Edition of | James Whitcomb Riley's First Book | Presented | December 11, 1909, to | The Indiana Society of Chicago | With the Compliments of | The Bobbs-Merrill Company | and the Author | *auto-graph* |

Identical with the first edition except that a leaf containing the above description is pasted between the first two blank leaves, and also that two lines at the bottom of the "Preface" differ : in the reproduction, the words "Indianapolis, Ind." are one inch in length; in the original they are 1⅛ inches. The date "July, 1883." in the reproduction is $\frac{9}{16}$ inches long; in the original ⅝ inches.

2. Character Sketches | The Boss Girl | A Christmas Story | and | Other Sketches | by | James Whitcomb Riley | Author of "The Old Swimmin' Hole," etc. | Indianapolis | The Bowen-Merrill Co | 1886 | [c. 1885]

5 x 7. Pictorial paper cover with following caption on front and back | The | Boss Girl | A X-mas Story, and | An Adjustable Lunatic | Tod | A Remarkable Man | A Nestegg | Tale of A Spider | Mary Alice Smith | Eccentric Mr. Clark | The Boy From Zeeny | The old Man | &c. &c. &c. | By | James Whitcomb Riley | Indianapolis, Ind: | The Bowen-Merrill Co. 1886. | Chandler Sc. Indpls. | The design on the cover was drawn by Mr. Riley and represents an imp reaching out of a cloud with a feathered pen and touching an ink bottle, which is mounted as a cannon and is exploding in the direction of the above noted list of titles; pp. 263, (4). The last four pages contain a reprint of the title page of the third print of *"The Old Swimmin'- Hole" and 'Leven More Poems,* three stanzas of *Thoughts Fer the Discuraged Farmer,* and "Publishers' Note" on *"Old Swimmin'-Hole."*
A limited number of this edition was rebound in tan cloth with the design as above described on the front cover.
The first edition is distinguished by this mark on the verso of title page : "Stereotyped by Wanamaker & Marshall, Indianapolis." The "Third Edition," so marked on back, is similar to the cloth bound first edition.
Another very rare second edition has a brown cloth binding, marked on the front cover in gold | Character | Sketches | at top, and in the lower right-hand corner | James Whitcomb Riley | . The back reads | The | Boss Girl | and | Other | Sketches | J. W. Riley. |
A few were bound in black leather, full gilt, with the title | The Boss Girl | James Whitcomb Riley | stamped in gold on the front cover.
In 1891, this volume appeared as *Sketches in Prose and Occasional Verses.* See title No. 8.

3. Afterwhiles | by | James Whitcomb Riley | Indianapolis | Bowen-Merrill Co., Publishers | 1888 | [c. 1887]

4½ x 7. Cream-colored boards with brown cloth back; title and author's name stamped in brown on front cover, in gold on back; gilt top; pp. (2) blank leaves, (8), (1) blank leaf, 160, (2) blank leaves at end.

Afterwhiles | by | James Whitcomb Riley | Indianapolis | Bowen-Merrill Co., Publishers | 1888 |

Brown cloth cover similar to back of first edition, with a narrow beaded border in black at top of front cover and back. Identical in other respects.

Afterwhiles | by | James Whitcomb Riley | Indianapolis | Bowen-Merrill Co., Publishers | 1888 |

Identical with first edition except for cover,—art boards with green cloth back stamped in gold; | Afterwhiles | Riley | at top of back is the only printing on cover; gilt top.

Afterwhiles | by | James Whitcomb Riley | Fourth Thousand. | Indianapolis | Bowen-Merrill Co., Publishers | 1888 |

Identical with first edition except for the insertion of words "Fourth Thousand" on title page, and the substitution of a half-title page for blank page preceding text.

Afterwhiles | by | James Whitcomb Riley | Seventh Thousand | Indianapolis | Bowen-Merrill Co., Publishers | 1888 |

Identical with preceding edition except for the binding and for the words "Seventh Thousand" on title page. Cloth binding in several colors, with a small illustration at top of front cover representing a country scene, with title "Afterwhiles;" at lower right-hand corner author's full name.

4. Pipes O' Pan at Zekesbury | by | James Whitcomb Riley | Indianapolis | Bowen-Merrill Co., Publishers | 1889 | [c. 1888]

4½ x 7. Cloth binding, with a symbolic design at top of front cover of Pan attired as a Hoosier boy, showing his cloven feet, and his horns protruding through his old straw hat, seated on a rock playing on pipes. The idea, which was Mr. Riley's, was carried out by the artist, Mr. R. B. Gruelle; gilt top; pp. (2) blank leaves, 245, (3) blank leaves at end.

Pipes O' Pan at Zekesbury | by | James Whitcomb Riley | Indianapolis | Bowen-Merrill Co., Publishers | 1889 |

Same as first edition except that the binding is art boards and cloth back with wording and decorations stamped in gold.

Pipes O' Pan at Zekesbury | by | James Whitcomb Riley | Indianapolis | Bowen-Merrill Co., Publishers | 1889 |

Same as first edition except that it has a parti-colored cloth binding, with a conventional floral design stamped at top of front cover, and on the back the following is stamped in gold: Pipes | o' Pan | at | Zekesbury | James | Whitcomb | Riley. | It contains Mr. Riley's portrait as frontispiece.

5. Nye and Riley's | Railway Guide | by | Edgar W. Nye | and | James Whitcomb Riley | Illustrated by Baron DeGrimm E. Zimmerman | Walt. McDougall and others | Chicago | The Dearborn Publishing Company | 88 and 90 La Salle Street | New York 1888 San Francisco |

5¼ x 7½. Pictorial cloth binding with medallion portraits of Mr. Nye and Mr. Riley embossed in gold. pp. xvi, 203, (1) blank leaf, (2) advertisements, (2) blank leaves,

decorated lining paper front and back.  Two full page illustrations preceding title page, one showing "Bill Nye,"
bearing a harp, mounted on Pegasus; the other "J. W.
Riley," also bearing a harp, crowned with a laurel wreath
and mounted on a dolphin.  Also issued with paper covers.

Reissued as *Fun, Wit and Humor,* Chicago: Laird &
Lee, 1889; as *Nye and Riley's Wit and Humor,* Chicago:
Thompson & Thomas, 1904; as *On the "Shoe-String" Limited With Nye and Riley,* Chicago: Thompson & Thomas,
1905.

6.  Old-Fashioned  Roses | by | James  Whitcomb
Riley | *shamrock    design* | London | Longmans,
Green, and Co. | 1888 | All rights reserved |

3¾ x 6¼.  Blue cloth sides, vellum back with blue label
bearing title. pp. (1) blank leaf, ix, (1), 145, (1) blank
leaf.  Sheets were imported and issued with the title page
bearing The Bowen-Merrill Co. imprint under date of
1889, [c. 1888]

7.  Rhymes of | Childhood | by | James Whitcomb
Riley | Indianapolis | The Bowen-Merrill Co | 1891 |
[c. 1890]

4¾ x 7¼.  Dark blue silk cloth binding stamped in gold.
Title at top of front cover, below which is a child's face
surrounded by cloud and stars with name of author at
lower right side; gilt top; pp. (2) blank leaves, (2), portrait frontispiece, (12), 186, (2) blank leaves.

8.  Sketches in Prose | and | Occasional Verses |
by | James    Whitcomb    Riley | Indianapolis | The
Bowen-Merrill Co | 1891 | [c. 1891]

4¾ x 7.  Cloth binding; pp. (2) blank leaves, 263, (2)
blank leaves.

The contents of this volume was originally published
with the title *The Boss Girl,* in which the first story was
entitled *The Boss Girl* instead of *Jamesy.*  See title No. 2.

9. "The Old Swimmin'-Hole" and | 'Leven More Poems | Neghborly Poems | on Friendship | Grief and | Farm-Life | by | Benj. F. Johnson, of Boone | [James Whitcomb Riley.] | 1891 | The Bowen-Merrill Co | Indianapolis, Ind | [c. 1891]

4¾ x 7¼. Parti-colored cloth binding, darkest color forming upper third of cover on which is stamped in gold, | Neghborly Poems | James Whitcomb Riley | ; gilt top; pp. (2) blank leaves, (16), 90, (2) blank leaves. Five full page illustrations, three of which are by Mr. R. B. Gruelle. In 1897, when included in the Homestead Edition, the title of this book was changed to *Neghborly Poems and Dialect Sketches.*

The Old | Swimmin'-Hole | James Whitcomb Riley. | This Edition | Limited | to One Hundred | Copies | Number —— | The Bowen-Merrill Company, Publishers, Indianapolis | [c. 1895]

Autograph edition: the title page is printed in red, all wording excepting name and place of publishers being in center of page and enclosed in a design resembling a shield, surmounted by a woman's head. At the bottom of the page enclosed with fancy scroll design is a space for author's autograph. 4½ x 7. Bright red silk cloth binding stamped in gold; gilt top; shield and head design on cover containing | The Old | Swimmin'-Hole | James Whitcomb Riley. |, fancy scroll designs at corners, back stamped with monogram, B-M-Co. pp. (2) blank leaves, (2), photogravure of old swimming hole as frontispiece, v-ix, (9), 112, (2) blank leaves; contents same as that of preceding volume with the addition of the essay, *Dialect in Literature.*

10. The Flying Islands | Of the Night | by | James Whitcomb Riley | *"A thynge of wytchencref—an idle dreme."* | Indianapolis | The Bowen-Merrill Co. | 1892 | [c. 1891]

5 x 7½. Bristol boards stamped with design of winged heads, title and author's name lettered in silver at top of

front cover; pp. (3) blank leaves, (8), 88, (3) blank leaves. The edition was first put on sale at the Flower Mission Fair, Indianapolis, November 3, 1891.

The Flying Islands | Of the Night | by | James Whitcomb Riley | *"A thynge of wytchencref—an idle dreme."* | Indianapolis | The Bowen-Merrill Co. | 1892 |

Same as above except the cover is parti-colored cloth.

The Poems and Prose | Sketches of | James Whitcomb Riley | The Flying Islands | of the Night | Charles Scribner's | Sons New York 1898 | [c. 1898]

5 x 7½. Brown cloth binding, front cover margined by gold line with small gold design in center; gold lettering on back; gilt top; pp. (1) blank leaf, (12), 5-187, (1) blank leaf; uncut. Pages 113-187 are here added to those of the previous editions, and comprise a number of poems under the general title | Spirk and Wunk Rhymes | Rounds and Catches |.

A special edition, 1913, is described under title No. 63.

11. An Old | Sweetheart | James Whitcomb Riley | Indianapolis. | The Bowen-Merrill Co. | Copyright 1891 Armstrong & Co. Lith. Boston. |

7½ x 10. Parti-colored, illustrated, cloth binding; also half cloth and decorated boards; front cover worded: An Old | Sweetheart | of | Mine | by | James Whitcomb Riley |; full gilt; thirteen color and monotint plates, (unnumbered); leaves, (1) picture in color | An Old | Sweetheart | of | Mine |, title page, (11), decorated lining paper front and back. This edition contains the original eleven stanzas of the poem, one stanza to a leaf.

12. Green Fields and | Running Brooks | by ‖ James Whitcomb Riley | Indianapolis | The Bowen-Merrill Company | 1893 | [c. 1892]

4¾ x 7¼. Cloth binding; pp. (2) blank leaves, 224, (2) blank leaves.

13. Poems Here | at Home | by | James Whitcomb Riley | Pictures by E. W. Kemble | *publisher's seal* | New York | The Century Co. | 1893 | [c. 1893]

4½ x 7. Green cloth binding with a stamped floreated border. The design and wording on front and back covers is identical, except that on front cover and back of book it is printed in gold, and on back cover blank stamped; gilt top; pp. (2) blank leaves, (4), 187, (1) blank leaf; contains portrait of author. Same edition also bound in Japan vellum with similar cover design stamped in gold; uncut.

14. Armazindy | by | James Whitcomb Riley | Indianapolis | The Bowen-Merrill Co. | 1894 | [c. 1894]

4¾ x 7¼. Parti-colored cloth binding, darkest color forming upper third of cover on which is stamped in gold | Armazindy | James Whitcomb Riley | ; gilt top; pp. (1) blank leaf, i-ii, photogravure frontispiece, iii-viii, (1) blank leaf, 169, (1) blank leaf.

Armazindy | by | James Whitcomb Riley | Indianapolis | The Bowen-Merrill Co. | 1894 |

5 x 7½. Red buckram binding margined with gilt band, lettering in gold; gilt top; pp. (2) blank leaves, i-ii, portrait frontispiece, iii-viii, (1) blank leaf, (2), 169, (2) blank leaves; uncut; four photogravure illustrations added in body of book.

Armazindy. | James Whitcomb Riley | This Edition | Limited | to One Hundred | Copies | Number — |

Autograph edition: 4¾ x 7½; text identical with second edition, preliminary pages changed as follows: (2) blank leaves, title page as above described inserted, substitution of portrait for picture as frontispiece, 4 pages occupied by table of contents, half-title page and picture preceding first page of text; second title page and binding, except for change of title, identical with that of autograph edition of *The Old Swimmin'-Hole,* described under title No. 9.

15. A Child-World | by | James Whitcomb Riley | Longmans, Green, and Co. | London and Bombay | 1896 | All rights reserved |

3¾ x 6¼. Half vellum and cloth binding; gilt top; (size and binding identical with *Old-Fashioned Roses* described under title No. 6). pp. (2) blank leaves, (14), 135, (1) blank leaf. Sheets were imported and issued with title page bearing the imprint | Indianapolis and Kansas City | The Bowen-Merrill Company | 1896 |. Also published the same year by the latter company in both blue and red cloth bindings, printed in gold, [c. 1896].

A Child-World | James Whitcomb Riley | This Edition | Limited | to One Hundred | Copies | Number — |

Autograph edition: 4¾ x 7; text identical with first edition; changes in preliminary pages as follows: (3) blank leaves, above described title page substituted for original, half-title page just before frontispiece with the additional words "Limited Edition;" title page and binding, except for change of title, identical with that of autograph edition of *The Old Swimmin'-Hole,* described under title No. 9.

16. Rubáiyát of Doc Sifers | by James Whitcomb Riley | Illustrated | by | C. M. Relyea | Published by The Century Co. | New York MDCCCXCVII | [c. 1897]

5 x 7½. Green cloth binding, illustration in colors stamped on front cover, marginal lines of gold around picture and front cover, lettering in gold; gilt top; pp. (3) blank leaves, (8), ix-x, (1), 111, (1) blank leaf.

Rubáiyát | of Doc Sifers | James Whitcomb Ri-
ley | This Edition Limited | to One Hundred Copies
| No. — |

Autograph edition: same as first edition in text with the
addition of a second title page, as above described, and a
portrait as frontispiece; design of second title page identical with that of autograph edition of *The Old Swimmin'-
Hole,* described under title No. 9; has red silk cloth binding also identical with said special edition except for the
substitution of head of "Doc Sifers" for woman's head.

17.   The Golden Year | From the Verse and Prose
| of | James  Whitcomb  Riley | compiled  by | Clara
E. Laughlin | "When wealth no more shall rest in
mounded heaps, | But smit with freër light shall
slowly melt | In many streams to fatten lower lands,
| And light shall spread, and man be liker man |
Thro' all the season of the golden year." | Tenny-
son | Longmans, Green, and Co. | 39 Paternoster
Row, London | New York and Bombay | 1898 | All
rights reserved |

3¾ x 6¼.  Blue cloth sides, vellum back with blue label
bearing title; gilt top (size and binding identical with *Old-
Fashioned Roses* described under title No. 6); pp. (2)
blank leaves, (9), viii, (2), 176, (2), (2) blank leaves.
Sheets were imported and issued with title page bearing
the imprint of The Bowen-Merrill Company, [c. 1898].

18.   Riley | Child-Rhymes | James Whitcomb Ri-
ley | with | Hoosier Pictures | by | Will Vawter | In-
dianapolis and Kansas City | The Bowen-Merrill
Company | MDCCC XC IX | [c. 1898]

5 x 7½.   Green ornamental cloth binding, stamped in
gold, design of boy and girl on front cover, figures in
green outlined in black with a background of gold; pp.
(3) blank leaves. (10), xv-xx, (2), 23-188, (3) blank
leaves.

Riley | Child-Rhymes | James Whitcomb Riley | with | Hoosier Pictures | by | Will Vawter | Indianapolis | The Bobbs-Merrill Company | Publishers | [c. 1905]

This edition is distinguished by marginal drawings on the dedication page and throughout the volume, and by the binding, which was a cloth of darker green. This edition was also bound in green leather, bearing the title in gold upon a smooth shield.

19. Riley | Love-Lyrics | James Whitcomb Riley | with | Life Pictures | by | William B. Dyer | Indianapolis, Indiana, U. S. A. | The Bowen-Merrill Company | [c. 1899]

5¼ x 7¾. Green ornamental cloth binding, stamped in gold; design on front cover of girl's head in brown and black on a background of gold, heart-shaped, surrounded by a cluster of marguerites in white; marginal gold line on front cover; pp. (2) blank leaves, (12), xv-xx, (2), 23-190, (2), (3) blank pages.

Riley | Love-Lyrics | James Whitcomb Riley | with | Life Pictures | by | William B. Dyer | Indianapolis, Indiana, U. S. A. | The Bobbs-Merrill Company |

Similar to first edition except for title page. Published in 1902.

Riley | Love-Lyrics | James Whitcomb Riley | with | Life Pictures | by | William B. Dyer | Indianapolis | The Bobbs-Merrill Company | Publishers | [c. 1905]

Similar to first edition except that the frontispiece and many illustrations have been changed. Also bound in leather.

20. Home-Folks | James Whitcomb Riley | Indianapolis | The Bowen-Merrill Company | Publishers | [c. 1900]

4¾ x 7. Red cloth binding, marginal gold line on front cover, ornamental gold scroll on back, lettering in gold; gilt top; pp. (1) blank leaf, (18), 166, (2) blank leaves.

21. Riley | Farm-Rhymes | James Whitcomb Riley | with | Country Pictures | by | Will Vawter | Indianapolis | The Bowen-Merrill Company | Publishers | [c. 1901]

5 x 7½. Green ornamental cloth binding, gold lettering; pp. (3) blank leaves, (10), (xv)-(xix), (3), 23-187, (1), (3) blank leaves.

Riley | Farm-Rhymes | James Whitcomb Riley | with | Country Pictures | by | Will Vawter | Indianapolis | The Bobbs-Merrill Company | Publishers | [c. 1905]

Similar to first edition except for title page and list of copyrights. Also bound in leather.

22. The Book | of Joyous Children | James | Whitcomb | Riley | Illustrated by | J. W. Vawter | New York | Charles Scribner's Sons | 1902 | [c. 1902]

5 x 7½. Illustrated cloth binding, design and lettering on cover in gold, gilt top, illustrated title page, book profusely illustrated, each poem having one or more pictures; pp. (1) blank leaf, (8), (ix)-(xiv), (2), 3-176, (2) blank leaves; uncut.

The Book of | Joyous Children | by | James Whitcomb Riley | Author's Edition | Charles Scribner's Sons | New York . . . . 1903 |

4½ x 7. Dark green limp leather stamped in gold, "Author's Edition" in small type at lower right-hand corner of front cover; gilt top; pp. (2) blank leaves, (4), vii-x, (2), 3-154, (1) with publisher's seal, (1), (2) blank leaves; uncut. This volume contains nine poems not in the first edition.

This book was issued in the Homestead Edition of *The Poems and Prose Sketches of James Whitcomb Riley* in the same year; text identical with second edition. See *Collected Works.*

23.  An Old | Sweetheart of Mine | James Whitcomb Riley | Drawings by | Howard Chandler Christy | Decorations by | Virginia Keep | The Bowen-Merrill Company | Publishers Indianapolis | [c. 1902]

6¼ x 9. Decorated cloth cover, lettered in gold, illustrated inlay cover surrounded by heart-shaped decorations; pp. (unnumbered) (20) preliminary pages, (70) text proper, (6), lining paper front and back; in text proper each alternate leaf bears illustration only, one stanza to a page enclosed in pink floreated border.

An Old | Sweetheart of Mine | James Whitcomb Riley | Drawings by | Howard Chandler Christy | Decorations by | Virginia Keep | The Bobbs-Merrill Company | Publishers Indianapolis |

Same as first edition except for title page and color of binding which is dark red.

An Old | Sweetheart of Mine | James Whitcomb Riley | Drawings by | Howard Chandler Christy | Decorations by | Virginia Keep | The Bobbs-Merrill Company | Publishers Indianapolis |

7 x 9½. Same as second edition except that front cover bears a large illustrated inlay in full color, with title, author's and illustrator's names stamped in gold leaf. Also bound in red English leather.

An Old | Sweetheart | of Mine | James Whitcomb Riley | Drawings by | Howard Chandler Christy | Decorations by | E. Stetson Crawford | The Bobbs-Merrill Company | Publishers Indianapolis | [c. 1903]

Autograph edition limited to 400 copies: 9 x 11½. Heavy paper boards in two tones of sepia with large inlay in gold in center of front cover bearing title and author's name; pp., (unnumbered), (18), (70), lining paper front and back; in text proper each alternate leaf bears illustration in sepia, tipped in; one stanza to a page enclosed in ornamental border.

24. His Pa's Romance | James Whitcomb Riley | With Illustrations by | Will Vawter and a Portrait by | John Cecil Clay | Indianapolis | The Bobbs-Merrill Company | Publishers | [c. 1903]

4¾ x 7. Red cloth binding, marginal gold line on front cover, ornamental gold scroll on back, lettering in gold; pp. (2) blank leaves, (14), 168, (2) blank leaves; oval portrait frontispiece in yellow and orange.

25. A Defective Santa Claus | James Whitcomb Riley | With Pictures by | C. M. Relyea | and | Will Vawter | Indianapolis | The Bobbs-Merrill Company | Publishers | [c. 1904]

5¼ x 7¾. Green cloth cover, front stamped in conventional holly design, lettering in gold; pp. (1) blank leaf, (14), 78, (4), (1) blank leaf.

26. Out to | Old Aunt Mary's | By | James Whitcomb Riley | Drawings by | Howard Chandler Christy | Decorations by | Margaret Armstrong | The Bobbs-Merrill Company | Indianapolis | [c. 1904]

6 x 8¾. Decorated cloth cover, lettered in gold, inlay oval picture of "Aunt Mary" on cover surrounded by heart-shaped decorations in white; pp. (unnumbered) (1) blank leaf, (13), (78), (1) blank leaf, decorated lining paper front and back; in text proper each alternate page bears illustration only, one stanza to a page printed on verso enclosed in floreated border.

Out to | Old Aunt Mary's | By | James Whitcomb Riley | Drawings by | Howard Chandler Christy | Decorations by | Margaret Armstrong | The Bobbs-Merrill Company | Indianapolis |

7 x 9½. Same as first edition except that front cover bears a large inlay illustration in full color with title, author's and illustrator's names stamped in gold leaf. Also bound in red English leather.

27. Riley | Songs O' Cheer | James Whitcomb Riley | With Pictures by | Will Vawter | Indianapolis | The Bobbs-Merrill Company | Publishers | [c. 1905]

5 x 7¾. Green ornamental cloth cover, gold lettering; pp. (3) blank leaves, (16), 19-195, (1), (4) blank leaves. Also bound in red cloth.

28. While the Heart Beats Young | By | James Whitcomb Riley | With Pictures By | Ethel Franklin Betts | Indianapolis | The Bobbs-Merrill Company | Publishers | [c. 1906]

6¾ x 9¼. Green cloth cover, with large inlay picture of boy and girl playing in field of grasses and white flowers, lettering in gold; pp. (18), 17-110, decorated, illustrated lining paper front and back.

While the Heart Beats Young | By | James Whitcomb Riley | With Pictures By | Ethel Franklin

Betts | Indianapolis | The Bobbs-Merrill Company | Publishers |

Identical with first edition except for inlay on cover, which shows a boy and girl before a hedge of hollyhocks, and for verso of title page, which is blank.

29. The Boys of | The Old | Glee Club | By James Whitcomb Riley | Indianapolis | The Bobbs-Merrill Company | Publishers | [c. 1907]

5½ x 9. Green cloth binding, stamped design on front cover in two colors with white inlay edged with gold, at top, bearing title; all lettering in gold; printed on one side of leaf only; pp. (unnumbered) (1) blank leaf, (16), (64), (2) blank leaves, decorated lining paper front and back, 13 full page half-tone illustrations, also marginal illustrations.

30. Morning | James Whitcomb Riley | Indianapolis | The Bobbs-Merrill Company | Publishers | [c. 1907]

4½ x 7. Red cloth binding, marginal gold line on front cover, ornamental gold scroll on back, lettering in gold; pp. (1) blank leaf, (16), 162, (1) blank leaf. Portrait by Sargent as frontispiece. Also bound in red leather.

31. The Raggedy Man | By | James Whitcomb Riley | With illustrations by | Ethel Franklin Betts | Indianapolis | The Bobbs Merrill Company | Publishers | [c. 1907]

10¼ x 11½. Cloth back, illustrated board sides, same full color illustration on front and back of cover; pp. (unnumbered), (1) blank page, (10), (36), (2) blank leaves; illustrated title page, 8 full page color illustrations; text enclosed in colored border.

The Raggedy Man | By | James Whitcomb Riley | With illustrations by | Ethel Franklin Betts | Indianapolis | The Bobbs-Merrill Company | Publishers |

Full cloth binding, color illustration same as that of first edition on front cover only with gold line border; text identical with first edition.

32. Riley Child Verse | By | James Whitcomb Riley | With Pictures by Ethel Franklin Betts | First Series | Indianapolis | The Bobbs-Merrill Company | Publishers |

Published in 1908; received by the Copyright Department, January 25, 1909. The copyright page of the volume bears the date 1906.
6¾ x 9½. Bright blue buckram binding, inlay front cover illustration in full color of "Little Orphant Annie" telling stories to the children; pp. (unnumbered) (1) blank leaf, (8), (39), (1) 1 blank leaf; illustrated and decorated title page, 8 full page color illustrations, also smaller color illustrations.

Riley Child Verse | By | James Whitcomb Riley | With Pictures by Ethel Franklin Betts | First Series | Indianapolis | The Bobbs-Merrill Company | Publishers |

Identical with first edition except for inlay on cover which shows a little girl sitting in the grass.

33. The Runaway Boy | By | James Whitcomb Riley | With Pictures by Ethel Franklin Betts | Riley Child Verse—Second Series | Indianapolis | The Bobbs-Merrill Company | Publishers |

Published in 1908; received by the Copyright Department, January 25, 1909. The copyright page in volume bears the date 1906.
6¾ x 9½. Green buckram binding, full color inlay illustration on front cover, with title and author's name

printed in bright blue at top; pp. (unnumbered) (1) blank leaf, (6), (50), (1) blank leaf; illustrated and decorated title page, 8 full page color illustrations, also smaller color illustrations.

34. Home | Again With Me | By | James Whitcomb Riley | Drawings by | Howard Chandler Christy | Decorations by Franklin Booth | Indianapolis | The Bobbs-Merrill Company | [c. 1908]

6 x 8½. Cloth binding, with oval inlay head of girl enclosed in heart-shaped decorations similar to first edition of *An Old Sweetheart of Mine,* [title No. 23]; title at top of front cover in gold, author's and illustrator's names at bottom in white; pp. (unnumbered) (9), (84), (1), (1) blank leaf, illustrated lining paper front and back, each alternate leaf of text proper bearing color illustration; text within ornamental borders.

Home | Again With Me | By | James Whitcomb Riley | Drawings by | Howard Chandler Christy | Decorations by Franklin Booth | Indianapolis | The Bobbs-Merrill Company |

Same as first edition except that front cover bears a large illustrated inlay in full color, with title, author's and illustrator's names stamped in gold.

35. The Orphant Annie Book | By James Whitcomb Riley | illustrated by | Ethel Franklin Betts | Indianapolis | The Bobbs-Merrill Company | Publishers | [c. 1908]

10 x 11¼. Cloth back, illustrated board sides, same full colored illustration on front and back of cover; pp. (unnumbered) (2) blank leaves, (44), lining paper front and back, illustrated title page, eight full page color illustrations, also smaller color illustrations in text; text within ornamental border.

Little Orphan Annie | By James Whitcomb Riley | illustrated by | Ethel Franklin Betts | Indianapolis | The Bobbs-Merrill Company | Publishers |

Full cloth binding, inlay color illustration same as that of first edition on front cover with gold line border; title on cover, and title page changed to | Little Orphan Annie | ; text and size identical with first edition. This edition was later divided into two parts and printed as *Ef You Don't Watch Out* and *The Boy Lives On Our Farm.* (See Nos. 45 and 46.)

36. Riley | Songs of Summer | James Whitcomb Riley | With Pictures by | Will Vawter | Indianapolis | The Bobbs-Merrill Company | Publishers | [c. 1908]

5 x 7¾. Ornamental green cloth cover, gold lettering; pp. (3) blank leaves, (14), 19-190, (2) blank leaves.

37. Old | School Day | Romances | by | James Whitcomb Riley | Illustrated & | Decorated | by | E Stetson Crawford | Indianapolis | The Bobbs-Merrill Company | Publishers | [c. 1909]

6¼ x 8¾. Brown cloth cover with large inlay of reddish brown and gold on front cover bearing title and author's name; title and author's surname in gold running lengthwise on back; pp. (unnumbered) (8), (40), brown lining papers front and back bearing author's monogram in large brown letters on gold; decorated title page, five full page color illustrations, also illustrations with each page of text. Also bound in red English leather.

Old | School Day | Romances | by | James Whitcomb Riley | Illustrated & | Decorated | by | E Stetson Crawford | Indianapolis | The Bobbs-Merrill Company | Publishers |

Same as first edition except that front cover bears a large inlay illustration in full color by Worth Brehm with title and author's name printed in gold.

38. Riley Roses | By James Whitcomb Riley | Illustrated by | Howard Chandler Christy | Decorations by Franklin Booth | Indianapolis | The Bobbs-Merrill Company | Publishers | [c. 1909]

6¾ x 9¼. Green cloth binding; pp. (unnumbered) (2) blank leaves, (10), (35), (1), (1) blank leaf; color illustrations; text with ornamental border.

The second edition has a rose-colored binding stamped with rose and stem design (see Nos. 42, 44, 48, 50, 51, 52); a girl carrying roses as frontispiece; rearrangement of text and illustrations. Both editions bound in red English leather.

39. The | Girl I Loved | By | James Whitcomb Riley | Drawings by | Howard Chandler Christy | Decorations by Margaret Armstrong | The Bobbs-Merrill Company | Publishers | [c. 1910]

6 x 8½. Green cloth binding with inlay oval head of girl enclosed in heart-shaped decorations in white and maroon, similar to first edition of *An Old Sweetheart of Mine* [title No. 23]; title in gold at top of front cover, author's and illustrator's names in white at bottom; pp. (unnumbered) (9), (84), (1) blank leaf, illustrated lining paper front and back; each alternate leaf of text bearing a color illustration; text within ornamental borders.

The | Girl I Loved | By | James Whitcomb Riley | Drawings by | Howard Chandler Christy | Decorations by Margaret Armstrong | The Bobbs-Merrill Company | Publishers |

7 x 9½. Same as first edition except that front cover bears a large inlay illustration in full color with title, author's and illustrator's names stamped in gold leaf. Also bound in red English leather.

40. A Hoosier Romance | 1868 | Squire Hawkins's Story | By James Whitcomb Riley | With Illustrations by | John Wolcott Adams | Published by The Century Co. | New York. . . . M CM X | [c. 1910]

5¾ x 8¾. Lavender cloth binding, decorated front cover with lettering in white; pp. (10), 3-87, decorated lining paper front and back; text and illustrations with a design in tint on margin.

A Hoosier Romance | By James Whitcomb Riley | With Illustrations by | John Wolcott Adams | Published by | The Bobbs-Merrill Company | [c. 1912]

6 x 7¾. Green cloth binding, mounted color illustration on front cover, bordered with heavy gold lines, lettering in gold; pp. (unnumbered) (1) blank leaf, (8), (56), (1) blank leaf; text and illustrations printed over a design in tint; except for front page text printed on verso of leaf only.

41. Riley | Songs of Home | James Whitcomb Riley | With Pictures by | Will Vawter | Indianapolis | The Bobbs-Merrill Company | Publishers | [c. 1910]

5 x 7¾. Illustrated green cloth cover, gold lettering; pp. (3) blank leaves, (14), 19-190, (2) blank leaves.

42. Down around the | River | and Other Poems | by | James Whitcomb Riley | With Pictures by | Will Vawter | Indianapolis | The Bobbs-Merrill Company | Publishers | [c. 1911]

4¾ x 7½. Cloth back, board sides, front cover illustrated in colors; pp. (2) blank leaves, (4), 7-29, (1), (2) blank leaves.

Down around the | River | and Other Poems |
by | James Whitcomb Riley | With Pictures by |
Will Vawter | Indianapolis | The Bobbs-Merrill
Company | Publishers |

Same as first edition except for cover which is brown
cloth stamped with rose and stem design [design same as
*Riley Roses,* title No. 38], lettering in white; illustrations
in color.

43. The Lockerbie Book | Containing Poems Not
in Dialect | By | James Whitcomb Riley | Collected
and Arranged by | Hewitt Hanson Howland | Indi-
anapolis | The Bobbs-Merrill Company | Publish-
ers | [c. 1911]

4 x 6½. Dark blue cloth with narrow marginal decoration and lettering in gold; full gilt; printed on Bible
paper; pp. (1) blank leaf, (10), 646, (1) blank leaf. Also
bound in limp morocco. In the first imprints of this edition, the index of titles was given by pages.

44. A Summer's Day | and Other Poems | by |
James Whitcomb Riley | With Pictures by | Will
Vawter | Indianapolis | The Bobbs-Merrill Company
| Publishers | [c. 1911]

4¾ x 7½. Cloth back, board sides, front cover illustrated in colors; pp. (2) blank leaves, (4), 7-29, (1), (2)
blank leaves. Uniform with *Down around the River,* title
No. 42.

A Summer's Day | and Other Poems | by | James
Whitcomb Riley | With Pictures by | Will Vawter |
Indianapolis | The Bobbs-Merrill Company | Pub-
lishers |

Same changes in binding and illustrations as in *Down
around the River,* title No. 42.

**45.** Little Orphan Annie | By James Whitcomb Riley | illustrated by | Ethel Franklin Betts | Indianapolis | The Bobbs-Merrill Company | Publishers |

Published in 1911. Copyright page bears the date 1908. 10 x 11¼. Green buckram binding with mounted full-color illustration on front cover bearing in gold letters | Ef You Don't Watch Out | by | James | Whitcomb | Riley |; pp. (unnumbered) (2) blank leaves, (8), (14), (1) blank leaf; text with ornamental border. (See title No. 35.)

**46.** The Boy Lives On Our Farm | By James Whitcomb Riley | illustrated by | Ethel Franklin Betts | Indianapolis | The Bobbs-Merrill Company | Publishers |

Published in 1911. Copyright page bears the date 1908. 10 x 11¼. Blue buckram binding with full color inlay illustration on front cover bearing title and author's name in gold letters; pp. (unnumbered) (1) blank leaf, (4), (24), (1) blank leaf; text with ornamental border. (See title No. 35.)

**47.** When | She Was About | Sixteen | by | James Whitcomb Riley | Illustrated by | Howard Chandler Christy | The Bobbs-Merrill Company | Publishers | [c. 1911]

7 x 9½. Brown cloth binding, full color inlay illustration on front cover with title, author's and illustrator's names stamped in gold leaf; pp. (unnumbered) (1) blank leaf, (9), (84), (2) blank leaves; the obverse side of each leaf bears an illustration, each alternate illustration having ornamental border; text with ornamental border printed on verso of leaf. Also bound in red English leather.

**48.** When the Frost Is | on the Punkin | and Other Poems | by | James Whitcomb Riley | With Pictures by | Will Vawter | Indianapolis | The Bobbs-Merrill Company | Publishers | [c. 1911]

4¾ x 7½. Cloth back, board sides, front cover illustrated in colors; pp. (2) blank leaves, (4), 7-29, (1), (2) blank leaves. Uniform with *Down around the River* and *A Summer's Day,* titles Nos. 42 and 44.

When the Frost Is | on the Punkin | and Other Poems | by | James Whitcomb Riley | With Pictures by | Will Vawter | Indianapolis | The Bobbs-Merrill Company | Publishers |

Same changes in binding and illustrations as in *Down around the River,* title No. 42.

49. All the Year | Round | by James | Whitcomb | Riley | With Twelve Illustrations Cut | on Wood and Printed in Colors | by Gustave Baumann | The Bobbs Merrill Company | Publishers Indianapolis | [c. 1912]

8½ x 10½. Parti-color cloth binding, back white, sides dark blue with lettering stamped in gold leaf; text hand-lettered, printed on heavy mauve paper, folded at the top; leaves (unnumbered) (3), (12), (1), cream lining paper front and back.

50. Knee-Deep in June | and Other Poems | by | James Whitcomb Riley | With Pictures by | Will Vawter | Indianapolis | The Bobbs-Merrill Company | Publishers | [c. 1912]

4¾ x 7½. Brown cloth binding stamped with rose and stem design (design same as *Riley Roses,* title No. 38) ; pp. (2) blank leaves, (4), 7-29, (1), (2) blank leaves. Uniform with second edition of *Down around the River, A Summer's Day* and *When the Frost Is on the Punkin,* Nos. 42, 44, 48.

51. The | Old Swimmin'-Hole | and Other Poems | by | James Whitcomb Riley | With Pictures by | Will Vawter | Indianapolis | The Bobbs-Merrill Company | Publishers | [c. 1912]

4¾ x 7½. Brown cloth binding stamped with rose and stem design (design same as *Riley Roses,* title No. 38) ; pp. (2) blank leaves, (4), 7-29, (1), (2) blank leaves. Uniform with second edition of *Down around the River, A Summer's Day, When the Frost Is on the Punkin* and *Knee-Deep in June,* Nos. 42, 44, 48, 50.

52. The Prayer Perfect | and Other Poems | by | James Whitcomb Riley | With Pictures by | Will Vawter | Indianapolis | The Bobbs-Merrill Company | Publishers | [c. 1912]

4¾ x 7½. Brown cloth binding stamped with rose and stem design (design same as *Riley Roses,* title No. 38) ; pp. (2) blank leaves, (4), 7-29, (1), (2) blank leaves. Uniform with second edition of *Down around the River, A Summer's Day, When the Frost Is on the Punkin, Knee-Deep in June* and *The Old Swimmin'-Hole,* Nos. 42, 44, 48, 50, 51.

53. Good-bye, Jim | By | James Whitcomb Riley | Illustrated by | Howard Chandler Christy | Decorations by | Bertha Stuart | The Bobbs-Merrill Company | Publishers | [c. 1913]

5¾ x 7¾. Cloth binding, title and author's name stamped in gold on center of top cover enclosed by heavy gold line ; pp. (unnumbered) (12), (44), (2) blank leaves, decorated lining paper front and back; every alternate leaf bears color illustration; text printed over a design in tint. Also bound in red English leather.

54. A Song | of Long Ago | By | James Whitcomb Riley | Decorated by | Emily Hall Chamberlain | The    Bobbs-Merrill    Company | Publishers ‖ [c. 1913]

3¾ x 6¾. Illuminated boards, raised lettering in color ; pp. (8) folded leaves printed on one side only, every leaf decorated in colors. The booklet is enclosed in an envelope of illuminated paper decorated and printed in colors, with one stanza of poem on lower left-hand corner. Also

4 x 7; bound in ooze leather stamped in gold and black; gilt top. On the envelope and box this booklet is numbered 1 of the series.

55. He and I | By | James Whitcomb Riley | Decorated by | Emily Hall Chamberlain | The Bobbs-Merrill Company | Publishers | [c. 1913]

Uniform with *A Song of Long Ago* [title No. 54.] No. 2.

56. When My Dreams | Come True | By | James Whitcomb Riley | Decorated by | Emily Hall Chamberlain | The Bobbs-Merrill Company | Publishers | [c. 1913]

Uniform with *A Song of Long Ago* [title No. 54.] No. 3.

57. The Rose | By | James Whitcomb Riley | Decorated by | Emily Hall Chamberlain | The Bobbs-Merrill Company | Publishers | [c. 1913]

Uniform with *A Song of Long Ago* [title No. 54.] No. 4.

58. Her Beautiful | Eyes | By | James Whitcomb Riley | Decorated by | Emily Hall Chamberlain | The Bobbs Merrill Company | Publishers | [c. 1913]

Uniform with *A Song of Long Ago* [title No. 54.] No. 5.

59. Away | By | James Whitcomb Riley | Decorated by | Emily Hall Chamberlain | The Bobbs-Merrill Company | Publishers | [c. 1913]

Uniform with *A Song of Long Ago* [title No. 54.] No. 6.

60. Do They Miss Me | By | James Whitcomb
Riley | Decorated by | Emily Hall Chamberlain |
The Bobbs-Merrill Company | Publishers | [c. 1913]

Uniform with *A Song of Long Ago* [title No. 54.]
No. 7.

61. The | Riley Baby Book | Autograph Verses |
Reproduced in Facsimile | By | James Whitcomb
Riley | Illustrated by | William Cotton | Indianap-
olis | The Bobbs-Merrill Company | Publishers |
[c. 1913]

6½ x 8¼. Red cloth binding, floral design and lettering
on front cover in gold; pp. (unnumbered) (1) blank leaf,
(7), (30), (1), (1) blank leaf. Each leaf bears a child's
picture and on the page opposite a stanza in facsimile of
Mr. Riley's handwriting.

62. The Flying | Islands of | the Night | by |
James Whitcomb Riley | With Illustrations | by
Franklin Booth | Indianapolis : The Bobbs-Merrill
Co·· Publishers. | [c. 1913]

7 x 9¾. Buckram and cloth, decorated and lettered in
gold; pp. (1) blank leaf, (10), 3-124, (2) blank leaves;
brown decorated lining paper front and back; text enclosed
in brown decorated border; full color illustrations, tipped
in, and bordered with lines of brown.

# COLLECTED WORKS

Since 1891 various editions of Mr. Riley's collected works have been issued. The most important and extensive are the Homestead, Greenfield and Biographical Editions.

In 1891, a collection of six volumes was uniformly bound, comprising: *Afterwhiles* (12th Thousand), *Pipes o' Pan at Zekesbury* (1891 edition), *Rhymes of Childhood* (first edition rebound), *Neghborly Poems* (first edition rebound), *Sketches in Prose* (first edition rebound), *The Flying Islands of the Night* (second edition rebound).

4¾ x 7. Full calf binding, with a ruled border of two gold lines and blank beading on sides; title and author's name on back only, where it appears in gold on a red background; conventional ornamental design in gold on back; gilt edges.

The following year, 1892, this collection was issued printed on uniform paper bound in both cloth and full morocco, with a border of one gold line on front and back cover and a simpler ornamentation in gold on back, the title and author's name in gold on a red background as before; gilt edges and rounded corners on volumes bound in leather.

In 1893, the same collection, with the addition of *Green Fields and Running Brooks,* was issued in cloth, full calf and half morocco with the title in gold on a colored background on the back.

In 1895, the foregoing collection, with the addition of *Armazindy* (eight volumes in all) was issued with a red cloth binding bearing a heavy gold line about the sides, lettering on front side and back and floral ornamentation on back in gold; gilt top. In 1896, *A Child-World* was added; in 1900, *Home-Folks;* in 1903, *His Pa's Romance;* in 1907, *Morning,* making twelve volumes in uniform style.

In 1897, the first two volumes of the Homestead Edition were published by Charles Scribner's Sons; *Neghborly Poems* and *Sketches in Prose.* In 1898 were added *Afterwhiles, Pipes o' Pan at Zekesbury, Rhymes of Childhood, The Flying Islands of the Night, Green Fields and Running Brooks, Poems Here at Home, Armazindy* and *A Child-World;* in 1902, *The Book of Joyous Children* and *Rubáiyát of Doc Sifers and Home Folks;* in 1908, *His Pa's Romance* and *Morning,*—in all fourteen volumes. The title page follows:—

The Poems and Prose | Sketches of | James Whitcomb Riley | *title printed in red* | Charles Scribner's | Sons New York *date of publication* |

5 x 7½. Brown cloth, and half Levant bindings; front cover margined with a heavy gold rule and marked in center with a design of three ears of corn in gold; the only lettering on binding being in gold on back as follows: at top | The Works | of | James | Whitcomb | Riley | *with a design of an ear of corn | and title of volume;* at bottom | Scribner's gilt top; uncut. Watermarked with monogram.
The first 204 sets of this edition were printed on Japan paper and bound in half vellum.

In 1905, the first eleven volumes of the Greenfield Edition were published as follows: *Neghborly Poems, Afterwhiles, Sketches in Prose, Pipes o' Pan at Zekesbury, Rhymes of Childhood, The Flying Islands of the Night, Green Fields and Running Brooks, Armazindy, A Child-World, Home-Folks,*

*His Pa's Romance.* In 1908, *Morning* was added. The title page follows:—

*title* | James Whitcomb Riley | Indianapolis | The Bobbs-Merrill Company | Publishers |

5 x 7½. Green cloth binding with lettering and a floral decoration in gold on back; gilt top; uncut. Also bound in red leather.

In 1913, appeared the Biographical Edition in six volumes with the following title page:—
The Complete Works | of | James Whitcomb Riley | In Which the Poems, Including a Number Heretofore Unpublished, | Are Arranged in the Order in Which They Were Written, | Together with Photographs, Bibliographic Notes | and a Life Sketch of the Author | Collected and Edited by | Edmund Henry Eitel | Biographical Edition | Volume *number* | Indianapolis | The Bobbs - Merrill Company | Publishers |

5 x 7¾. Light sage green cloth binding; gold stamped lettering and blank stamped decorations on back. Intaglio bee medallion in gold and black on front cover; uncut edges with gilt top. Also bound in red cloth with gold stamped lettering and decorations on side and back; three-quarters Turkey morocco, three-quarters calf and full morocco with plain sides and gold stamped lettering on back.

# MISCELLANEOUS

A Buckeye Ballad | By James Whitcomb Riley.
The Hoosier Poet. | Compliments of Passenger De-
partment Buckeye Route | Tale of a Million |

Copyright 1890 by W. H. Fisher, G. P. and T. A.
A pamphlet 9 x 6 with the above described lettering
on cover; (22) pages; illustrated by W. H. Mullay; tied
with brown ribbon which passes through a buckeye
stamped Buckeye Route.
This is one of the rarest of Mr. Riley's souvenirs. Mr.
W. H. Fisher, General Passenger and Ticket Agent of The
Hocking Valley Railway Company, formerly known as
The Columbus, Hocking Valley & Toledo R. R., or "The
Buckeye Route," was associated with Mr. Riley on *The
Indianapolis Journal,* and it was through this association
that the poem came to be written and pamphlet prepared.

## Poems.

A booklet, 6 x 6, pp. (24), issued by The Indianapolis
Flower Mission in 1890, containing poems by a number of
Indiana authors, among which is the poem *Home,* by Mr.
Riley.

Golden-rod. | The Magazine of the | Indianapolis
Flower Mission | "The Riley Booth." | Baker-Ran-
dolph Litho. and Eng. Co. |

6 x 9. Issued November 3, 1891, with yellow cover
stamped as above described. A collection of poems and
stories. Contains portrait of Mr. Riley, his poem, *Going
to the Fair,* and the prose sketch, *Tale of a Manuscript*
*("Twiggs and Tudens").*

444

A Christmas Story. | What | Chris'mas | Fetched | the | Wigginses | By James Whitcomb Riley. | Illustrated by | E. W. Kemble. | Louisville: | Press of Courier-Journal Job Printing Co. | 1891. | [c. 1891]

A Christmas pamphlet 6¾ x 9½ with pictorial cardboard cover, across the front of which is a miniature facsimile of a portion of the first page of *The Louisville Times* of November 23, 1891; (14) pages.

A Tinkle of Bells | and Other Poems | by | James Whitcomb Riley | Chicago: | E. A. Weeks & Company | 521-531 Wabash Avenue |

Pirated edition, suppressed by law. (Copyright, 1895, by E. A. Weeks & Company).
4¼ x 6¾. Dark blue buckram binding, front cover and back decorated and lettered in gold; gilt top; pp. (1) blank leaf, illustration frontispiece, (2), iii-v, (1), 210, (3) blank leaves, uncut.

The Days Gone By | and Other Poems | by | James Whitcomb Riley | Chicago: | E. A. Weeks & Company | 521-531 Wabash Avenue |

Pirated edition, suppressed by law. (Copyright, 1895, by E. A. Weeks & Company).
4¼ x 6¾. Dark blue buckram binding, front cover and back decorated and lettered in gold; gilt top; pp. (1) blank leaf, illustration frontispiece, (2), iii-v, (3), 214, (2) blank leaves.

Dialect in Literature | James Whitcomb Riley |

A booklet, 4½ x 6¾; paper back with wording as above described; no title page; first page worded as follows: | Originally Contributed to the FORUM—| and by Permission Now Reprinted | and Included in | NEGHBORLY POEMS | Indianapolis, The | Bowen-Merrill Co. | Publishers | M DCCC XC VI | ; pp. (unnumbered) (20); gilt top.

Riley's | First Poems | Collected and Published by | Dory Biddle, | Anderson, Indiana, | Christmas, 1901. |

A pamphlet 9 x 6¾. Gray paper cover with portrait of author on center of front cover and decorative design of roses to left of portrait enclosed by red and green lines; pp. (1) blank leaf, (4), 17 leaves printed on obverse page only, (1) blank leaf. This is a rare souvenir.

A Souvenir of | Lockerbie Fair |

A small booklet with red cover, issued by The Indianapolis Flower Mission and sold at The Lockerbie Street Fair in June, 1903. It contains a portrait of Mr. Riley and his poem, *Lockerbie Fair.*

A booklet of quotations has been published under various titles by various lithographic companies, as follows:

Gems from Riley, published by DeWolfe, Fiske & Co., Boston. [c. 1904]

Jewels from Riley, published by Berger Publishing Company, Buffalo. [c. 1907]

Flowers and Fruits from Riley, published by Cupples & Leon Co., New York. [c. 1909]

Wild Roses from Riley, published by The Hayes Lithographic Co., Buffalo. [1910]

Seymour-Riley Panels [c. 1905]

Six poems, hand-lettered and decorated by Ralph Fletcher Seymour: *As Created, Ike Walton's Prayer, God Bless Us Every One, The Prayer-Perfect, Wet Weather Talk, Kissing the Rod.* Printed as separate panels, 7¼ x 10, in four colors on cream Florentine cardboard. Each enclosed in an envelope.

James | Whitcomb | Riley | Calendar |

A calendar composed of fourteen sheets of heavy white bristol board, 10¾ x 16½, bearing in addition to the calendar for 1912 quotations from Mr. Riley's poems. The first sheet is lettered in gold as above quoted, with marginal lines of gold; second sheet has a border of heavy gold lines, and bears a portrait of Mr. Riley with the tribute to him written by Henry van Dyke, beneath which is a floral design with Mr. Riley's monogram in large letters, all in gold. Of the remaining sheets each alternate one has a large full color illustration by Ethel Franklin Betts with a gold line border. A limited number of these was printed with calendar for 1913. [c. 1911]

Mrs. Miller | By | James Whitcomb Riley | Indianapolis | The Bobbs-Merrill Co. | Publishers | [c. 1911]

4¼ x 7. Red cloth binding, front cover lettered in gold as follows | The Indiana Society of Chicago | Mrs. | Miller | James Whitcomb Riley | The Bobbs-Merrill Company | ; pp. (1) blank leaf, (8), 79, (1), (1) blank leaf. This volume, which contains the prose sketches *Mrs. Miller* and *Jamesy*, is one of a set of eleven volumes, each being by a different Indiana author. The set was prepared for The Indiana Society of Chicago and given away as a souvenir at its annual banquet in 1912.

A card of greeting containing *Child's Christmas Carol,* beneath which appear the words in facsimile | With Christmas greetings, | —James Whitcomb Riley. | Christmas of | 1912 |

The poem is printed in black and enclosed in a green border. A heavy gold band margins the card, the dimensions of which are 7 x 8¼.

Out To | Old Aunt Mary's |

A booklet, 5¾ x 7, of cream paper, containing the poem *Out to Old Aunt Mary's* in facsimile of the author's writing. It is composed of six leaves tied with a silk cord. Each page has a heavy border of gold. The front cover bears the title; inside of cover is a portrait of Mr. Riley; on the opposite page are the words | With greetings, | James Whitcomb Riley. | Enclosed in envelope. This is a personal souvenir of the author's and has never been put on sale. Issued in December, 1912.

In October, 1913, a new print of this was made. Mr. Riley presented this to the school children of Indianapolis in appreciation of their tribute of parade, poetry shower and exercises on his birthday, October seventh. The changes made were the substitution of a recent picture of the author as frontispiece; the insertion on the opposite page of a stanza in greeting composed for the occasion; and the changing of the gold marginal band to nile green.

Eccentric Mr. Clark | Stories in Prose | By | James Whitcomb Riley | New York | The New York Book Co. | 1913 |

4¾ x 7¼. Cloth binding with large square in black on front cover containing title and author's name; pp. (1) blank leaf, (2), 189, (1), (1) blank leaf. This book is a re-arrangement of the prose sketches contained in *Sketches in Prose*.

A card of appreciation in reply to the poetry shower, 1913.

5¾ x 3¼. Contains oval portrait; the verses beginning "Dear singing friend,"; | With greetings, | —James Whitcomb Riley. | in facsimile.

# PART II

## Rileyana

---

## SKETCHES AND REFERENCES IN BOOKS AND PAMPHLETS

Abernathy, J. W. *American Literature.* New York: Maynard, Merrill & Company, 1902, p. 463.

Adams, Oscar Fay. *Brief Hand-Book of American Authors.* Boston and New York: Houghton, Mifflin Company, 1901, p. 315.

Avary, Myrta Lockett. *Uncle Remus and The Wren's Nest: Joel Chandler Harris and His Home.* Atlanta: The Uncle Remus Memorial Association and Mrs. Joel Chandler Harris, 1913, p. 18. (Sketch and portrait.)

Barr, James. *Humour of America.* New York: Charles Scribner's Sons, 1894, p. 456.

Bates, K. L. *American Literature.* New York: The Macmillan Company, 1898, p. 204.

Beers, Henry Augustin. *Studies in American Letters.* Meadville Pa.: Flood & Vincent [The Chatauquan Century Press], 1895, pp. 210-212.

Beveridge, A. J. *Meaning of the Times.* Indianapolis: The Bobbs-Merrill Company, 1908, pp. 254-60.

Clemens, Samuel L. *How to Tell a Story, and Other Essays.* New York: Harper Brothers, 1897, pp. 3-12.

Ford, Robert. *American Humorists, Recent and Living.* Paisley, Scotland: A. Gardner, 1897, pp. 295-304.

Gugler, Julius. *Wie's die Stunde gab.* Milwaukee: Julius Gugler, 1910, pp. 135-139. (Poems translated into German.)

Harringshaw, T. W. *Poets of America.* Chicago: American Publishing Association, 1892, p. 513.

Howland, J. A. *James Whitcomb Riley in Prose and Picture.* Chicago: Handy & Higgings, 1903.

Lawton, Wm. Cranston. *Introduction to the Study of American Literature.* Yonkers-on-the-Hudson: Globe School Book Company, 1902, pp. 329-330.

Levering, Julia Henderson. *Historic Indiana.* New York: G. P. Putnam's Sons, 1909, pp. 331, 355, 369-70, 372, 384, 390-1.

McFee, Inez N. *Studies in American and British Literature.* Chicago: A. Flanagan Company, 1905, pp. 165-177.

Mason, Harriet L. *American Literature—A Laboratory Method.* Philadelphia: Harriet L. Mason, 1901, pp. 47, 54.

Marsden, O. S. *How They Succeeded.* Boston: Lothrop, Lee & Shepard, 1901, pp. 357-365.

Nicholson, Meredith. *The Hoosiers.* New York: The Macmillan Company, 1900, pp. 156-76.

Nicholson, Meredith. *Poems.* Indianapolis: The Bobbs-Merrill Company, 1906. (Dedicatory poem, *To James Whitcomb Riley.*)

Nicholson, Meredith. *James Whitcomb Riley.* Address by Meredith Nicholson at Manual Training High School, Indianapolis, October 6, 1911. (Pamphlet issued by the Indianapolis Public Schools.)

Nicholson, Meredith. *A Hoosier Chronicle.* Boston and New York: Houghton, Mifflin Company, 1912, p. 194.

Noble, Charles. *Studies in American Literature.* New York: The Macmillan Company, 1898, p. 357.

Onderdock, J. L. *History of American Verse.* Chicago: A. C. McClurg & Company, 1901, pp. 351-52.

Parker, B. S., and Heiney, E. B. *Poets and Poetry of Indiana.* Boston: Silver, Burdett & Company, 1900, p. 454.

Pond, J. B. *Eccentricities of Genius.* New York: W. Dillingham Company, 1900, pp. 241-259.

Ridgeway, Major. *Early Recollections of James Whitcomb Riley.* Wm. R. Hartpence, Harrison, Ohio, 1902.

Rutherford, Mildred. *American Authors.* Atlanta, Georgia: The Franklin Printing & Publishing Company, 1894, pp. 615-18.

Simonds, A. B. *American Song.* New York: G. P. Putnam's Sons, 1894, pp. 284-285.

Sladen, Douglas. *Younger American Poets.* New York: Cassell & Company, 1891, pp. 295-306.

Smith, Wm. Henry. *History of the State of Indiana.* Indianapolis: B. L. Blair Co., 1897, pp. 844.

Stedman, Edmund Clarence. *American Anthology.* Boston and New York: Houghton, Mifflin Company, 1900, p. 818.

Stedman, Edmund Clarence. *Poets of America.* Boston and New York: Houghton, Mifflin Company, 1885, p. 455.

Whitcomb, S. L. *Chronological Outlines of American Literature.* New York: The Macmillan Company, 1894.

Wilder, Marshall P. *The Sunny Side of the*

*Street.*  New York and London: Funk & Wagnalls Company, 1905, pp. 139, 159.

*In Honor of James Whitcomb Riley.*  Indianapolis: The Bobbs-Merrill Company, 1906.  Booklet containing addresses by Henry Watterson, Senator Albert J. Beveridge, Meredith Nicholson and others, and a Sketch of James Whitcomb Riley's Life.

# ARTICLES IN ENCYCLOPÆDIAS

Allibone, S. A. Supplement to *Allibone's Critical Dictionary of English Literature and British and American Authors,* by John Foster Kirk. 1891.

*Appleton's Cyclopædia of American Biography,* by J. G. Wilson and John Fiske. 1888.

*Century Cyclopædia of Names,* by B. E. Smith. 1894.

*Chamber's Cyclopædia of English Literature.* 1904.

*Columbian Cyclopædia.* 1897.

*Encyclopædia Americana.* 1904.

*Encyclopædia Britannica, The. New American Supplement to The Encyclopædia Britannica.* The Werner Company, publishers. 1898.

*Encyclopædia Britannica, The.* 1911.

*Herringshaw's Encyclopædia of American Biography of the Nineteenth Century,* by T. W. Herringshaw. 1902.

*International Cyclopædia,* by H. T. Peck. 1899.

*Johnson's Universal Cyclopædia.* 1895.

*Lamb's Biographical Dictionary of the United States,* by John Howard Brown. 1903.

*Literature of All Nations and All Ages, The,* by Julian Hawthorne, John Russell Young and John Porter Lamberton. 1900.

*A Library of American Literature,* by Edmund Clarence Stedman and Ellen Mackey Hutchinson. 1890.

*Library of the World's Best Literature,* by Charles Dudley Warner. 1897.

*Men of America,* by L. R. Hamersly & Company. 1907.

*Men and Women of America,* by L. R. Hamersly & Company. 1909.

*National Cyclopædia of American Biography, The.* 1892.

*New Century Book of Facts.* 1911.

*Nelson's Encyclopædia.* 1907.

*New International Encyclopædia, The.* 1905.

*Standard Dictionary of Facts,* by H. N. Ruoff. 1912.

*Twentieth Century Home Encyclopædia and Gazetteer.* 1904.

*Universal Cyclopædia.* 1899.

*Universal Pronouncing Dictionary of Biography and Mythology,* by Joseph Thomas. 1901.

*Winston's Cumulative Encyclopædia.* 1912.

*Who's Who.* 1899 and subsequent editions.

*Who's Who in America.* 1899 and subsequent editions.

# ARTICLES AND PORTRAITS IN MAGAZINES

## ACADEMY

Carmen, Bliss. *James Whitcomb Riley's Poetry.* Vol. l (1898), p. 272.

Thompson, Maurice. *James Whitcomb Riley.* Vol. lv (1898), p. 472.

## ARENA

*James Whitcomb Riley.* Vol. xvii (1897), pp. 1121-30.

## ATLANTIC MONTHLY

Carmen, Bliss. *Mr. Riley's Poetry.* Vol. lxxxii (1898), pp. 424-28.

## THE BELLMAN

Edgar, E. C. *A Message and Some Memories.* Vol. xi (1911), pp. 746-9.

## BOOK BUYER

Paine, D. L. *James Whitcomb Riley.* Vol. v (1888), pp. 96-7.

Laughlin, C. E. *James Whitcomb Riley as a Poet of Childhood.* Vol. xvii (1898), p. 181.

## BOOKMAN

Portrait. Vol. v (1897), p. 282.

Richards, L. P. *Riley on a Country Newspaper.* Vol. xx (1904), pp. 18-24.

Howland, Hewitt Hanson. *How Riley Came into His Own.* Vol. xxxiii (1911), pp. 666-75.

Guterman, Arthur. *James Whitcomb Riley* [a poem]. Vol. xxxiii (1911), p. 511.

Tevis, C. V. *"Jim Riley" (An Appreciation).* Vol. xxxv (1912), pp. 637-45.

Hyman, Herbert R. *James Whitcomb Riley's Complete Works.* xxxviii (1913), pp. 163-8.

## BOOK NEWS

Ridpath, J. C. *James Whitcomb Riley.* Vol. x (1892), pp. 278-80.

van Dyke, Henry. *James Whitcomb Riley.* Vol. xxv (1907), pp. 429-30.

Miller, Elizabeth. *A Typical Indianian.* Vol. xxv (1907), pp. 431-32.

Carmen, Bliss. *Riley—Poet of the People.* Vol. xxv (1907), pp. 433-5.

Howland, Hewitt Hanson. *Riley the Humorist.* Vol. xxv (1907), p. 436.

McCoy, Samuel Duff. *More about the Riley Humor.* Vol. xxv (1907), pp. 437-8.

Hitt, George C. *Mr. Riley as a Public Reader.* Vol. xxv (1907), pp. 439-40.

Chambers, D. L. *The Darlington Collection of the Works of James Whitcomb Riley.* Vol. xxix (1911), pp. 246-9.

## THE CATHOLIC SCHOOL JOURNAL

Smith, Elsie May. *Authors Your Pupils Should Know. James Whitcomb Riley.* Vol. xii (1912), pp. 102-3.

## CENTURY

Portrait. Vol. xli (1901), p. 63.
Portrait. Vol. lxxii (1906), p. 941.
Portrait. Vol. lxxvii (1909), p. 892.

## THE CONTINENT

Kane, Thomas. *When Poet Riley Was a Boy.* (1912), p. 1736.

## THE CRITIC

Portrait. Vol. xxviii (1896), p. 429.
Thompson, Maurice. *Poetry of James Whitcomb Riley.* Vol. xxxiii (1898), p. 460.
Portrait. Vol. xxxix (1901), p. 203.
Portrait. Vol. xl (1902), p. 496.
Portrait. Vol. xlii (1903), p. 230.

## CURRENT LITERATURE

Hopkins, F. M. *American Poets of To-day.* Vol. xxiv (1898), pp. 208-9.
How He Got His Start (*General Gossips of Authors and Writers*). Vol. xxviii (1900), p. 44.
A Sketch (*General Gossips of Authors and Writers*), Vol. xxix (1900), p. 415.
*Dr. James Whitcomb Riley.* (Poem.) Vol. xxxvi (1904), p. 470.
Carmen Bliss. *Much Loved Personality.* Vol. xli (1906), pp. 160-2.

## DELINEATOR

Daggett, Mabel Potter. *In Lockerbie Street.* Vol. lxxii (1908), pp. 391-4, 454-5. Also published in booklet form.

## FORTNIGHTLY REVIEW

Wallace, A. R. *Leonainie Problem.* Vol. lxxxi (1904), pp. 706-11.

## GENTLEMAN'S MAGAZINE

Urban, Sylvanus. Estimate of James Whitcomb

Riley (*Table Talk*). Vol. cclxxxii (1897), pp. 311-12.

## GOOD HOUSEKEEPING

Fletcher-Berry, Mrs. R. M. *The Best Beloved Poet.* Vol. lv (1912), pp. 456-60.

## GREAT THOUGHTS

*James Whitcomb Riley, a Favorite American Poet.* Vol. iv (1899), pp. 148.

## HARPER'S MAGAZINE

Portrait. Vol. lxxviii (1889), p. 495.

## HARPER'S WEEKLY

MacArthur, J. *Estimate of James Whitcomb Riley.* Vol. xlviii (1904), p. 1099.

## KNIGHTHOOD

(Sturgis, Mich.)

McManus, Hon. S. B. *When James Was Jim.* Vol. i, No. 2 (1897), p. 2.
McManus, Hon. S. B. *How "Jim" Became James.* Vol. i, No. 3 (1897), p. 2.

## LADIES' HOME JOURNAL

Mitchell, J. F. Jr. *Riley's Home Folks.* Vol. xix, No. 1 (1902), p. 7.

## LAMP

Chomel, M. C. *Interview with Riley.* Vol. xxvi (1903), pp. 289-95.
*James Whitcomb Riley.* Vol. xxvi (1903), p. 454. With portrait by J. F. Sargent.

## LITERARY DIGEST

Nesbit, Wilbur D. *To James Whitcomb Riley.* (Poem.) Vol. xlv (1912), p. 728.

## LITERARY WORLD

Milburn, N. F. *Open Letter to James Whitcomb Riley* (Poem). Vol. xxxi (1900), p. 104.

## McCLURE'S MAGAZINE

Garland, Hamlin. *James Whitcomb Riley.* Vol. ii (1894), pp. 219-34.

## MUNSEY'S MAGAZINE

Wilson, R. R. *James Whitcomb Riley.* Vol. xiii (1895), pp. 380-85.
*Sketch of James Whitcomb Riley.* Vol. xix (1898), p. 278.

## NATIONAL MAGAZINE

Chapple, J. M. *James Whitcomb Riley.* Vol. ix (1899), pp. 322-28.

## NEW ENGLAND MAGAZINE

Portrait. Vol. xxiv (1901), p. 79.

## NORTH AMERICAN REVIEW

Howells, W. D. James Whitcomb Riley (*The New Poetry*). Vol. clxviii (1899), p 588.

## OHIO MAGAZINE

McCormick, E. *James Whitcomb Riley, His Literary Hoax, "Leonainie."* Vol. iii (1877), pp. 219-22.

### PRIMARY PLANS

Tristram, Elizabeth. *October Birthday Story— James Whitcomb Riley.* Vol. xi, No. 3 (1913), pp. 25, 49.

### PUBLIC OPINION

Carmen, Bliss. *James Whitcomb Riley's Poetry.* Vol. xxv (1898), p. 372.

### SCRIBNER'S MAGAZINE

van Dyke, Henry. *To James Whitcomb Riley, Gardener* (poem). Vol. xxxiii (1903), p. 156.

### SUCCESS

Fawcett, Waldon. *James Whitcomb Riley, the "Hoosier Poet," tells the story of his early struggles and of his beginning as a Bard.* Vol. ii, p. 63.
Portrait. Vol. iv (1901), p. 1052.
Galeshore, Roger. *James Whitcomb Riley and His Children.* Vol. vi (1903), p. 720.

### WORLD'S WORK

McCoy, Samuel Duff. *The Boy Who Was Born in Our Town.* Vol. xxv (1913), pp. 565-7.

### WORLD TODAY

Portrait. Vol. viii (1905), p. 262.

### THE WRITER'S MAGAZINE

Masterson, Kate. *To James Whitcomb Riley.* Vol. v. (1913), pp. 8-9.

# POEMS SET TO MUSIC

*Babyhood.* R. J. Jose. Boston, New York, Chicago: White-Smith Music Publishing Co., 1894.

*Bee-Bag, The.* Fritz Krull. Indianapolis: Fritz Krull, 1913.

*Billy and His Drum.* G. Smith. Boston: A. P. Schmidt, 1906.

‡*Billy Goodin'.* Rupert Hughes. New York: Edward Schuberth & Co., 1902.

*\*Billy Goodin'.* Archie A. Mumma. Dayton: Archie A. Mumma & Co., 1913.

*Childhood.* Leigh Hilton. New York: Carl Fischer, 1909.

*Christmas Glee, A.* James Whitcomb Riley. *The Reader* (magazine), Vol. vii, No. 1 (1905), pp. 45-48.

‡*Coffee Like His Mother Used to Make.* Rupert Hughes. New York: Edward Schuberth & Co., 1902.

*Cradle Song.* Mary V. Fuller. New York: Luckhardt & Belder, 1896.

*\*Cradle Song.* Archie A. Mumma. Dayton: Archie A. Mumma & Co., 1913.

*Days Gone By, The.* H. N. Bartlett, Boston: Oliver Ditson Co., 1895.

‡*Dead Lover, The.* Rupert Hughes. New York: Edward Schuberth & Co., 1902.

*Dead Wife, The.* Fritz Krull. Indianapolis: Fritz Krull [to be published shortly].

*Dearth.* Fritz Krull. Indianapolis: Fritz Krull [to be published shortly].

*Don't Cry.*   Mary K. Wood.   Boston: Oliver Ditson Co., 1893.

\*Dwainie—A Sprite Song.*   Archie A. Mumma. Dayton: Archie A. Mumma & Co., 1913.

*Ever a Song Somewhere.*   E. L. Ashford.   Dayton, New York: The Lorenz Publishing Co., 1903.

*Fool Youngens.*   Fidella Dario.   New York: Luckhardt & Belder, 1907.

†*Funny Little Fellow, The.*   F. F. Churchill, Clara Grindell.   Platteville, Wis.: Churchill-Grindell Co., 1905.

*Gobble-uns 'll Git You Ef You Don't Watch Out, The.*   E. J. Appleton.   Cincinnati: George B. Jennings Co., 1892.

‡*Granny's Come to Our House.*   Rupert Hughes. New York: Edward Schuberth & Co., 1902.

‡*Griggsby's Station.*   Rupert Hughes. New York: Edward Schuberth & Co., 1902.

*Her Beautiful Eyes.*   Carl Hahn.   Cincinnati: The John Church Company, 1897.

*Humble Singer, A.*   Lulu Maye Lockwood.   Boston: C. W. Thompson & Co., 1912.

*Impetuous Resolve, An.*   Carrie B. Adams.   Dayton: Lorenz Publishing Company, 1911.

†*Impetuous Resolve, An.*   F. F. Churchill, Clara Grindell.   Platteville: Churchill-Grindell Co., 1905.

‡*Impetuous Resolve, An.*   Rupert Hughes.   New York: Edward Schuberth & Co., 1902.

*In the Orchard Where the Children Used to Play.* Barclay Walker.   New York: Jos. W. Stern & Co., 1909.

*I Will Walk with You, My Lad.*   Edw. Baxter Felton.   Cincinnati: The John Church Company, 1900.

*Jolly Miller, The.*   Fritz Krull.   Indianapolis: Fritz Krull [to be published shortly].

*Last Night and This.* Laura Dye Carpenter. New York: Globe Music Co., 1905.

*Leave-Taking, A.* Fritz Krull, Indianapolis: Fritz Krull [to be published shortly].

*Life-Lesson, A.* J. Jordan. Boston: A. P. Schmidt, 1897.

*Life Lesson, A.* Fritz Krull. Indianapolis: Fritz Krull, 1913.

*\*Little Girly-Girl.* Archie A. Mumma. Dayton: Archie A. Mumma & Co., 1913.

†*Little Orphant Annie.* F. F. Churchill, Clara Grindell. Platteville: Churchill-Grindell Co., 1905.

*Little Orphant Annie.* B. Margaret Hoberg. New York, Chicago, London: M. Whitmark & Sons, 1911.

*Little Orphant Annie.* Fritz Krull. Indianapolis: Fritz Krull, 1913.

*Little Orphant Annie.* Alicia Adélaide Needham. New York and London: Boosey & Co., 1899.

*Little Orphant Annie.* Clayton Thomas. Boston: A. P. Schmidt, 1913.

*Little Orphant Annie.* Barclay Walker, Indianapolis. [To be published shortly.]

*Little Red Apple Tree, The.* Carrie B. Adams. Terre Haute: The C. B. Adams Music Co., 1912.

‡*Little Tiny Kickshaw, The.* Rupert Hughes. New York: Edward Schuberth & Co., 1902.

*Lullaby.* Fritz Krull. Indianapolis: Wulschner-Stewart Co., 1907.

*\*Max and Jim.* Archie A. Mumma. Dayton: Archie A. Mumma & Co., 1913.

*Maymie's Story of Red-Riding Hood.* Incidental music by George Edwards. Cincinnati: The Willis Music Company, 1913.

*The Messiah of Nations.* John Philip Sousa. Cincinnati: The John Church Co., 1902.

†*Mr. Hammond's Parable.* F. F. Churchill, Clara Grindell. Platteville: Churchill-Grindell Co., 1905.

*O Heart of Mine.* Tod B. Galloway. Philadelphia: Theo. Presser Co., 1905.

*Old Sweetheart of Mine, An* [Monologue]. Fritz Krull. Indianapolis: Fritz Krull, 1913.

*Old Trundle Bed, The.* H. N. Bartlett. Boston: Oliver Ditson Co., 1895.

‡*Our Own.* Rupert Hughes. New York: Edward Schuberth & Co., 1902.

*Out to Old Aunt Mary's.* R. Atkinson. Boston: Oliver Ditson Co., 1897.

*Out to Old Aunt Mary's.* Barclay Walker, Indianapolis. [To be published shortly.]

*Prayer Perfect, The.* Teresa Del Riego. New York: Chappell & Co., 1908.

*Prayer Perfect, The.* Alexander Russell. Cincinnati: The John Church Company, 1912.

*Primrose, A.* G. L. Brown. Philadelphia: Theo. Presser Co., 1900.

*Raggedy Man, The.* Carrie B. Adams. Terre Haute: The C. B. Adams Music Co., 1912.

*Raggedy Man, The.* Fritz Krull. Boston: The Boston Music Company, 1908.

*\*Raggedy Man, The.* Archie A. Mumma. Dayton: Archie A. Mumma & Co., 1913.

*Ribbon, the Ring and the Rose, The.* Charles Willeby. Cincinnati: The John Church Company, 1909.

‡*Scrawl, A.* Rupert Hughes. New York: Edward Schuberth & Co., 1902.

*Sea Song from the Shore, A.* E. Harold Davies. London: Novello & Co., Ltd., 1912.

*Sea Song from the Shore, A.* E. E. Starr. Boston: Oliver Ditson Co., 1895.

*\*She "Displains" It.* Archie A. Mumma. Dayton: Archie A. Mumma & Co., 1913.

*Silver Lining, The.* Charles Willeby. Cincinnati: The John Church Company, 1905.

*Song, A.* Sidney C. Durst. Cleveland, Chicago: J. H. Rogers; Lyon & Healy, 1892.

*Song, A.* Fritz Krull. Indianapolis: Fritz Krull, 1913.

*Song of the Road, A.* Jean Bohannan. Boston: B. F. Wood Music Co., 1913.

*Song of the Road, A.* Kate Vannah. Philadelphia: Theo. Presser Co., 1900.

*There Little Girl, Don't Cry.* Edward Campion. Cleveland: Rogers & Eastman, 1906. (Assigned to New York: G. Schirmer Co.)

*There Little Girl Don't Cry.* C. Forsyth. Indianapolis: Wulschner & Son, 1900.

*\*There! Little Girl; Don't Cry!* Archie A. Mumma. Dayton: Archie A. Mumma & Co., 1913.

*There Little Girl Don't Cry.* H. A. Norris. Philadelphia: Theo. Presser Co., 1893.

*There Little Girl, Don't Cry.* Caro Roma. New York: M. Whitmark & Sons, 1903.

*There Little Girl Don't Cry.* Alvah Glover Salmon. Boston: Louis H. Ross & Co., 1893. (Assigned to Boston: White-Smith Music Publishing Co.)

*There Little Girl Don't Cry.* P. A. Schnecker. New York: G. Schirmer Co., 1889.

*There Little Girl Don't Cry.* C. Sobeski. Boston: Oliver Ditson Co., 1898.

*There Little Girl Don't Cry.* Pier A. Tirindelli. Cincinnati: The John Church Company, 1901.

*There Little Girl Don't Cry.* H. B. Vincent. Philadelphia: Theo. Presser Co., 1896.

*There Is Ever a Song Somewhere.* John Hyatt Brewer. Boston: A. P. Schmidt, 1897.

*There Is Ever a Song Somewhere.* W. H. Pontius. Philadelphia: Theo. Presser Co., 1895.

‡*Uncle Sidney*.  Rupert Hughes.  New York: Edward Schuberth & Co., 1902.

*Uncle Sidney's Logic*.  Archie A. Mumma. Dayton: Archie A. Mumma & Co., 1913.

*Very Youthful Affair, A*.  John Barnes Wells. Cincinnati: The John Church Company, 1911.

*Weather, The*.  Elizabeth L. Skinner.  New York: G. Schirmer Co., 1908.

*When Our Baby Died*.  Archie A. Mumma. Dayton: Archie A. Mumma & Co., 1913.

*When She Comes Home*.  Fritz Krull. Indianapolis: Fritz Krull [to be published shortly].

*When She Comes Home Again*.  Herbert J. Wrightson.  New York: The Wm. Maxwell Music Co., 1913.

†*When the Frost Is on the Punkin*.  F. F. Churchill, Clara Grindell.  Platteville: Churchill-Grindell Co., 1905.

*Where Shall We Land*.  Fritz Krull. Indianapolis: Fritz Krull [to be published shortly].

*Wind of the Sea*.  Clayton Johns.  Boston: C. C. Birchard & Co., 1902.

---

‡ In *A Riley Album* by Rupert Hughes.
* In *Ten Songs of Childhood* by Archie A. Mumma.
† In *Churchill-Grindell Song Book No. 1* by F. F. Churchill and Clara Grindell.

## PHONOGRAPH RECORDS

*Little Orphant Annie.*
*Out to Old Aunt Mary's.*
*The Happy Little Cripple.*
*The Raggedy Man.*
    The Victor Talking Machine Co., 1912.

INDEXES

# COMPLETE INDEX OF TITLES

*Indicates that the poem appears in this edition under a
different title or that the one specified is the subtitle.*

(N) *Indicates that the poem is printed in the NOTES.*

471

# INDEX OF FIRST LINES

*First lines thus designated do not start a new poem but
are sections of a larger one.*

(N) *The poem is found in the notes, not in the body
of the volume.*

# INDEX BY TOPICS

*In this table of contents the poems are classified
under the following heads:—*

# INDEX BY TOPICS

*\* Indicates a Subtitle.*

## POEMS FOR AND ABOUT CHILDREN

### GENERAL

## "Raggedy Man," " 'Lizabuth Ann" and "Little Orphant Annie" Poems

## "Uncle Sidney" Poems

## NARRATIVE AND DRAMATIC POEMS

# NATURE POEMS

## Out of Doors

### Winter

### The Sun, the Wind and Rain

### Dawn, Noon and Dewfall

# HOLIDAY POEMS

# POEMS ABOUT PERSONS

*Italicized names in this section do not form a part of the title.*

558

# POEMS OF SENTIMENT

## LOVE

## FRIENDSHIP

### REFLECTION

### HOME

### PATRIOTISM

# HUMOROUS POEMS IN DIALECT

## ART, POETRY AND MUSIC

# MISCELLANEOUS

# INDEX OF ILLUSTRATIONS

## VOLUME I

## VOLUME II

584

## VOLUME III

## VOLUME IV

## VOLUME V

## Date Loaned

| | | | |
|---|---|---|---|
| Ap 9 | | | |
| FEB 1 6 '62 | | | |
| | | | |
| | | | |
| | | | |
| | | | |
| | | | |
| | | | |
| | | | |
| | | | |
| | | | |
| | | | |
| | | | |
| | | | |
| | | | |
| | | | |
| | | | |
| | | | |